CONCISE INORGANIC CHEMISTRY

by

J. D. LEE

Lecturer in Inorganic Chemistry
University of Loughborough

ENGLISH LANGUAGE BOOK SOCIETY

AND

D. VAN NOSTRAND COMPANY LTD.

LONDON

D. VAN NOSTRAND COMPANY LTD.
Windsor House, 46 Victoria St., London

D. VAN NOSTRAND COMPANY INC.
120 Alexander Street, Princeton, New Jersey
24 West 40th Street, New York 18

D. VAN NOSTRAND COMPANY (CANADA) LTD.
25 Hollinger Road, Toronto 16

D. VAN NOSTRAND AUSTRALIA PTY. LTD.
12 Denman St. Mitcham, Victoria

Library of Congress Catalog Card No. 64–15138

First Published 1964
Second Edition 1965
Reprinted 1966, 1968, 1969
E.L.B.S. edition first published 1968
Reprinted 1969

Made and printed in Great Britain by
Compton Printing Ltd.
London and Aylesbury

CONCISE INORGANIC CHEMISTRY

Some E.L.B.S. Textbook Titles

PREFACE

THIS book discusses the arrangement of electrons in atoms, the factors which determine how many bonds an atom may form, the various types of bonds, and the structure of ionic, covalent and co-ordination compounds. Various theories of bonding are discussed. The valence bond theory is used in most cases in preference to the molecular orbital approach, because the former is simpler and more readily understood by students.

The value of a theory lies not in its truth but in its usefulness. A knowledge of valence theory is no substitute for a knowledge of chemical facts; the two are complementary. This book does not seek to teach a mass of unrelated facts about chemical elements, but to compare in groups the properties of those elements which have similar electronic arrangements. The long form of the periodic table, which is based on the electronic theory of matter, is used in this book. Once the trends in properties and the reasons underlying these trends have been grasped, it is possible to use known facts about one element to deduce probable facts about an unfamiliar element.

Few books cater for students in their early stages of inorganic chemistry courses for degree or Higher National Certificate examinations in Great Britain, or their equivalents elsewhere. This book is primarily intended for the early part of a degree course, though parts of it should be useful to good sixth-form students and, if suitably supplemented, it may also be read profitably by senior undergraduates. A limited number of references to other more specialized articles, reviews and textbooks are included.

It is impossible to cover everything in a book of this size, but it is hoped that this present work is long enough to cover the essentials and short enough to be interesting.

J.D.L.

CONTENTS

CHAPTER 1

ATOMIC STRUCTURE AND THE PERIODIC TABLE

The Atom as a Nucleus with Orbital Electrons

All atoms consist of a central nucleus surrounded by one or more orbital electrons. The nucleus always contains protons and usually contains neutrons, and both together make up most of the weight of the atom. Both protons and neutrons are particles of unit weight, but a proton has a unit positive charge and a neutron is electrically neutral (i.e. carries no charge). Thus the nucleus always carries a positive charge which is exactly balanced by negative charges carried by each of the orbital electrons. Electrons are relatively light—about 1/1840 the weight of a proton, and they circle the nucleus in orbits.

The 103 elements at present known are all built up from these three fundamental particles in a simple way. The first and most simple element, hydrogen, consists of a nucleus containing one proton and therefore has one positive charge, which is balanced by one negatively-charged orbital electron. The second element, helium, has two protons (and two neutrons) in the nucleus and hence a charge of +2, which is balanced by two negatively charged orbital electrons. This pattern is repeated for the rest of the

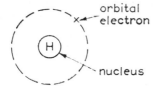

Fig. 1.1.   Hydrogen: Atomic No. 1
Symbol H

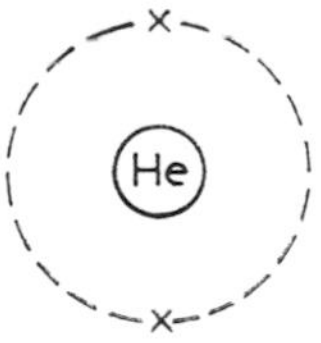

Fig. 1.2.   Helium: Atomic No. 2
Symbol He

elements, and Element 103, Lawrencium, has 103 protons in the nucleus (and some neutrons); hence the nuclear charge is +103 and is balanced by 103 orbital electrons. The number of positive charges on the nucleus of an atom always equals the number of orbital electrons, and is called the Atomic Number of the element.

One may think of the orbital electrons as being arranged in certain well-defined orbits. Thus hydrogen (Fig. 1.1) and helium (Fig. 1.2) have one and two electrons respectively in their first orbit. The first orbit is then full, and in the atoms of lithium, beryllium, boron, carbon, nitrogen, oxygen, fluorine and neon, subsequent electrons go into a second orbit (Fig. 1.3). Similarly in the atoms of Elements 11 to 18 the additional electrons enter a third shell.

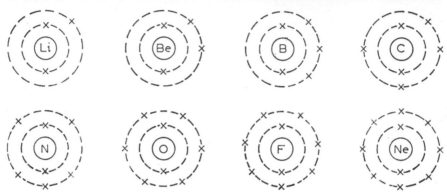

Fig. 1.3

The negatively-charged electrons are attracted to the positive nuclei by electrostatic attraction. An electron near the nucleus is strongly attracted by the nucleus and has a low potential energy. An electron distant from the nucleus is less firmly held and has a high potential energy.

Quantum Numbers

The quantum theory states that electrons bound to a nucleus cannot have all possible values of energy, but can only exist in certain definite energy levels. If an electron moves from one energy level to another, a definite quantity of energy corresponding to a particular frequency of radiation will be emitted or absorbed. The frequency of the radiation is given by:

$$E = h\nu$$

where E is the energy difference between the two levels, h is Planck's constant and ν the frequency. From a study of the frequencies of the lines in the atomic spectra it is possible to find what energy levels are available to electrons in atoms.

s, p, d and f Orbitals

These energy levels are found to occur in groups. All the levels in one group are described by a principal quantum number n, which has values

1, 2, 3 ... corresponding to the first, second, third ... orbits, already de-scribed.

These main energy levels are divided into sub-levels, each being denoted by a subsidiary or azimuthal quantum number l. Electrons do not really travel in circular orbits. The volume of space where there is a high proba-bility of finding the electron is called an *orbital*. The subsidiary quantum number l describes the shape of the orbital occupied by the electron. l may have values 0, 1, 2 or 3. When $l = 0$, the orbital is spherical and is called an *s* orbital; when $l = 1$, the orbital is dumb-bell-shaped and is called a *p* orbital; when $l = 2$, the orbital is double dumb-bell-shaped and is called a *d* orbital and when $l = 3$ a more complicated *f* orbital is formed (see Fig. 1.4). The letters *s*, *p*, *d* and *f* come from the spectroscopic terms *s*harp, *p*rincipal, *d*iffuse and *f*undamental, which were used to describe the lines in the atomic spectra.

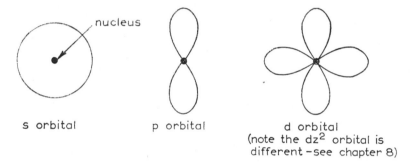

s orbital   p orbital   d orbital
(note the dz^2 orbital is different – see chapter 8)

Fig. 1.4. *s*, *p* and *d* Orbitals

Each main level has a number of sub-levels equal to the principal quantum number. In the first shell of electrons $n = 1$, and there is thus only one value for the subsidiary quantum number. Thus $l = 0$ and this shell contains only *s* electrons. In the second shell of electrons $n = 2$; hence $l = 0$ and 1, so that both *s* and *p* orbitals exist. Similarly when $n = 3$, $l = 0$, 1 and 2, and *s*, *p* and *d* orbitals exist.

Each sub-level is further subdivided, the subdivisions being denoted by a magnetic quantum number m and a spin quantum number s. The magnetic quantum number is determined by the way in which the lines in the atomic spectrum split up under the influence of a magnetic field. m can only have the values $-l, \ldots, -3, -2, -1, 0, +1, +2, +3, \ldots, +l$, where l is the subsidiary quantum number. There are therefore $2l + 1$ values for the magnetic quantum number. The spin quantum number may be regarded as the direction of spin of an electron on its own axis. It has values of $+\frac{1}{2}$ or $-\frac{1}{2}$ corresponding to clockwise and anti-clockwise spin.

Pauli Exclusion Principle

Thus four quantum numbers are needed to define the energy of an electron in an atom. According to the Pauli exclusion principle, no two electrons in one atom can have all four quantum numbers the same. By permutating the quantum numbers, the maximum number of electrons which can be contained in each main energy-level can be calculated (see Fig. 1.5).

Build-up of the Elements, Hund's Rule

When atoms are in their ground state, the electrons occupy the lowest possible energy levels. The simplest element, hydrogen, has one electron, which occupies the $1s$ level; this level has the principal quantum number $n = 1$, and the subsidiary quantum number $l = 0$. Helium has two electrons, the second one also occupying the $1s$ level. This is possible because the two electrons have opposite spins. This level is now full, so in the next atom, lithium, which has three electrons, the third electron occupies the next lowest level. This is the $2s$ level, which has the principal quantum number $n = 2$ and subsidiary quantum number $l = 0$. The fourth electron in beryllium also occupies the $2s$ level. Boron must have its fifth electron in the $2p$ level since the $2s$ level is full. The sixth electron in carbon is also in the $2p$ level. According to Hund's rule, the number of unpaired electrons in a given energy level is a maximum. In other words, the negatively-charged electrons tend to keep away from one another. Thus in the ground state the two p electrons in carbon are unpaired, i.e. they occupy separate p orbitals and have parallel spins. Similarly in nitrogen the three p electrons are unpaired and have parallel spins.

To show the positions of the electrons in an atom, the symbols $1s$, $2s$, $2p$, etc. are used to denote the main energy level and sub-level. An index figure is added to show the number of electrons in each set of orbitals. The electronic structures of the first few atoms in the periodic table are:

H $1s^1$
He $1s^2$
Li $1s^2 2s^1$
Be $1s^2 2s^2$
B $1s^2 2s^2 2p^1$
C $1s^2 2s^2 2p^2$
N $1s^2 2s^2 2p^3$
O $1s^2 2s^2 2p^4$
F $1s^2 2s^2 2p^5$
Ne $1s^2 2s^2 2p^6$
Na $1s^2 2s^2 2p^6 3s^1$

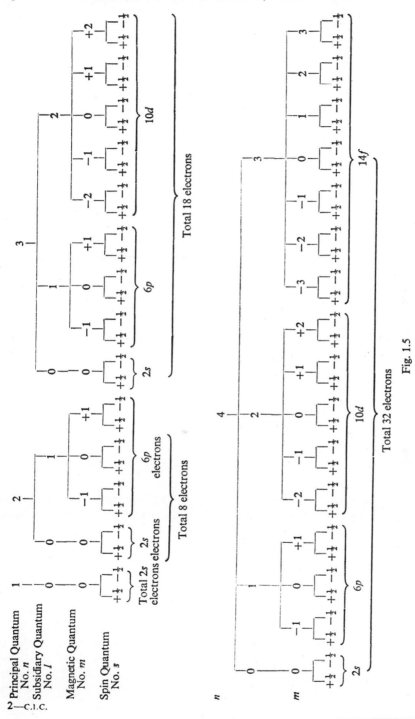

Fig. 1.5

Sequence of Energy Levels

It is important to know the sequence in which the energy levels are filled. Figure 1.6 is a useful aid:

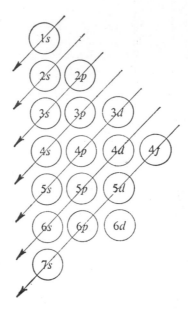

Fig. 1.6.   Sequence of Filling Energy Levels

From this, it can be seen that the order of filling of energy levels is: 1s, 2s, 2p, 3s, 3p, 4s, 3d, 4p, 5s, 4d, 5p, 6s, 4f, 5d, 6p, 7s, etc.

After the 1s, 2s, 2p, 3s and 3p levels have been filled at argon, the next two electrons go into the 4s level, and give potassium and calcium, since the 4s levels are lower in energy than the 3d levels.   Only when the 4s level is full does the 3d level start filling, at scandium.   The elements from scandium to copper have two electrons in the 4s level and an incomplete 3d level, and all behave in a similar manner chemically.   Such a series of atoms is known as a transition series.

A second transition series starts after the 5s orbital has been filled, at strontium, because in the next element, yttrium, the 4d level begins to fill up. A third transition series starts at lanthanum where the electrons start to fill the 5d level after the 6s level has been filled with two electrons.   A further complication arises here because after lanthanum which has one electron in the 5d level, the 4f level begins to fill giving the elements from cerium to lutetium which range from one to fourteen f electrons.   These are sometimes called the inner transition elements, but are usually known as the lanthanides or rare earth metals.

Arrangement of the Elements in Groups in the Periodic Table

The chemical and physical properties of an element are governed by the number and arrangement of the orbital electrons, that is by the atomic number. If the elements are arranged in groups, each group having a characteristic electronic arrangement, then elements within a group should show similarities in chemical and physical properties. One great advantage of this is that initially it is only necessary to learn the properties of each group rather than the properties of each individual element.

Elements with one s electron in their outer shell are called Group I (the alkali metals) and elements with two s electrons in their outer shell are called Group II (the alkaline earth metals). These two groups are known as the s block elements, because their properties result from the presence of s electrons.

Elements with three electrons in their outer shell (two s electrons and one p electron) are called Group III, and similarly Group IV elements have four outer electrons, Group V elements have five outer electrons, Group VI elements have six outer electrons and Group VII elements have seven outer electrons. Group 0 elements have a full outer shell of electrons so that the next shell is empty; hence the group name. Groups III, IV, V, VI, VII and 0 all have p orbitals filled and because their properties are dependent on the presence of p electrons, they are called jointly the p block elements.

In a similar way, elements where d orbitals are being filled are called the d block, or transition elements. In these, d electrons are being added to the penultimate shell.

Finally, elements where f orbitals are filling are called the f block, and here the f electrons are entering the antepenultimate (or second from the outside) shell.

In the periodic table (Table 1.1), the elements are arranged in order of increasing atomic number, that is in order of increased nuclear charge, so that each element contains one more orbital electron than the preceding element. Instead of listing the 103 elements, the periodic table arranges them into several rows or periods, in such a way that each row begins with an alkali metal and ends with an inert gas. The sequence in which the various energy levels are filled determines the number of elements in each period, and the periodic table can be divided into four main regions according to whether the s, p, d or f levels are being filled.

1st period	$1s$			elements in this period 2
2nd period	$2s$		$2p$	elements in this period 8
3rd period	$3s$		$3p$	elements in this period 8
4th period	$4s$	$3d$	$4p$	elements in this period 18
5th period	$5s$	$4d$	$5p$	elements in this period 18
6th period	$6s$	$4f$ $5d$	$6p$	elements in this period 32

TABLE 1.1   Periodic Table

Period	s block 1	2	d block										p block 3	4	5	6	7	0
1	1 H																1 H	2 He
2	3 Li	4 Be											5 B	6 C	7 N	8 O	9 F	10 Ne
3	11 Na	12 Mg											13 Al	14 Si	15 P	16 S	17 Cl	18 Ar
4	19 K	20 Ca	21 Sc	22 Ti	23 V	24 Cr	25 Mn	26 Fe	27 Co	28 Ni	29 Cu	30 Zn	31 Ga	32 Ge	33 As	34 Se	35 Br	36 Kr
5	37 Rb	38 Sr	39 Y	40 Zr	41 Nb	42 Mo	43 Tc	44 Ru	45 Rh	46 Pd	47 Ag	48 Cd	49 In	50 Sn	51 Sb	52 Te	53 I	54 Xe
6	55 Cs	56 Ba	57 La	72 Hf	73 Ta	74 W	75 Re	76 Os	77 Ir	78 Pt	79 Au	80 Hg	81 Tl	82 Pb	83 Bi	84 Po	85 At	86 Rn
7	87 Fr	88 Ra	89 Ac	90 Th	91 Pa	92 U												

f block

Lanthanides	58 Ce	59 Pr	60 Nd	61 Pm	62 Sm	63 Eu	64 Gd	65 Tb	66 Dy	67 Ho	68 Er	69 Tm	70 Yb	71 Lu
Transuranium Elements				93 Np	94 Pu	95 Am	96 Cm	97 Bk	98 Cf	99 Es	100 Fm	101 Md	102 No	

The alkali metals appear in a vertical column labelled Group I, which all have one *s* electron in their outer shell, and hence all have similar properties. Thus when one element in a group reacts with a reagent, the other elements in the group will probably react similarly, forming compounds which have similar formulae. Thus reactions of new compounds and their formulae may be predicted by analogy with known compounds. Similarly the inert gases all appear in a vertical column labelled Group 0, and all have a complete outer shell of electrons. This form of the periodic table has many advantages. The similarity of properties within a group and the relation between the group and the electron structure is emphasized. The *d* block elements are referred to as the transition elements since they are situated between the *s* and *p* blocks.

Hydrogen and helium differ from the rest of the elements because there are no *p* orbitals in the first shell. Helium obviously belongs to Group 0, the inert gases, which are chemically inactive because their outer shell of electrons is full. Hydrogen is more difficult to place in a group. It could be included in Group I because it has one *s* electron in its outer shell, or in Group VII because it is one electron short of a complete shell. Hydrogen is included in both these groups in the periodic table, although it resembles neither the alkali metals nor the halogens very closely. The unique properties of hydrogen are largely due to the extremely small size of hydrogen atoms. Thus there is a case for placing hydrogen in a group on its own, or omitting it from the periodic table altogether.

PROBLEMS

1. What is an orbital, and what are the shapes of *s*, *p* and *d* orbitals respectively?
2. The first shell may contain up to two electrons, the second shell up to eight, the third shell up to eighteen, and the fourth shell up to thirty-two electrons. Explain this arrangement in terms of quantum numbers.
3. Give the sequence in which the energy levels in an atom are filled with electrons. Write the electronic configurations for the elements of atomic number 6, 11, 17 and 25, and from this decide to which group in the periodic table each element belongs.
4. Suggest reasons for and against the inclusion of hydrogen in the main groups of the periodic table. (See p. 55.)

CHAPTER 2

VALENCY

Attainment of a Stable Configuration

How do atoms combine together to form molecules and why do atoms form bonds? The molecule formed must be more stable than the individual atoms, or molecules would not be formed, i.e. the process must be energetically favourable and lead to a minimum energy.

To understand what is happening in terms of electronic structure, consider first the Group 0 elements. These comprise the inert gases helium, neon, argon, krypton, xenon and radon which are noted for their lack of chemical properties. Atoms of the inert gases do not normally react with any other atoms and their molecules are monatomic—that is, they contain only one atom. The lack of reactivity indicates that these atoms are extremely stable, and their energy being so favourable that it cannot be improved by compound formation. The inert gases all have a complete outer shell of electrons, so that we can conclude that this is a very stable arrangement.

The electrons in the outermost shell of an atom are generally the ones concerned with bond and compound formation, and from energy considerations molecules are formed only if each atom acquires a stable electron configuration in the process. The atoms which have the most stable arrangements of electrons are the inert gases. (Less stable arrangements than this are commonly attained by the transition elements.)

Types of Bonds

There are several ways in which atoms may obtain a stable electronic configuration: by losing, gaining or sharing electrons. If the elements are divided into (a) electropositive elements, whose atoms give up one or more electrons fairly readily, (b) electronegative elements which take up electrons, and (c) elements which neither tend to lose nor gain electrons, we can classify the kinds of bonds formed into the following ideal types:

Electropositive element
+
Electronegative element } Ionic bond

10

Electronegative element
+   } Covalent bond
Electronegative element

Electropositive element
+   } Metallic bond
Electropositive element

Ionic Bonds

Consider the sodium atom, which has the electronic configuration $1s^2\, 2s^2$ $2p^6\, 3s^1$. The first and second shells of electrons are full, but the third shell contains only one electron. When this atom reacts it will do so in such a way that a stable electron configuration is attained. The inert gases have a very stable electron arrangement and the nearest inert gas is neon whose configuration is $1s^2\, 2s^2\, 2p^6$. If the sodium atom can lose one electron from its outer shell, it will attain this configuration except that the sodium ion as it is now called has a net charge of $+1$ because there are eleven positive charges on the nucleus and only ten electrons. When supplied with energy sodium atoms tend to do this, so sodium is an electropositive element:

$$Na \;\rightarrow\; Na^+ \;+\; electron$$
$$\text{Sodium atom} \qquad \text{Sodium ion}$$

Chlorine atoms have the electronic configuration $1s^2\, 2s^2\, 2p^6\, 3s^2\, 3p^5$. They are only one electron short of the stable inert gas configuration of argon $1s^2\, 2s^2\, 2p^6\, 3s^2\, 3p^6$, and chlorine atoms tend to react and gain electrons (that is they are electronegative):

$$Cl \;+\; electron \;\rightarrow\; Cl^-$$
$$\text{Chlorine atom} \qquad\qquad \text{Chloride ion}$$

By gaining an electron, an electrically neutral chlorine atom becomes a chloride ion with a net charge of -1.

When sodium and chlorine react together the outer electron of the sodium atoms is transferred to the chlorine atoms to produce sodium ions Na^+ and chloride ions Cl^-, which are held together by the electrostatic attraction of their opposite charges. Since both sorts of atoms attain a very stable inert gas configuration, the process is energetically favourable, and sodium chloride Na^+Cl^- is formed readily. This may be illustrated diagrammatically showing the outer electrons only:

$$Na\text{×} \qquad \text{×}\overset{\times\,\times}{\underset{\times\,\times}{Cl}}\text{×} \quad\rightarrow\quad \left[Na\right]^+ \; \left[\overset{\times\,\times}{\underset{\times\,\times}{\text{×}Cl\text{×}}}\right]^-$$
$$\text{Sodium atom} \quad \text{Chlorine atom} \qquad \text{Sodium ion} \quad \text{Chloride ion}$$

In a similar way, a calcium atom may lose two electrons to two chlorine atoms forming a calcium ion Ca^{2+} and two chloride ions Cl^-, that is calcium chloride $CaCl_2$. Showing the outer electrons only, this may be represented:

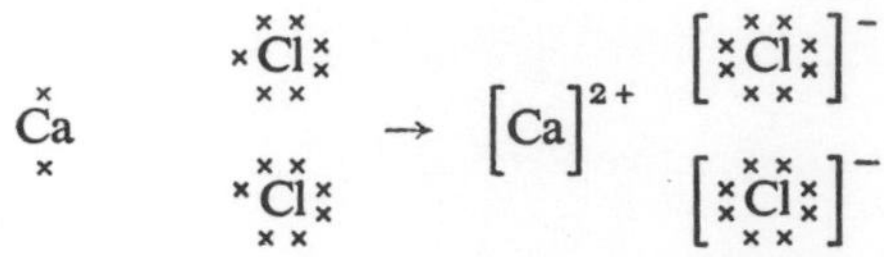

$$
\overset{\times}{\underset{\times}{Ca}} \qquad \overset{\times\ \times}{\underset{\times\ \times}{\times \overset{}{Cl} \times}} \qquad \overset{\times\ \times}{\underset{\times\ \times}{\times \overset{}{Cl} \times}} \quad \rightarrow \quad \left[Ca \right]^{2+} \quad \left[\times \overset{\times\ \times}{\underset{\times\ \times}{Cl} } \times \right]^{-} \quad \left[\times \overset{\times\ \times}{\underset{\times\ \times}{Cl} } \times \right]^{-}
$$

Calcium atom   Chlorine atoms   Calcium ion   Chloride ions

Ionic bonds are formed when electropositive elements react with electronegative elements.

Covalent Bonds

When two electronegative atoms react together, ionic bonds are not formed because both atoms have a tendency to gain electrons. In such cases, an inert gas configuration may be obtained by sharing electrons. First consider diagrammatically how chlorine atoms Cl react to form chlorine molecules Cl_2 (the outer electrons only are shown in the following diagrams):

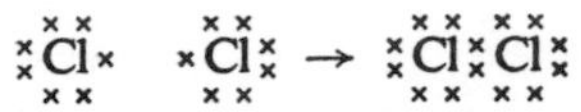

$$
\overset{\times\ \times}{\underset{\times\ \times}{\times \overset{}{Cl} \times}} \quad \overset{\times\ \times}{\underset{\times\ \times}{\times \overset{}{Cl} \times}} \rightarrow \overset{\times\times\ \ \times\times}{\underset{\times\times\ \ \times\times}{\times \overset{}{Cl} \times \overset{}{Cl} \times}}
$$

Chlorine atoms   Chlorine molecule

Each chlorine atom gives a share of one of its electrons to the other atom. Thus a pair of electrons are shared equally between both atoms, and each atom in the molecule has in its outer shell six electrons which completely belong to it plus a share in two more electrons, thereby making a stable octet—the inert gas structure of argon. In a similar way a molecule of carbon tetrachloride CCl_4 is made up of one carbon and four chlorine atoms:

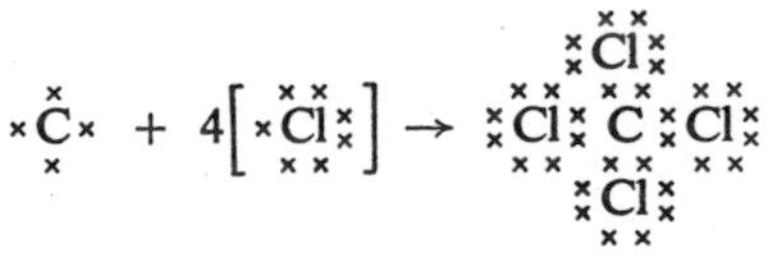

$$
\overset{\times}{\underset{\times}{\times C \times}} + 4\left[\times \overset{\times\ \times}{\underset{\times\ \times}{Cl} } \times \right] \rightarrow \overset{\times\times\ \ \times\times\ \ \times\times}{\underset{\times\times\ \ \times\times\ \ \times\times}{\times Cl \times C \times Cl \times}}
$$

The carbon atom is four electrons short of the inert gas structure, so it forms four bonds, and the chlorine atoms are one electron short, so they each form one bond. By sharing electrons in this way, both the carbon and all four chlorine atoms attain an inert gas structure. It must be emphasized that although it is possible to build up molecules in this way, and to understand their electronic structures, it does not follow that the atoms will react together directly. In this case, carbon and chlorine do not react directly and carbon tetrachloride is made by indirect reactions.

A molecule of ammonia NH_3 is made up of one nitrogen and three hydrogen atoms:

$$\overset{\times\ \times}{\underset{\times}{\times}} \text{N} \times \ + \ 3\left[\times\text{H}\right] \ \rightarrow \ \text{H}\overset{\times\ \times}{\underset{\times\ \times}{\times}}\text{N}\overset{}{\underset{}{\times}}\text{H} \\ \overset{}{\text{H}}$$

A nitrogen atom is three electrons short and hydrogen atoms are one electron short of an inert gas structure. Thus nitrogen forms three bonds, and the hydrogen atoms one bond each, thus attaining a stable configuration. In this case, one pair of electrons is not involved in bond formation, and this is called a lone pair of electrons.

A covalent bond results from the sharing of an electron pair, where each atom contributes one electron to the bond, as described above. It is also possible to have an electron pair bond in which a pair of electrons is shared by two atoms, although both electrons came originally from one atom and none from the other. Such bonds are called co-ordinate-covalent or dative-covalent bonds, and once they have been formed they are identical to normal covalent bonds.

Co-ordinate Bonds

Even though the ammonia molecule has a stable electron configuration, it can react with hydrogen ions H^+ by donating a share in the lone pair of electrons, forming the ammonium ion $NH_4{}^+$

$$\underset{\text{H}}{\overset{\text{H}}{\text{H}\overset{\times\ \times}{\underset{\times\ \times}{\times}}\text{N}\times}} + \left[\text{H}\right]^+ \rightarrow \left[\underset{\text{H}}{\overset{\text{H}}{\text{H}\overset{\times\ \times}{\underset{\times\ \times}{\times}}\text{N}\times\text{H}}}\right]^+ \ \text{or} \ \left[\underset{\text{H}}{\overset{\text{H}}{\text{H}-\text{N}\rightarrow\text{H}}}\right]^+$$

Frequently, covalent bonds are depicted as straight lines joining the two atoms, and co-ordinate bonds as arrows indicating which atom is donating the electrons. Similarly ammonia may donate its lone pair to boron trifluoride, and by this means the boron atom attains a share in eight electrons:

$$\underset{\text{H}}{\overset{\text{H}}{\text{H}\overset{\times\ \times}{\underset{\times\ \times}{\times}}\text{N}\times}} + \underset{\text{F}}{\overset{\text{F}}{\overset{\times\ \times}{\underset{\times\ \times}{\text{B}}}\text{F}}} \rightarrow \underset{\text{H}\ \ \text{F}}{\overset{\text{H}\ \ \text{F}}{\text{H}-\text{N}\rightarrow\text{B}-\text{F}}}$$

Metallic Bonds

Metals are made up of positive ions packed together, usually in one of the three following geometrical arrangements: (1) face-centred cubic (cubic close-packed); (2) hexagonal close-packed; or (3) body-centred cubic. Negatively charged electrons hold the ions together, and the positive and negative charges are balanced, since the electrons originated from the neutral metal atoms. The outstanding feature of metals is their very high electrical conductivity, which is due to the mobility of these electrons through the lattice. Reviews of the theories of bonding in metals and alloys have been given by W. Hume-Rothery in *The Metallurgist*, **3**, 11 (1964), and by B. L. Mordike in *Research*, **13**, 179 (1960).

It is important to realize that bonds are not necessarily 100% covalent or 100% ionic and that bonds of intermediate character exist. In a molecule made up of two identical atoms, both atoms have an equal tendency to gain electrons, so that the electron pair forming the bond is equally shared by both atoms. This constitutes a 100% covalent bond. In molecules formed between different atoms, the tendency to gain electrons differs—hence the bond pair of electrons is unequally shared by the two atoms, one atom having a very small negative charge $\delta-$ and the other a small positive charge $\delta+$

$$\overset{\delta+}{A}\text{——}\overset{\delta-}{B}$$

This covalent bond is therefore partly ionic in character.

Double and Triple Bonds

Sometimes more than two electrons are shared between a pair of atoms. If four electrons are shared (that is, there are two bonds), this arrangement is called a double bond, and if six electrons are shared (that is, there are three bonds) it is called a triple bond:

Ethylene molecule (double bond)

Acetylene molecule (triple bond)

General Properties of Ionically and Covalently Bonded Compounds

Compounds containing ionic linkages are made up of positive and negative ions arranged together in a regular way in a lattice. The attraction between ions is electrostatic and non-directional, and extends equally in all directions. Thus to melt the compound it is necessary to break the lattice—this requires considerable energy, and so the melting-point and boiling-point are usually high, and the compounds very hard. Compounds with covalent bonds are usually made up of discrete molecules. The bonds are directional, and strong covalent bonding forces exist between the atoms in a molecule. In the solid, the only forces between one molecule and another are weak Van der Waals forces. Thus the heat energy required to melt or boil the compound is the small amount needed to overcome the Van der Waals forces. Hence covalently bonded compounds are often gases, liquids or soft solids with low melting-points.   In a few cases infinite three-dimensional covalent structures are formed rather than discrete molecules.   In these cases there are strong forces operating in all directions, hence diamond and silica, SiO_2, are covalent but very hard and have a high melting-point.

Ionic compounds conduct electricity because ions migrate towards the electrodes when the compound is melted or in solution.   At the electrodes, the ions are neutralized; for example, in a solution of sodium chloride, the sodium ion gains an electron at the cathode, and forms a sodium atom while the chloride ion loses an electron at the anode, and becomes a chlorine atom. These changes amount to the transfer of electrons from cathode to anode, but the ionic mechanism involving both sorts of ions is in apparent contrast to the direct movement of electrons, and accounts for the conductivity of metals. In an ionic crystal, the ions are trapped in fixed places in the crystal lattice; hence they cannot migrate and therefore cannot conduct electricity.   If the crystal is not perfect (most crystals have defects) and a lattice site is left vacant, that is an ion is missing, some very slight conduction may occur by migration of an ion from its lattice site to the vacant site.   In contrast, covalent compounds are insulators.   They have no electric charges and carry no current in either the solid, liquid or gaseous state.

Ionic compounds are usually soluble in polar solvents: that is, solvents of high dielectric constant such as water.   Covalent compounds are not normally soluble in these solvents but are soluble in non-polar (organic) solvents: that is, solvents of low dielectric constant such as benzene and carbon tetrachloride.

Ionic reactions are usually rapid, since the reacting species have only to collide.   Covalent compounds usually react slowly since the reaction usually involves breaking a bond and substituting or adding another group.   Thus collisions between the reactant molecules will only cause reaction if they have sufficient energy.

Structures of Ionic Solids (Limiting Radius Ratios)

In an ionic solid, positive ions are surrounded by negative ions, and vice versa.   Normally each ion is surrounded by the greatest possible number of oppositely-charged ions and this number is called the co-ordination number. The co-ordination numbers of positive and negative ions are the same if there are equal numbers of both ions, as in NaCl, and are different when there are different numbers of positive and negative ions, as in $CaCl_2$.   The co-ordination number is related to the relative sizes of the ions.   When the co-ordination number is three in an ionic compound AX, three X^- ions are in contact with one A^+ ion (Fig. 2.1).   A limiting case arises (Fig. 2.2) when the X^- ions are also in contact with one another.   By simple geometry this gives the ratio $\dfrac{\text{radius } A^+}{\text{radius } X^-} = 0\cdot155$. If the ratio falls below this value then the structure is unstable (Fig. 2.3). Co-ordination numbers of 3, 4, 6 and 8 are common, and the appropriate limiting radius ratios can be worked out.

Fig. 2.1   Fig. 2.2

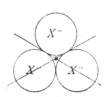

Fig. 2.3

Some of these numbers and their limiting radius ratios are given in Table 2.1.

TABLE 2.1

Co-ordination number	Shape	Limiting radius ratio r^+/r^-
3	Planar triangle	$0\cdot155\rightarrow$
4	Tetrahedral	$0\cdot225\rightarrow$
4	Square planar	$0\cdot414\rightarrow$
6	Octahedral	$0\cdot414\rightarrow$
8	Body-centred cubic	$0\cdot732\rightarrow$

If the ionic radii are known, the radius ratio can be calculated and hence the co-ordination number and shape may be predicted. It is convenient to divide ionic compounds into groups AX, AX_2, AX_3 depending on the relative numbers of positive and negative ions.

Ionic Compounds of the Type AX (ZnS, NaCl, CsCl)

Three structural arrangements commonly found are the zinc sulphide, sodium chloride and caesium chloride structures. In zinc sulphide, ZnS, the radius ratio of 0·40 suggests a tetrahedral arrangement.   Each Zn^{2+} ion is tetrahedrally surrounded by four S^{2-} ions and each S^{2-} ion is tetrahedrally surrounded by four Zn^{2+} ions.   This is therefore a 4:4 arrangement since the co-ordination number of both ions is four.   Actually two different forms of zinc sulphide exist, both 4:4 arrangements, one being called zinc blende and the other wurtzite (Fig. 2.4).

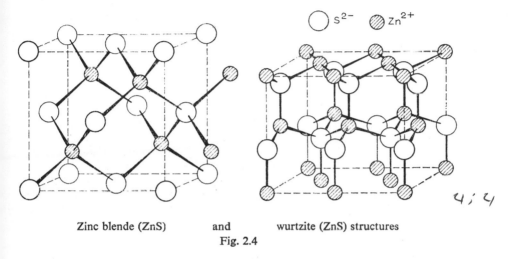

Zinc blende (ZnS)   and   wurtzite (ZnS) structures

Fig. 2.4

The radius ratio of sodium chloride, NaCl, is 0·52 and suggests an octahedral arrangement.   Each Na^+ ion is surrounded by six Cl^- ions at the

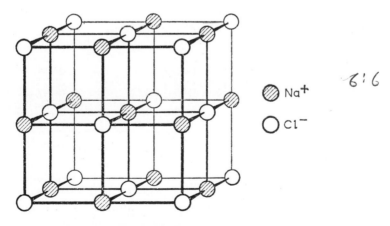

Fig. 2.5.   Rock-salt (NaCl) structure

corners of a regular octahedron and similarly each Cl^- ion is surrounded by six Na^+ ions (Fig. 2.5).

In caesium chloride CsCl, the radius ratio is 0·93, indicating a body-centred cubic arrangement where each Cs^+ ion is surrounded by eight Cl^- ions and vice versa (Fig. 2.6).

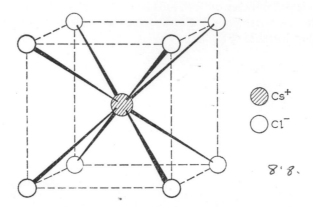

Fig. 2.6. Caesium chloride (CsCl) structure

The relative sizes of the ions are obviously important, but is size the only factor for consideration, and how well does the radius-ratio concept fit the observed facts? The radius ratios of the alkali metal halides and the alkaline earth metal oxides, sulphides, selenides and tellurides are shown in Table 2.2:

TABLE 2.2

	F^-	Cl^-	Br^-	I^-		O^{2-}	S^{2-}	Se^{2-}	Te^{2-}
Li^+	0·44	0·33	0·31	0·28	Be				
Na^+	0·70	0·52	0·49	0·44	Mg^{2+}	0·46	0·35	0·33	0·29
K^+	0·98	0·73	0·68	0·62	Ca^{2+}	0·71	0·54	0·50	0·45
Rb^+	0·92*	0·82	0·76	0·69	Sr^{2+}	0·81	0·61	0·57	0·51
Cs^+	0·80*	0·93	0·87	0·79	Ba^{2+}	0·96	0·73	0·68	0·61

(* Indicates reciprocal value r^-/r^+ since the normal ratio is greater than unity.)

Except for CsCl, CsBr and CsI which have a caesium chloride structure and MgTe which has a zinc sulphide structure, all the above compounds have a sodium chloride lattice at normal temperatures. Only those crystals with a radius ratio between 0·41 and 0·73 (enclosed by full line in above table) would be expected to have the sodium chloride structure. The explanation why some salts fail to adopt the co-ordination number indicated by their radius ratios is to be found in the lattice energy of the crystal. Presumably there is little difference in stability and lattice energy between co-ordination numbers six and eight since RbCl and RbBr have a co-ordination number of six at normal temperatures and pressures, but adopt the higher co-ordination number if crystallized at high pressures or temperatures. *for Crystal shape.*

Thus radius ratios and geometry are not the only factors. The gain in potential energy when oppositely-charged ions are brought together and the repulsion between like charges play their part. Since ionic radii cannot be measured absolutely, but are estimated, and since they vary with the co-ordination number, conclusions based on them, though often useful, are not rigorous. (Note that the apparent ionic radius increases 3% if the co-ordination number is changed from six to eight and decreases 6% when the co-ordination number changes from six to four.)

Ionic Compounds of the Type AX_2 (CaF$_2$, TiO$_2$)

There are two very common structures: fluorite, CaF_2 (Fig. 2.7), and rutile, TiO_2 (Fig. 2.8). Many difluorides and dioxides have one of these

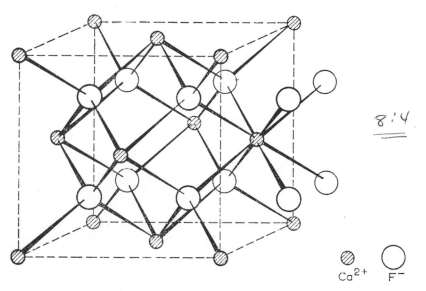

8:4

Ca^{2+} F^-

Fig. 2.7.   Fluorite (CaF$_2$) structure

structures. In fluorite each Ca^{2+} ion is surrounded by eight F^- ions in a body-centred cubic arrangement. Since there are twice as many F^- ions as Ca^{2+} ions, the co-ordination number of both ions is not the same, and four Ca^{2+} ions are tetrahedrally arranged round each F^- ion. The co-ordination numbers are eight and four and this is called an 8:4 arrangement. The fluorite structure is found when the radius ratio is 0·73 or above.

The rutile structure is found where the radius ratio is between 0·73 and 0·41. The co-ordination numbers are six and three, each Ti^{4+} ion being octahedrally surrounded by six O^{2-} ions and each O^{2-} ion having three Ti^{4+} ions round it in a plane triangular arrangement.

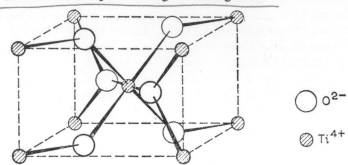

Fig. 2.8. Rutile (TiO_2) structure

There are only a few cases where the radius ratio is below 0.41, examples being silica SiO_2 and beryllium fluoride BeF_2. These have co-ordination numbers of four and two, but radius ratio predictions are uncertain, as they are appreciably covalent.

Layer Structures

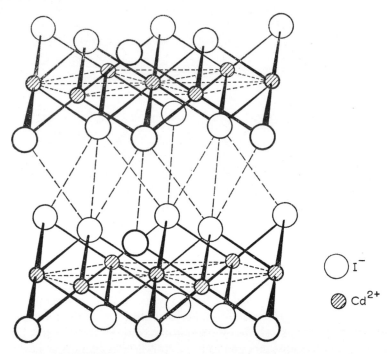

Fig. 2.9. Part of two layers of cadmium iodide (CdI_2) structure

Many AX_2 compounds are not sufficiently ionic to form the perfectly regular ionic structures described. Many chlorides, bromides, iodides and sulphides crystallize into structures very different from those described. Thus cadmium iodide, CdI_2, does not form the fluorite structure like CdF_2. The radius ratio 0·45 indicates a co-ordination number of six for cadmium, but the structure is made up of electrically neutral layers of Cd^{2+} ions sandwiched between layers of I^- ions. This is therefore called a layer structure, and since the negatively charged I^- ions of one layer are adjacent to those of the next layer, and there are only weak Van der Waals forces holding the sheets together, the crystal cleaves into parallel sheets quite easily. Most hydroxides of formula $M(OH)_2$ have similar layer structures.

Cadmium iodide may be regarded approximately as a hexagonal close-packed arrangement of I^- ions with the Cd^{2+} ions occupying octahedral sites between alternate layers of I^- ions. Cadmium chloride forms a closely related layer structure but with the chloride ions approximately in a cubic close-packed arrangement.

The CdI_2 structure is related to the nickel arsenide NiAs structure, where the arsenic atoms form a hexagonal close-packed type of lattice with nickel atoms occupying octahedral sites between all of the layers of arsenic atoms.

Layer structures are intermediate in type between the extreme cases of (1) a totally ionic crystal with a regular arrangement of ions and strong electrostatic forces in all directions, and (2) a crystal in which small discrete molecules are held together by weak residual forces such as Van der Waals forces and hydrogen bonds.

For details of other ionic structures such as perovskite and spinels the following sources are useful:

ADDISON, W. E., *Structural Principles in Inorganic Compounds*, Longmans, 1961.
HESLOP, R. B. and ROBINSON, P. L., *Inorganic Chemistry*, Elsevier, 1960.
WELLS, A. F., *Structural Inorganic Chemistry*, Clarendon Press, 1962.
[FIGURES 2·4–2·7 are reproduced, with permission, from this last book.]

The essential feature about crystalline solids is that the constituent molecules, atoms or ions are arranged in a completely regular three-dimensional pattern. Models built to show the detailed structure of crystalline materials are usually grossly misleading, for they imply a perfect, static pattern. Since the atoms or ions have a considerable degree of thermal vibration, the crystalline state is far from static, and the pattern is seldom perfect. Many of the most useful properties of solids are related to the thermal vibration of atoms, the presence of impurities or the existence of defects.

Stoichiometric Defects

In stoichiometric compounds, i.e. ones where the numbers of positive and negative ions are exactly in the ratios indicated by their chemical formulae, two types of defects may be observed. They are called Schottky and Frenkel defects respectively. At absolute zero, crystals tend to have a perfectly ordered arrangement. As the temperature increases, the chance that a lattice site may be unoccupied by an ion increases. This constitutes a defect, and since the number of defects depends on the temperature, they are sometimes called thermodynamic defects. The number of defects formed per cm³ (n) is given by

$$n = N \exp(-W/2kT)$$

where N is the number of sites per cm³ which could be left vacant, W is the work necessary to form a defect, k is the gas constant and T the absolute temperature.

Schottky Defects

A pair of 'holes' exist in the crystal lattice due to one positive ion and one negative ion being absent from the crystal lattice (see Fig. 2.10).

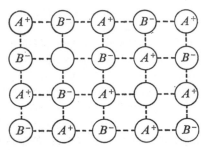

Fig. 2.10. Schottky defect

This sort of defect tends to be formed in highly ionic compounds with a high co-ordination number, and where the positive and negative ions are of similar size, e.g. NaCl and CsCl.

Frenkel Defects

A 'hole' may exist in the lattice because an ion occupies an interstitial position rather than its correct lattice site (see Fig. 2.11).

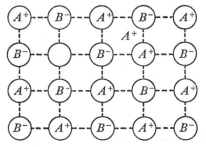

Fig. 2.11. Frenkel defect

This type of defect is favoured by a large difference in size between the positive and negative ions. Since positive ions are generally smaller than negative ions, it is more common to find the positive ions occupying interstitial positions. Small positive ions are highly polarizing and large negative ions are readily polarized; hence these compounds have some covalent character. This distortion of ions, and the proximity of like charges leads to a high dielectric constant. It is easier to form Frenkel defects in compounds which have a low co-ordination number, since fewer attractive forces have to be broken. Examples of this type of defect are ZnS and AgBr.

The energy needed to form a Schottky defect is usually less than that to form a Frenkel defect, and in a given compound one type generally predominates. In NaCl, the energy to form a Schottky defect is about 40 kcal/g mol compared with a lattice energy of approx. 180 kcal/g mol. It is therefore much easier to form a defect than to break the lattice. The number of defects is relatively small, and at room temperature NaCl has only one defect in 10^{15} lattice sites, this value rising to one in 10^6 sites at 500°C and one in 10^4 sites at 800°C.

A consequence of these defects is that a crystalline solid which has defects, may conduct electricity to a small extent, by an ionic mechanism. If an ion moves from its lattice site to occupy a 'hole', it creates a new 'hole', and in this way a 'hole' may migrate across a crystal, which is effectively moving a charge in the opposite direction.

The density of a defect lattice should be lower than for a perfect lattice, because of the 'holes' present. However, the presence of an interstitial ion may expand the lattice and increase the unit cell dimensions, or the presence of too many 'holes' may allow a partial collapse or distortion of the lattice —in which case the change in density is unpredictable.

Non-Stoichiometric Defects

Non-stoichiometric or Berthollide compounds exist over a range of chemical composition, and do not therefore obey the law of constant composition. The ratio of positive and negative ions present in a compound differs from that indicated by the ideal chemical formula, and the balance of + and − charges is maintained either by having extra electrons or extra positive charges present. This makes the structure irregular in some way, i.e. it contains defects, which are in addition to the normal thermodynamic defects already discussed. Non-stoichiometry implies that either the metal or the non metal atoms are present in excess.

Metal Excess

This may occur in either of two ways. In the first, a negative ion may be absent from its lattice site, leaving a 'hole' which is occupied by an electron thereby maintaining the electrical balance (see Fig. 2.12).

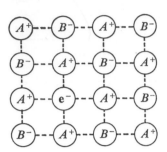

Fig. 2.12. Metal excess defect due to absent anion.

This is rather similar to a Schottky defect in that there are 'holes' and not interstitial ions, but only one 'hole' is formed rather than a pair. This type of defect is formed by crystals which would be expected to form Schottky defects. Examples are uncommon, but if NaCl is treated with Na vapour, a yellow non-stoichiometric form of NaCl is obtained, and a lilac-coloured non-stoichiometric form of KCl may be prepared by analogous means.

A second way in which metal excess defects may occur is if an extra positive ion occupies an interstitial position in the lattice. Electrical neutrality is maintained by an electron also in an interstitial position (see Fig. 2.13).

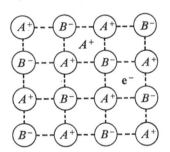

Fig. 2.13. Metal excess defect caused by interstitial cation.

This type of defect is rather like a Frenkel defect in that ions occupy interstitial positions, but there are no 'holes', and there are also interstitial electrons. This second kind of metal excess defect is much more common than the first, and is formed in crystals which would be expected to form Frenkel defects, e.g. ZnO.

Crystals with either type of metal excess defect contain free electrons, and if these migrate, they conduct an electric current. Since there are relatively few defects and hence few free electrons which can conduct electricity, the amount of current carried is very small compared with that in metals, fused salts or salts in aqueous solutions, and these materials are called semiconductors. Since the mechanism is normal electron conduction, these are called n-type semiconductors. These free electrons may be excited to higher energy levels giving absorption spectra, and in consequence their compounds are often coloured, e.g. non-stoichiometric NaCl is yellow, non-stoichiometric KCl lilac, and ZnO is white when cold but yellow when hot.

Metal Deficiency

Theoretically metal deficiency can occur in two ways. Both require variable valency of the metal, and might therefore be expected with the transition metals. In the first way, a positive ion is absent from its lattice site, and the charges are balanced by an adjacent metal ion having two charges instead of one (see Fig. 2.14).

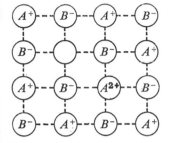

Fig. 2.14. Metal deficiency defect because positive ion is missing.

Semiconductivity

Examples of this are FeO, FeS and NiO.

The second possibility is to have an extra negative ion in an interstitial position and to balance the charges by means of an extra charge on an adjacent metal ion (see Fig. 2.15).

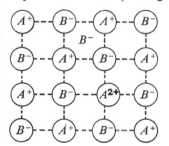

Fig. 2.15. Metal deficiency defect caused by interstitial negative ion.

Negative ions are usually large, and it would be expected to be difficult to fit them into interstitial positions. In fact no examples of crystals containing such negative interstitial ions are known at present.

Crystals with metal deficiency defects are semiconductors because of the moving of an electron from an A^+ ion to an A^{2+} ion, i.e. an apparent movement of A^{2+}. This is called positive hole, or p-type semiconduction.

For details of non-stoichiometric compounds see *Advances in Chemistry, No. 39*, 'Non Stoichiometric Compounds', edited by Gould, published by the American Chemical Society, 1963.

Semiconductors and Transistors

Semiconductors are solids which are insulators at absolute zero, but which conduct electricity by the passage of electrons at normal temperatures. Germanium and silicon are the most common practical examples. The atoms of both have four electrons in the outer shell of their atoms, which form four covalent bonds to other atoms and give rise to a tetrahedral structure like diamond. Given sufficient energy, some of the covalent bonds break, and electrons are ejected from their normal sites. These electrons can then migrate, leaving behind a positive charge where a bond is missing. Electrical conduction takes place by the migration of electrons one way, and the migration of 'positive holes' in the other. This is termed intrinsic conduction.

Germanium and silicon are obtained very pure by zone refining. If some impurity is added deliberately, for example, the addition of some atoms with five electrons in their outer shell such as arsenic, four of the electrons form bonds and the fifth can carry current quite readily. This is extrinsic conduction, and is much greater than intrinsic conduction. Since the current is carried by excess electrons, it is n-type semiconduction.

Alternatively if some atoms, such as indium, with only three outer electrons, are introduced, they are unable to complete the covalent structure. Some sites normally occupied by electrons are left empty and so constitute 'positive holes'. If adjacent electrons fill these 'holes', they form other 'holes', and by migration in this way, the current is carried. This is p-type semiconduction.

If a single crystal has a variable concentration of impurity such that one part is a p-type and the other an n-type, the p-n junction will only allow current from an outside source to flow through it in one direction, i.e. it acts as a rectifier. Other transistors have three zones and p-n-p and n-p-n transistors are widely used in radio and electrical circuits.

Structures of Simple Covalent Molecules

The chance of finding an s electron in any particular direction from the nucleus (the angular distribution probability) is the same for all directions. In other words there is a high probability of finding an s electron within a spherical volume of space, that it occupies a spherical orbital.

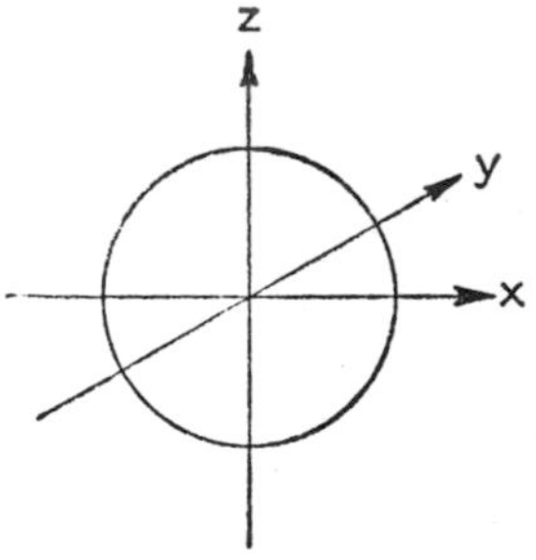

The six p electrons which can fill each shell occupy three orbitals which are mutually at right-angles pointing along the x, y and z axes (Fig. 2.16). The orbitals are dumb-bell shaped and are called p_x, p_y and p_z respectively (Fig. 2.17).

Fig. 2.16. Angular distribution probability for s orbitals

When a covalent bond is formed, electrons are shared between two atoms and the atoms must approach sufficiently closely for the orbitals of one atom to overlap the orbitals of the other. Thus the distribution in space of the orbitals

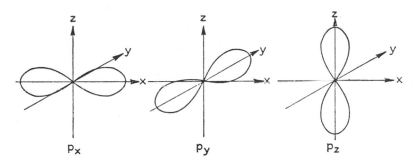

Fig. 2.17. Angular distribution probability for p orbitals

determines the shape of the resultant molecule. Since an orbital can only contain two electrons at most, it follows that in covalent bond formation an orbital containing one electron on one atom overlaps with a singly-occupied orbital on the other atom, and thus both orbitals have a share in two electrons.

Sidgwick-Powell Theory and Theory of Hybridization

In 1940 Sidgwick and Powell pointed out that the shape of a molecule was related to the number of electrons in the outer shell of the central atom. Pairs of electrons occupy orbitals and since the occupied orbitals repel each other they are orientated in space as far apart as possible. This applies irrespective of whether the electron pair is shared (bond pair) or is not shared (non-bonding or lone pair). If the distribution of orbitals about the central atom can be predicted, the shape of the molecule and bond angles can also be predicted. Table 2.3 shows well-known arrangements of electron pairs. This can now be explained in terms of the theory of hybridization of orbitals.

Consider the structure of a gaseous molecule of beryllium fluoride BeF_2. The beryllium atom is the central atom in this molecule and the electronic structure of a beryllium atom in its ground state (lowest energy state) is $1s^2 2s^2$. This may be shown diagrammatically, using arrows for electrons and boxes for energy levels:

Beryllium atom—ground state

$1s$ $2s$ $2p$

When two electrons occupy the same orbital, they must have opposite spins, due to the Pauli exclusion principle which states that in an atom, no two electrons can have all four quantum numbers the same. Since there are no unpaired electrons, this atom cannot form any covalent bonds. It follows

TABLE 2.3

Number of electron pairs in outer shell	Shape of molecule		Bond angles
2	linear		180°
3	plane triangle		120°
4	tetrahedron		109° 28′
5	trigonal bipyramid		120° and 90°
6	octahedron		90°
7	pentagonal bipyramid		72° and 90°

that in BeF_2 the Be atom is not in the ground state, but is in an excited state, with sufficient extra energy to unpair a $2s$ electron.

Beryllium atom—excited state

Here there are two unpaired electrons, so Be can form two covalent bonds.

Beryllium atom in BeF_2

↓ Electrons gained by bonding with fluorine atoms

Since there are two filled orbitals in the outer shell, these would be expected to be at 180° to each other, but if one s and one p bond have been formed, these should be of different strengths, and since s bonds are non-directional, the bond angle cannot be predicted.

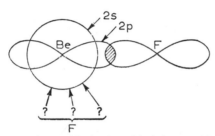

Fig. 2.18.   One F atom overlaps with the $2p$ orbital, but position of overlap of other F atom with $2s$ orbital uncertain

Hybridization

In fact both bonds are of equal strength and the molecule is linear, the bond angle F–Be–F being 180°. This is explained by hybridization. The energy of the s and p orbitals is combined, and two hybrid orbitals of the same shape and energy are formed. Combination of one s and one p orbital is called sp hybridization and the resultant sp hybrid orbitals, which have one lobe much larger than the other, point in opposite directions (see Fig. 2.19).

More effective overlapping of orbitals is now possible, and since the two electron pairs are as far apart as they can be, repulsion between them is minimized, and thus sp hybrid orbitals form stronger bonds than those formed by overlap of s or p orbitals.

Consider the structure of a boron trifluoride molecule. The boron atom is the central atom in the molecule and has the electronic structure $1s^2 2s^2 2p^1$.

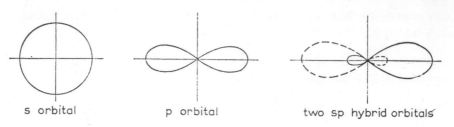

s orbital   p orbital   two sp hybrid orbitals

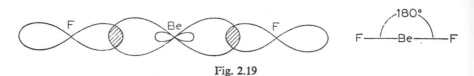

Fig. 2.19

The atom in its ground state has only one unpaired electron, so that it can form only one covalent bond, but in the excited state shown, there are three unpaired electrons; hence three bonds can be formed.

	1s	2s	2p
Electronic structure of Boron atom—ground state	↑↓	↑↓	↑
Boron atom—excited state	↑↓	↑	↑ ↑
Boron atom—having gained three electrons from fluorine atoms in BF₃ molecule	↑↓	↑↓	↑↓ ↑↓

Since there are three orbitals in the outer shell, they should be distributed at 120° to each other, according to the Sidgwick-Powell theory. The three

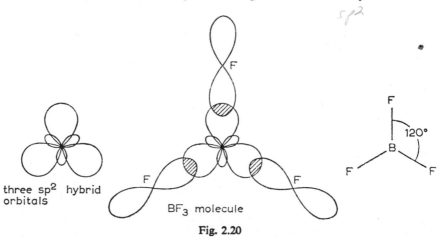

three sp² hybrid orbitals

BF₃ molecule

Fig. 2.20

orbitals used for bonding do not retain their s and p characteristics, but are hybridized, giving three sp^2 hybrid orbitals, which are 120° apart; this minimizes the repulsion between electron pairs. Since these sp^2 hybrid orbitals overlap with orbitals from F atoms to form the bonds, it follows that the bond angles are also 120° and the molecule is triangular and planar (Fig. 2.20).

Carbon, the central atom in a molecule of methane CH_4, has only two unpaired electrons in the ground state. The two electrons in the $2p$ level are not paired, i.e. put into the same box, in accordance with Hund's rule, which states that in a given energy level, e.g. $2p$, we always get the maximum number of unpaired electrons. In the excited state carbon can form four bonds, but the s orbital and the three p orbitals are not used to form them. Instead, bond hybridization occurs and four equivalent sp^3 hybrid orbitals are formed (Fig. 2.21).

	$1s$	$2s$	$2p$	
Electronic structure of carbon atom—ground state	↑↓	↑↓	↑ ↑ ☐	
Carbon atom—excited state	↑↓	↑	↑ ↑ ↑	Sp^3.
Carbon atom having gained four electrons from H atoms in CH_4 molecule	↑↓	↑↓	↑↓ ↑↓ ↑↓	

The repulsion between four orbitals is smallest if they point to the corners of a regular tetrahedron, and make a bond angle of 109° 28′.

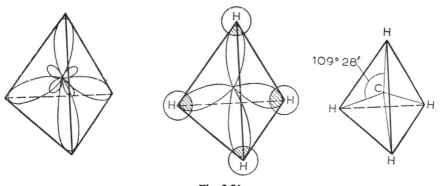

Fig. 2.21

In a molecule of ammonia, nitrogen, the central atom, has three unpaired electrons in its ground state—sufficient to form three bonds; so it is not necessary to excite the atom.

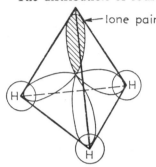

Electronic structure of the nitrogen atom—ground state

Nitrogen atom having gained three electrons from three H atoms in NH_3 molecule

hybridization may occur between orbitals energy levels of same p.q. no.

The distribution of four orbitals should be tetrahedral according to the Sidgwick-Powell theory, and the hybridization of one *s* and three *p* orbitals gives this arrangement. Three of the orbitals are used for bonding, and contain a shared pair of electrons, whilst the fourth orbital contains a lone pair of electrons (Fig. 2.22).

This shape is either called pyramidal or described as tetrahedral with one corner occupied by a lone pair. Repulsions between these orbitals are not all of equal strength because all four orbitals are not in the same environment.

Fig. 2.22

In general the repulsion between two lone pairs is greater than that between a lone pair and a bond pair, which in turn is greater than that between two bond pairs of electrons. On passing from methane to ammonia, a bond pair is replaced by a lone pair which repels the other bond pairs more strongly, thus reducing the bond angle $H\hat{N}H$ from 109° 28′ to 106° 45′.

In a molecule of water, oxygen, the central atom, has two unpaired electrons, which are sufficient to form the two bonds required.

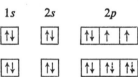

Electronic structure of oxygen atom—ground state

Oxygen atom, having gained two electrons from hydrogen atoms in H_2O molecule

Once again the four outer orbitals are hybridized and are distributed tetrahedrally (Fig. 2.23). The structure is called either tetrahedral with two positions occupied by lone pairs, or V-shaped. Here the two lone pairs distort the bond angle more than it was distorted by the one lone pair in ammonia; the bond angle $H\hat{O}H$ in water is 104° 27′.

Distortion of the ideal shape may be related also to electronegativity (see next chapter). In a series of molecules such as NH_3, PH_3, AsH_3, because the electronegativity of the central atom

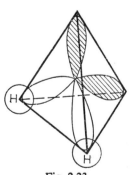

Fig. 2.23

decreases, N → P → As, the bonding electrons are drawn nearer to the hydrogen atoms, that is further away from the central atom. Repulsion between bond pairs of electrons therefore decreases and the bond angles decrease progressively from 106° 45′ in NH_3 to 93° 50′ in PH_3 to 91° 35′ in AsH_3.

In a gaseous molecule of phosphorus pentachloride, PCl_5 (Fig. 2.24), phosphorus, the central atom, has only three unpaired electrons in its ground state. An electron must be unpaired to provide the correct number of unpaired electrons for bond formation; and the $3d$ level is used rather than following in the order in which energy levels are filled when electrons are added to atoms.

	3s	3p	3d
Electronic structure of phosphorus atom—ground state	[↑↓]	[↑][↑][↑]	[ ][ ][ ][ ][ ]
Phosphorus atom —excited state	[↑]	[↑][↑][↑]	[↑][ ][ ][ ][ ]
Phosphorus having gained five electrons from chlorine atoms in PCl_5 molecule	[↑↓]	[↑↓][↑↓][↑↓]	[↑↓][ ][ ][ ][ ]

Five orbitals are being used and sp^3d hybridization occurs, giving a trigonal bipyramid structure.

This is not a completely regular structure, since some bond angles are 90° and others 120°. Symmetrical structures are usually more stable than unsymmetrical ones; thus PCl_5 is highly reactive, and in the solid state splits into PCl_4^+ and PCl_6^- ions, which have tetrahedral and octahedral structures respectively.

In a molecule of chlorine trifluoride (Fig. 2.25), the chlorine atom must be excited to provide the right number of unpaired electrons.

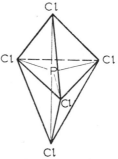

Fig. 2.24. Phosphorus pentachloride molecule

	3s	3p	3d
Electronic structure of chlorine atom— ground state	[↑↓]	[↑↓][↑↓][↑]	[ ][ ][ ][ ][ ]
Electronic structure of chlorine atom— excited state	[↑↓]	[↑↓][↑][↑]	[↑][ ][ ][ ][ ]
Chlorine atom having gained three electrons from fluorine atoms in ClF_3 molecule	[↑↓]	[↑↓][↑↓][↑↓]	[↑↓][ ][ ][ ][ ]

Once again there are five orbitals in the outer shell which are hybridized, giving five sp^3d hybrid orbitals and a trigonal bipyramid arrangement.

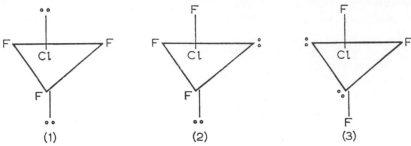

Fig. 2.25.   Chlorine trifluoride molecule

Three orbitals contain bond pairs and two contain lone pairs. Since the bond angles are not all the same, all the corners are not equivalent, and several arrangements are theoretically possible.

One cannot predict which of these is the actual structure, but because the bond angles have been found to be 87° 40′, the structure must be (3), and the slight distortion from a right-angle must be due to the repulsion of the two lone pairs.

In sulphur hexafluoride, SF_6 (Fig. 2.26), the sulphur atom is excited to provide sufficient unpaired electrons.

	3s	3p	3d
Electronic structure of sulphur atom—ground state	↑↓	↑↓ ↑ ↑	☐ ☐ ☐ ☐ ☐
Electronic structure of sulphur atom—excited state	↑	↑ ↑ ↑	↑ ↑ ☐ ☐ ☐
Sulphur atom having gained six electrons from fluorine atoms in SF_6 molecule	↑↓	↑↓ ↑↓ ↑↓	↑↓ ↑↓ ☐ ☐ ☐

sp^3d^2 hybridization occurs and the six hybrid orbitals are directed to the corners of a regular octahedron.

Figure 2.26.   Sulphur hexafluoride molecule

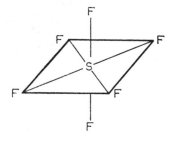

Iodine heptafluoride is perhaps the only example of seven orbitals and sp^3d^3 hybridization. The number of outer orbitals and commonly occurring shapes and types of hybridization are summarized in Table 2.4.

TABLE 2.4

Number of outer orbitals	Shape	Hybridization
2	Linear	sp
3	Plane triangle	sp^2
4	Tetrahedron	sp^3
5	Trigonal bipyramid	$sp^3 d$
6	Octahedron	$sp^3 d^2$
7	Pentagonal bipyramid	$sp^3 d^3$
(4	Square planar	dsp^2)

Sigma and Pi Bonds

All the bonds formed in these examples result from end to end overlap of orbitals and are called sigma (σ) bonds. When double or triple bonds occur, some orbitals overlap laterally giving pi (π) bonds.

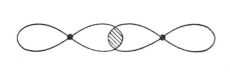 

Fig. 2.27

π bonds are never included in hybridization, but apart from this all the orbitals in the outer shell are hybridized.

Further information on the shapes of covalent molecules may be obtained from the following sources:

ADDISON, W. E., *Structural Principles in Inorganic Compounds*, Longmans, 1961.
CARTMELL, E. and FOWLES, G. W. A., *Valency and Molecular Structure*, Butterworths, 1961.
GILLESPIE, R. J. and NYHOLM, R. S., *Quarterly Reviews of the Chemical Society*, **11**, 339, 1957.

Molecular Orbital Method

The previous section described the valence bond or electron pair theory. There the molecule was regarded as composed of atoms, which to some extent retained their character even when chemically bonded. In the molecular orbital theory, the valency electrons are considered to be associated with all the nuclei concerned.

Electrons may be considered either as particles or waves. An electron in an atom may therefore be described as occupying an atomic orbital, or by a wave function ψ, which is a solution to the Schrödinger wave equation. Electrons in a molecule are said to occupy molecular orbitals. The wave function describing a molecular orbital may be obtained by one of two procedures:

1. Linear combination of atomic orbitals (L.C.A.O.).
2. United atom method.

L.C.A.O. Method

Consider two similar atoms 1 and 2 which have atomic orbitals described by the wave functions $\psi(1)$ and $\psi(2)$. When these atoms form a bond, the electrons originally in the atomic orbitals now occupy molecular orbitals, and the molecular orbital is formed by a linear combination of the atomic orbitals $\psi(1)$ and $\psi(2)$.

$$\psi = N\{C(1)\psi(1) + C(2)\psi(2)\}$$

where N is a normalizing constant chosen to ensure that the probability of finding the electron in the whole of the space is unity, and $C(1)$ and $C(2)$ are constants chosen to give a minimum energy for ψ.

The atomic orbitals $\psi(1)$ and $\psi(2)$ will only combine effectively if they have similar energy, if they overlap, and if the orbitals have the same symmetry. When a pair of atomic orbitals $\psi(1)$ and $\psi(2)$ combine, they give rise to a pair of new molecular orbitals $\psi+$ and $\psi-$ of different energy.

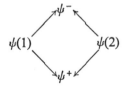

In a very simple case such as H_2^+ (which has only one electron), when the atomic orbitals overlap, two molecular orbitals are formed.

$$\psi + = \frac{1}{\sqrt{2}} \{\psi(1) + \psi(2)\}$$

and

$$\psi - = \frac{1}{\sqrt{2}} \{\psi(1) - \psi(2)\}.$$

The function $\psi+$ is a bonding molecular orbital and is associated with a decrease in energy, whilst $\psi-$ is an antibonding orbital and is associated with an increase in energy (Fig. 2.28).

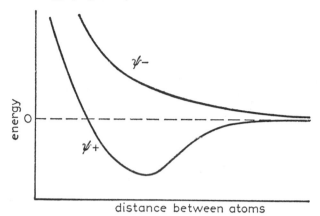

Fig. 2.28. Energy of $\psi+$ and $\psi-$ molecular orbitals

The functions $\psi+$ and $\psi-$ are in M.O. language often called ψg and ψu. g stands for gerade (even) and u for ungerade (odd). g and u refer to the symmetry of the orbital about its centre. If the sign of ψ is unchanged when the orbital is reflected about its centre (i.e. x, y and z are replaced by $-x$, $-y$ and $-z$) it is gerade. If the process reverses the sign, the orbital is ungerade.

Some further symbols are necessary to describe the way in which the atomic orbitals overlap. Overlap of orbitals along the axis joining the nuclei produces σ molecular orbitals, whilst lateral overlap of atomic orbitals forms π molecular orbitals. Table 2.5 indicates the formation of both σ and π orbitals and bonding and antibonding molecular orbitals.

Note that the atomic orbitals $2pz$ will also give π bonding and π antibonding orbitals of the same energy as the $2py$ ones. Thus both the $\pi2p$ and the π^*2p orbitals are doubly degenerate.

Each molecular orbital has a definite energy, and is defined by four quantum numbers. The principal quantum number n and the subsidiary quantum number l are retained from atomic orbitals and have the same significance. The magnetic quantum number of atomic orbitals is replaced by a new quantum number λ. In a diatomic molecule, the line joining the nuclei is taken as a reference direction and λ represents the quantization of angular momentum in $h/2\pi$ units with respect to this axis. λ takes the same values as m takes for atoms, i.e.

$$\lambda = -l, \ldots, -3, -2, -1, 0, 1, 2, 3, \ldots, l.$$

When $\lambda = 0$, the orbitals are symmetrical around the axis and are called σ orbitals. When $\lambda = \pm 1$ there are π orbitals and when $\lambda = \pm 2$ there are

TABLE 2.5. M.O.'s for homonuclear diatomic molecule using the second shell of electrons

Atomic orbitals	Molecular orbitals		Symbol
  2s 2s		σ overlap bonding g	σ2s
		σ overlap antibonding u	σ*2s
  2px 2px		σ overlap bonding g	σ2px
		σ overlap antibonding u	σ*2px
  2py 2py		π overlap bonding u	π2py
		π overlap antibonding g	π*2py

δ orbitals. The spin quantum number which may have values of $\pm\frac{1}{2}$ is the same as for atomic orbitals. The Pauli exclusion principle is applied to molecular orbitals; no two electrons in the same molecule can have all four quantum numbers the same.

The order of energy of molecular orbitals has been determined mainly from spectroscopic data. In simple homonuclear diatomic molecules, the order is:

$$\sigma 1s, \ \sigma^*1s, \ \sigma 2s, \ \sigma^*2s, \ \sigma 2px, \ \begin{cases} \pi 2py \\ \pi 2pz \end{cases}, \ \begin{cases} \pi^*2py, \ \sigma^*2px. \\ \pi^*2pz \end{cases}$$

The *Aufbau* or build-up principle is used, the orbitals of lowest energy being filled up first.

Examples of molecular orbital treatment

$H_2{}^+$ $\sigma 1s^1$ one electron in $1s$ molecular orbital.

H_2 $\sigma 1s^2$ two electrons in $1s$ molecular orbital forming σ bond.

N_2 The filled K shell $\sigma 1s^2 \sigma^*1s^2$ which is non-bonding is written K,K. N_2 is thus:

$$K,K, \ \sigma 2s^2, \ \sigma^*2s^2, \ \sigma 2px^2, \ \pi 2py^2, \ \pi 2pz^2.$$

The effects of the $2s$ bonding and antibonding orbitals cancel one another, so that the two electrons in the $2px$ orbital form a σ bond, and the pair of electrons in the $2py$ and $2pz$ orbitals result in two π bonds.

O_2 $K,K,\ \sigma 2s^2,\ \sigma^* 2s^2,\ \sigma 2px^2,\ \pi 2py^2,\ \pi 2pz^2,\ \pi^* 2py^1,\ \pi^* 2pz^1.$

$\pi^* 2py$ and $\pi^* 2pz$ have the same energy; so each is singly occupied. These two antibonding electrons cancel the bonding effect of a π-bonding orbital, so the overall effect is one σ bond and one π bond.

F_2 $K,K,\ \sigma 2s^2,\ \sigma^* 2s^2,\ \sigma 2px^2,\ \pi 2py^2,\ \pi 2pz^2,\ \pi^* 2py^2,\ \pi^* 2pz^2.$

The $2s$ bonding and antibonding orbitals cancel each other as do the bonding and antibonding py and pz orbitals. The overall effect is therefore one σ bond.

United Atom Method

The L.C.A.O. method described above is tantamount to bringing the atoms from infinity to their equilibrium positions in the molecule. The

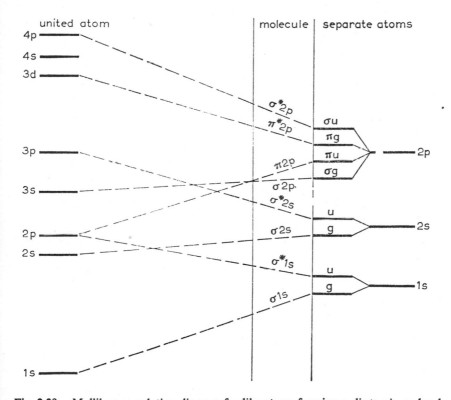

Fig. 2.29. Mulliken correlation diagram for like atoms forming a di atomic molecul

united atom method is an alternative approach. It starts with a hypothetical 'united atom' where the nuclei are superimposed, and then moved to their equilibrium distance apart. The united atom has the same number of orbitals as a normal atom, but it contains the electrons from two atoms. Thus some electrons must be promoted to higher energy levels in the united atom. Further, the energy of the united atom orbitals differs from that of the atomic orbitals because of the greater nuclear charge. Thus the molecular orbitals are in an intermediate position between the orbitals in the united atom and those in the separate atom. If lines are drawn between the energies of the electrons in the separate atoms and in the united atom (that is a graph of internal energy against the distance between the nuclei from $r = 0$ to $r = \infty$), a correlation diagram is obtained (Fig. 2.29).

For further details on the molecular orbital theory, the following sources are useful:

CARTMELL, E. and FOWLES, G. W. A., *Valency and Molecular Structure*, Butterworths, 1961.
COULSON, C. A., *Valence*, Clarendon Press, 1961.

PROBLEMS

1. Relate the tendency of atoms to gain or lose electrons to the types of bonds they form.
2. Indicate to what extent the following will conduct electricity, and give the mechanism of conduction in each case:
   (a) NaCl   (fused);
   (b) NaCl   (aqueous solution);
   (c) NaCl   (solid);
   (d) Cu   (solid);
   (e) CCl$_4$ (liquid).
3. Why are ionic compounds usually high melting, whilst most simple covalent compounds have low melting points? Explain the high melting point of diamond.
4. How are the minimum values of radius ratio arrived at for various co-ordination numbers, and what are these limits? Give examples of the types of crystal structure associated with each co-ordination number.
5. Do crystals always adopt the structures indicated by their radius ratios? If not, what generalizations can be made about the exceptions?
6. Predict the structure of each of the following, and indicate whether the bond angles are likely to be distorted from the theoretical values:
   (a) BeCl$_2$; (b) BCl$_3$; (c) SiCl$_4$; (d) PCl$_5$ (vapour); (e) PF$_3$; (f) F$_2$O; (g) SF$_4$; (h) IF$_5$; (i) SO$_2$.

CHAPTER 3

GENERAL PROPERTIES OF THE ELEMENTS

Size of Atoms and Ions

The size of atoms decreases from left to right across a period in the periodic table. For example, on moving from lithium to beryllium, the number of charges on the nucleus is increased by one, so that all the orbital electrons are pulled in closer to the nucleus. In a given period, the alkali metal is the largest atom and the halogen the smallest. When a row of ten transition elements, or fourteen inner transition elements occurs in a horizontal period, the contraction in size is even more marked.

On descending a group in the periodic table such as lithium, sodium, potassium, rubidium, caesium, the size of the atoms increases due to the effect of extra shells of electrons being added; this outweighs the effect of increased nuclear charge.

A positive ion is formed by removing one or more electrons from an atom. Normally the whole of the outer shell of electrons is removed in this way, and since the remaining inner shells do not extend so far in space, the cation is much smaller than the metal atom. In addition, the ratio of positive charges on the nucleus to the number of orbital electrons is increased. Thus the effective nuclear charge is increased and the electrons are pulled in. A positive ion is therefore smaller than the corresponding atom and the more electrons removed (that is, the greater the charge on the ion), the smaller it becomes.

> Atomic radius Na 1·57 Å   Atomic radius Fe 1·17 A
> Ionic radius Na^+ 0·98   Ionic radius Fe^{2+} 0·76
>   Ionic radius Fe^{3+} 0·64

When a negative ion is formed, one or more electrons are added to an atom, the effective nuclear charge is reduced and hence the electron cloud expands. Negative ions are bigger than the corresponding atom.

> Van der Waals non-bonded radius Cl   1·40 Å
> Ionic radius Cl^- 1·81 Å

41

TABLE 3.1

Period \ Group	1	2	Sc	Ti	V	Cr	Mn	Fe	Co	Ni	Cu	Zn	3	4	5	6	7	0
1	H ~0·30																	He 1·20
2	Li 1·23	Be 0·89											B 0·80	C 0·77	N 0·74	O 0·74	F 0·72	Ne 1·60
3	Na 1·57	Mg 1·36											Al 1·25	Si 1·17	P 1·10	S 1·04	Cl 0·99	Ar 1·91
4	K 2·03	Ca 1·74	Sc 1·44	Ti 1·32	V 1·22	Cr 1·17	Mn 1·17	Fe 1·17	Co 1·16	Ni 1·15	Cu 1·17	Zn 1·25	Ga 1·25	Ge 1·22	As 1·21	Se 1·14	Br 1·14	Kr 2·00
5	Rb 2·16	Sr 1·91	Y 1·62	Zr 1·45	Nb 1·34	Mo 1·29	Tc —	Ru 1·24	Rh 1·25	Pd 1·28	Ag 1·34	Cd 1·41	In 1·50	Sn 1·40	Sb 1·41	Te 1·37	I 1·33	Xe 2·20
6	Cs 2·35	Ba 1·98	La 1·69	Hf 1·44	Ta 1·34	W 1·30	Re 1·28	Os 1·26	Ir 1·26	Pt 1·29	Au 1·34	Hg 1·44	Tl 1·55	Pb 1·46	Bi 1·52	Po	At	Rn
7	Fr	Ra	Ac	Th 1·65	Pa 1·65	U 1·42												

Lanthanides	Ce	Pr	Nd	Pm	Sm	Eu	Gd	Tb	Dy	Ho	Er	Tm	Yb	Lu
	1·65	1·65	1·64	—	1·66	1·85	1·61	1·59	1·59	1·58	1·57	1·56	1·70	1·56

COVALENT RADII OF THE ELEMENTS

(Numerical values are given in Ångström units. The values for the inert gases are atomic radii.)
(Large circles indicate large radii and small circles small radii.)
After MOELLER, T., *Inorganic Chemistry*, Wiley, 1952.

Ionization Potentials

If energy is supplied to an atom, electrons may be promoted to a higher energy level. If sufficient energy is supplied the electron may be completely removed, giving a positive ion. The energy required to remove the most loosely bound electron from an isolated gaseous atom is called the ionization potential. These are determined from spectra and are measured in electron volts. (1 eV is the energy acquired by an electron falling through a potential of one volt and is equivalent to 23·06 kcal/mole.) Since it is possible to remove one, two or three ... electrons from most atoms there is a first, second or third ... ionization potential. Thus the first ionization potential is the energy required to convert $M \rightarrow M^+$; the second, $M^+ \rightarrow M^{2+}$; the third, $M^{2+} \rightarrow M^{3+}$ and so on.

The factors influencing the ionization potential are the size of the atom, the charge on the nucleus, the screening effect of inner electron shells and the type of electron involved. These factors are usually interrelated. In a small atom the electrons are tightly held, but the larger the atom, the less strongly are the electrons held; thus the ionization potential decreases with increased size. Thus in Group I metals, the ionization potential decreases with increased size, but the extra shells of electrons must also help to screen the outer electron from the nucleus (Table 3.2).

	First I.P.	Second I.P.
Li	5·39 eV	75·62 eV
Na	5·14	47·29
K	4·34	31·81
Rb	4·18	27·36
Cs	3·89	23·40

For this group it can be seen that removal of a second electron involves so much more energy that in practice it does not occur. This is related to the structure of the atom, for whilst it is fairly easy to remove the single outer electron, it is much more difficult to break into a completed octet.

The first, second and third ionization potentials for magnesium are 7·64, 15·03 and 80·12 eV respectively. The first I.P. is greater than the value for sodium, partly due to the increased nuclear charge and partly due to the smaller size of magnesium. Once the first electron has been removed, the effective nuclear charge is increased and the size of Mg^+ is less than a Mg atom, so that the second I.P. is greater than the first. Removal of a third electron is much harder because of the decreased size, increased nuclear charge and a completed shell would need to be broken.

Due to the shape of the orbital, an s electron penetrates nearer to the nucleus than a p, d or f electron and is more tightly held. Other factors being equal, the ionization potential decreases $s > p > d > f$.

In general, the ionization potential decreases on descending a group and

TABLE 3.2

Period \ Group	1	2											3	4	5	6	7	0
1	H 13·6																	He 24·6
2	Li 5·4	Be 9·3											B 8·3	C 11·3	N 14·6	O 13·6	F 17·4	Ne 21·6
3	Na 5·1	Mg 7·6											Al 6·0	Si 8·2	P 11·0	S 10·4	Cl 13·0	Ar 15·7
4	K 4·3	Ca 6·1	Sc 6·5	Ti 6·9	V 6·8	Cr 6·8	Mn 7·4	Fe 7·9	Co 7·9	Ni 7·6	Cu 7·7	Zn 9·4	Ga 6·0	Ge 8·1	As 10·0	Se 9·8	Br 11·8	Kr 14·0
5	Rb 4·2	Sr 5·7	Y 6·6	Zr 6·9	Nb 6·8	Mo 7·2	Tc 7·3	Ru 7·5	Rh 7·7	Pd 8·3	Ag 7·6	Cd 9·0	In 5·8	Sn 7·3	Sb 8·6	Te 9·0	I 10·4	Xe 12·1
6	Cs 3·9	Ba 5·2	La 5·6	Hf 5·5	Ta 6·0	W 8·0	Re 7·9	Os 8·7	Ir 9·2	Pt 9·0	Au 9·2	Hg 10·5	Tl 6·1	Pb 7·4	Bi 8·0	Po	At	Rn 10·8
7	Fr	Ra	Ac	Th	Pa	U												

FIRST IONIZATION POTENTIALS OF THE ELEMENTS

(Numerical values are given in electron volts 1 eV = 23·06 kcal/mole.)
(Large circles indicate high values and small circles low values.)
After SANDERSON, R. T., *Chemical Periodicity*, Reinhold, New York.

increases on crossing a period, although since s electrons are more difficult than p or d the change across a period may not be quite regular. Removal of successive electrons becomes more difficult and first I.P. < second I.P. < third I.P. . . .

Electron Affinity

The energy released when an extra electron is added to a neutral gaseous atom is termed the electron affinity. Usually only one electron is added, forming a uninegative ion. This repels further electrons and energy is needed to add on a second electron, hence the negative affinity of O^{2-}. Electron affinities depend on the size and effective nuclear charge. They cannot be determined directly, but are obtained indirectly from the Born-Haber cycle. Some values derived by Pauling are given below:

$$
\begin{array}{ll}
F \to F^- & 3\cdot62 \text{ eV} \\
Cl \to Cl^- & 3\cdot79 \\
Br \to Br^- & 3\cdot56 \\
I \to I^- & 3\cdot28 \\
H \to H^- & 0\cdot77 \\
O \to O^{2-} & -7\cdot28 \\
S \to S^{2-} & -3\cdot44
\end{array}
$$

The values for Li, Na, K, Rb and Cs are assumed to be 0.

(For further details see: PAULING, L., *The Nature of the Chemical Bond*, 3rd Edn., Oxford University Press, 1961.)

Born-Haber Cycle

This cycle devised by Born and Haber in 1919 relates the lattice energy of a crystal to other thermochemical data. The energy terms involved in building a crystal lattice such as sodium chloride may be taken in steps. The elements in their standard state are first converted to gaseous atoms, then to ions and finally packed into the crystal lattice.

The heats of sublimation, dissociation and ionization potential are positive since energy is supplied to the system. According to Hess's law, the overall energy change in a process depends only on the energy of the initial and final states and not on the route taken.   Thus the heat of formation Q is equal to the sum of the terms going the other way round the cycle.

$$-Q = +S + \tfrac{1}{2}D + I - E - U$$

All the terms except the lattice energy and electron affinity can be measured. Originally the lattice energy was calculated for known crystal structures and thus values were obtained for the electron affinity.   More recently when values for electron affinity had been found in this way the cycle has been used to calculate the lattice energy for unknown structures.   This is useful, for the lattice must be broken up when the substance dissolves.   If the lattice energy is high, it is unlikely that the heat of solvation will be big enough to offset this, so the substance will probably be insoluble.   The resistance of many transition metals to chemical attack is related to a similar series of energy changes and nobility is favoured by a high heat of sublimation, high ionization potential and low heat of solvation of the ions.   For further uses of the cycle see the article by L. BREWER, *Journal of Chemical Education*, **36**, 9, 446, 1959.

Electronegativity

The tendency of an atom to attract electrons to itself *when combined in a compound* is termed the electronegativity of the atom.   Generally, small atoms attract electrons more than large ones and are therefore more electronegative.   Atoms with nearly filled shells of electrons will tend to have higher electronegativities than those with sparsely occupied ones.   Ionization potentials and electron affinity may be regarded as measures of electronegativity and Mulliken regarded electronegativity as the average of the two. The commonly accepted values are more nearly obtained by I.P. + E.A./ 130, where the ionization potential and electron affinity are in kcal/mole. Since only a few electron affinities are known, it is more usual to use another approach based on bond energies.   It is worth remembering a few electronegativity values (see Table 3.3).   Covalent bonds are formed by elements which have similar electronegativity values, and ionic bonds are formed between elements with a large electronegativity difference.

Generally the bond formed between two atoms A and B will be intermediate between pure covalent A—B and pure ionic $A^+ B^-$.   Because of this partial ionic character, the bond is strengthened, that is the bond energy is increased.   The bond is in fact stabilized by resonance.

Resonance energy = Actual bond energy − Energy for 100% covalent bond

Pauling states that the electronegativity difference between two atoms equals $0 \cdot 18\sqrt{\Delta}$, where Δ is the resonance energy in k. cal/mole.   To evaluate the

TABLE 3.3

						H 2·1
Li 1·0	Be 1·5	B 2·0	C 2·5	N 3·0	O 3·5	F 4·0
Na 0·9						Cl 3·0
K 0·8						Br 2·8
Rb 0·8						I 2·5
Cs 0·7						

electronegativity difference, both the actual bond energy and the energy for a 100% covalent bond must be known. The actual bond energy can be measured, but the energy of a 100% covalent bond must be calculated. This was done as follows:

(1) It was assumed that the 100% covalent bond energy equals the arithmetic mean of the covalent energies of A—A and B—B molecules

$$E_{100\% \text{ covalent } A-B} = \tfrac{1}{2}(E_{A-A} + E_{B-B})$$

The bond energy in A—A and B—B molecules can be measured and so the resonance energy may be evaluated. Since the resonance energy must be positive, this assumption is incorrect because in some cases such as LiH, NaH, KH, the calculated energy is negative.

(2) Pauling suggested the geometric mean:

$$E_{100\% \text{ covalent } A-B} = \sqrt{(E_{A-A} \cdot E_{B-B})}$$

so resonance energy Δ = actual bond energy $- \sqrt{(E_{A-A} \cdot E_{B-B})}$ (in k.cals)
Pauling evaluated $0 \cdot 18\sqrt{\Delta}$ for a number of bonds and called this the electronegativity difference between A and B. He found for example:

Bond	Δ	$0 \cdot 18\sqrt{\Delta}$	
C—H	5·8	0·4	i.e. $\mathscr{X}C - \mathscr{X}H = 0 \cdot 4$ ($\mathscr{X}$ = electronegativity of atom)
H—Cl	25·4	0·9	i.e. $\mathscr{X}Cl - \mathscr{X}H = 0 \cdot 9$
N—H	30·1	1·0	i.e. $\mathscr{X}N - \mathscr{X}H = 1 \cdot 0$

If $\mathscr{X}H = 0$ then the electronegativity values of C, Cl and N would be 0·4, 0·9 and 1·0 respectively. The origin of the scale has been changed from $\mathscr{X}H = 0$ to $\mathscr{X}H = 2·05$ to make the values for C and F 2·5 and 4·0 respectively. Thus by adding 2·05 the usually accepted electronegativity values are obtained (see Table 3.4).

If two atoms have similar electronegativities, that is a similar tendency to attract electrons, the bond between them will be covalent. Similarly a large difference in electronegativity leads to an ionic bond. Rather than have the two extreme forms, Pauling introduced the idea that the ionic character of a bond varies with the difference in electronegativity as shown in Fig. 3.1. This graph is based on the ionic characters HI 4% ionic, HBr 11%, HCl 19% and HF 45%, which are known from dipole moment measurements. 50% ionic character occurs when the electronegativity difference

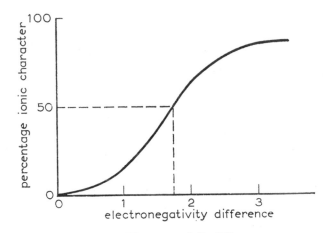

Fig. 3.1.   Electronegativity difference

between the atoms is about 1·7, so for a larger difference than this a bond is more ionic than covalent. Similarly if the electronegativity difference is less than this, the bond is more covalent than ionic. It is better to describe a bond such as one of those in BF_3 as 63% ionic, rather than just ionic.

The electronegativity values given are those stated by Pauling, but others have been calculated from different theoretical assumptions by Huggins, Mulliken and Sanderson. A review of electronegativity values is given by ALLRED, A. L., *Journal of Inorganic and Nuclear Chemistry*, **5**, 269, 1958, and **17**, 43 and 215, 1961.

Polarizing Power and Polarizability—Fajans' Rules

If the two ions A^+ and B^- are brought together to their equilibrium distance, the type of bond between them depends on the effect of one ion on

TABLE 3.4

Period \ Group	1	2											3	4	5	6	7	0
1	H 2·1																H 2·1	He
2	Li 1·0	Be 1·5											B 2·0	C 2·5	N 3·0	O 3·5	F 4·0	Ne
3	Na 0·9	Mg 1·2											Al 1·5	Si 1·8	P 2·1	S 2·5	Cl 3·0	Ar
4	K 0·8	Ca 1·0	Sc 1·3	Ti 1·5	V 1·6	Cr 1·6	Mn 1·5	Fe 1·8	Co 1·8	Ni 1·8	Cu 1·9	Zn 1·6	Ga 1·6	Ge 1·8	As 2·0	Se 2·4	Br 2·8	Kr
5	Rb 0·8	Sr 1·0	Y 1·2	Zr 1·4	Nb 1·6	Mo 1·8	Tc 1·9	Ru 2·2	Rh 2·2	Pd 2·2	Ag 1·9	Cd 1·7	In 1·7	Sn 1·8	Sb 1·9	Te 2·1	I 2·5	Xe
6	Cs 0·7	Ba 0·9	La 1·1	Hf 1·3	Ta 1·5	W 1·7	Re 1·9	Os 2·2	Ir 2·2	Pt 2·2	Au 2·4	Hg 1·9	Tl 1·8	Pb 1·8	Bi 1·9	Po 2·0	At 2·2	Rn
7	Fr 0·7	Ra 0·9	Ac 1·1	Th 1·3	Pa 1·5	U 1·7												

PAULING'S ELECTRONEGATIVITY VALUES

Electronegativity varies with the oxidation state of the element. The values given are for the most common oxidation states. (Large circles indicate high values and small circles small values.)

Copyright 1960, Cornell University. Adapted by permission of Cornell University Press.

the other.   The positive ion attracts the electrons on the negative ion and repels the nucleus, thus distorting or polarizing the negative ion.   If the polarization is quite small, then an ionic bond results.   If the degree of polarization is large, electrons are drawn from the negative ion to the positive ion and appreciable covalent character results.

The extent of ion distortion depends on both the power of an ion to distort the other, i.e. its polarizing power, and the susceptibility of an ion to distortion, i.e. its polarizability.   Generally the polarizing power increases as ions become smaller and more highly charged.   The polarizability of a negative ion is greater than that of a positive ion since the electrons are less firmly bound because of the differences in effective nuclear charge.   Large negative ions are more polarizable than small ones.   These trends are summarized in Fajans' rules which state that covalent bonding is favoured by:

1. Small positive ion.
2. Large negative ion.
3. Large charges on either ion.

Metallic Character

Metals are electropositive and have a tendency to lose electrons, if supplied with energy:

$$M \rightarrow M^+ + e$$

The stronger this tendency, the more electropositive and more metallic an element is.   The tendency to lose electrons depends on the ionization potential.   Since it is easier to remove an electron from a large atom than from a small one, metallic character increases as we descend the groups in the periodic table.   Thus in Group IV, carbon is a non-metal; germanium shows some metallic properties, and tin and lead are metals.   Similarly metallic character decreases from left to right across the periodic table because atomic size decreases and ionization potential increases.   Thus sodium and magnesium are more metallic than silicon, which, in turn, is more metallic than chlorine.   The most electropositive elements are found in the lower left of the periodic table and the most non-metallic in the top right.

Electropositivity is really the converse of electronegativity, but it is convenient to retain the concept of electropositivity when describing metals. Strongly electropositive elements give ionic compounds.   Metallic oxides and hydroxides are basic since they ionize, and give hydroxyl ions:

$$NaOH \rightarrow Na^+ + OH^-$$
$$CaO + H_2O \rightarrow Ca^{2+} + 2OH^-$$

Oxides which are insoluble in water are regarded as basic if they react with acids to form salts. Thus in the main groups of the periodic table, basic properties increase on descending a group because the elements become more electropositive and more ionic. However, this generalization does not hold for the *d* block, and particularly for the central groups of transition elements (Cr, Mn, Fe, Co, Ni) where basicity and the ability to form simple ions decreases on descending the group.

The degree of electropositivity is shown in a variety of ways. Strongly electropositive elements react with water and acids. They form strongly basic oxides and hydroxides, and they react with oxy-acids to give stable salts such as carbonates, nitrates and sulphates. Weakly electropositive elements are unaffected by water and are much less readily attacked by acids. Their oxides are frequently amphoteric, and react with both acids and alkalis. They are not basic enough to form stable carbonates.

The electropositive nature of a metal is also shown in the degree of hydration of the ions. In the change: M^+ to $[(H_2O)_n \rightarrow M]^+$ the positive charge becomes spread over the whole complex ion. Since the charge is no longer localized on the metal, this is almost the same as the change $M^+ \rightarrow M$. Strongly electropositive metals have a great tendency to the opposite change: $M \rightarrow M^+$, so that they are not readily hydrated. The less electropositive the metal, the weaker the tendency $M \rightarrow M^+$ and the stronger the degree of hydration. Thus the elements in Group II are more heavily hydrated than those in Group I, and the degree of hydration decreases down a group, e.g. $MgCl_2.6H_2O$ and $BaCl_2.2H_2O$.

Salts of strongly electropositive metals have little tendency to hydrolyse and form oxy-salts. Since the size of the metal ion is large it has little tendency to form complexes. On the other hand, salts of weakly electropositive elements hydrolyse and may form oxy-salts. Because they are smaller, the metal ions have a greater tendency to form complexes.

Standard Electrode Potentials and Electrochemical Series

When a metal is immersed in a solution containing its own ions, an electric potential is set up between the two. The size of the potential E for the electrode reaction $M^{n+} + ne \rightleftharpoons M$ is given by the Nernst equation:

$$E = Eo + \frac{RT}{nF}\ln_e a$$

where R is the gas constant, T the absolute temperature, n the valency of the ion and F the Faraday. For most purposes, the activity a may be replaced by the concentration of ions in solution. Eo is the standard electrode potential, which is a constant for any particular metal and is in fact the electrode potential at unit activity.

The standard electrode potential is thus a measure of the electropositive nature of the metal. The potential of a single electrode cannot be measured, but if a second electrode of known potential is put in the solution, the difference in potential between the two can be measured. The standard by which all electrode potentials are compared is the hydrogen electrode. (A platinized platinum electrode is saturated with hydrogen at one atmosphere pressure and immersed in a solution of H^+ at unit activity. The potential developed is arbitrarily fixed at zero.)

If the elements are arranged in order of decreasing standard electrode potentials, the resulting Table 3.5 is called the electrochemical series.

TABLE 3.5.   Standard electrode potentials at 25°C (European Sign Convention)

	volts
Li^+ | Li	-3.01
K^+ | K	-2.92
Ca^{2+} | Ca	-2.84
Al^{3+} | Al	-1.66
Mn^{2+} | Mn	-1.08
Zn^{2+} | Zn	-0.76
Fe^{2+} | Fe	-0.44
Cd^{2+} | Cd	-0.40
Co^{2+} | Co	-0.27
Ni^{2+} | Ni	-0.23
Sn^{2+} | Sn	-0.14
Pb^{2+} | Pb	-0.13
H^+ | H_2	0.00
Cu^{2+} | Cu	$+0.35$
Ag^+ | Ag	$+0.80$
Au^{3+} | Au	$+1.38$

Electrode potentials can also be measured for elements like oxygen and the halogens which form negative ions (Table 3.6).

TABLE 3.6.   Standard electrode potentials

	volts
O_2 | OH^-	$+0.40$
I_2 | I^-	$+0.57$
Br_2 | Br^-	$+1.07$
Cl_2 | Cl^-	$+1.36$
F_2 | F^-	$+2.85$

The sign conventions in Europe and the U.S.A. are exactly opposite. For example, Li has an electrode potential of -3.01 volts on the European scale and $+3.01$ on the American convention.

In the electrochemical series the most electropositive elements are at the top and the least electropositive at the bottom. The greater the negative value of the potential, the greater is the tendency for a metal to ionize. Thus a metal will displace another metal lower down the series from solution. For example, in recovering copper scrap iron is sacrificed.

$$Fe + Cu^{2+}SO_4^{2-} \rightarrow Fe^{2+}SO_4^{2-} + Cu\downarrow$$

In the Daniell cell zinc tends to displace copper from copper salts in solution. This causes the potential difference between the plates.

When a solution is electrolysed the externally applied potential has to overcome the electrode potential. The minimum voltage necessary to cause deposition is equal and opposite in sign to the potential between the solution and the electrode. Elements low down in the series discharge first, thus Cu^{2+} discharges before H^+, so copper may be electrolysed in aqueous solution. However, hydrogen and other gases often require a considerably higher voltage than the theoretical potential before they discharge. For hydrogen, this extra or over-voltage may be 0·8 volts, and thus it is possible to electrolyse zinc salts in aqueous solution.

Several factors affect the value of the standard potential. The conversion of $M \rightarrow M^+$ in aqueous solution may be considered in a series of steps:

1. Sublimation of a solid metal.
2. Ionization of a gaseous metal atom.
3. Hydration of a gaseous ion.

These are best considered in a Born-Haber type of cycle.

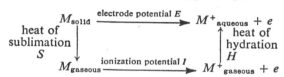

The heat of sublimation and the ionization potential are positive since energy is supplied, so

$$E = +S + I - H$$

Since S and I are high for transition metals, E is low, that is the metal has little tendency to form ions hence it is unreactive or noble. Among the s block metals (Groups I and II) S and I are small, so that E is high and the metals are reactive.

During oxidation electrons are lost, and during reduction they are gained. A reducing agent must therefore supply electrons, and elements having large negative electrode potentials are strong reducing agents. The strengths of oxidizing and reducing agents may be measured by the size of the potential between a solution and an inert electrode. Standard oxidation potentials are obtained when the concentrations of oxidized and reduced forms are equal, the standard hydrogen electrode being taken as zero. The most powerful oxidizing agents have a large positive oxidation potential and strong reducing agents have a large negative potential. Standard oxidation potentials allow us to predict which ions will oxidize or reduce other ions, but they do not indicate the rate of the reaction and a catalyst may be required, as in the oxidation of arsenites by ceric sulphate.

Horizontal, Vertical and Diagonal Relationships in the Periodic Table

On moving across a period in the periodic table, the number of electrons in the outer shell increases from one to eight. Thus Group I elements all have one electron in their outer orbital and when they react they are univalent, because the loss of one electron leaves an inert gas structure. Similarly Group II elements have two electrons in their outer shell and are divalent. The valency of an element in one of the main groups is either the group number which is the same as the number of outer electrons, or eight minus the group number. Group V elements (e.g. nitrogen) have five outer electrons. If three of these are shared in covalent bonds with other atoms, the nitrogen atom has a share in eight electrons and has a stable configuration. Thus nitrogen is trivalent, for example in ammonia NH_3. The halogens are in Group VII and have seven outer electrons. The valency should be $8 - 7 = 1$, and if one electron can be gained either by electrovalent or covalent bond formation, a stable structure is attained. The number of outer electrons thus determines the valency of the element.

On moving from left to right across a period, the size of the atoms decreases because of the additional nuclear charge. Thus the orbital electrons are more tightly held, and the ionization potential increases. The metallic character of the elements also decreases, and the oxides of the elements become less basic. Thus Na_2O is strongly basic; Al_2O_3 is amphoteric and reacts with both acids and bases; SO_2 is an acidic oxide since it dissolves in water to form sulphurous acid (H_2SO_3), and reacts with bases to form sulphites. Generally, metallic oxides are basic, whilst non-metallic oxides are acidic.

On descending a vertical group in the periodic table, the elements all have the same number of outer electrons and the same valency, but the size increases. Thus the ionization potential decreases and the metallic character increases. This is particularly apparent in Groups IV and V which begin with the non-metals carbon and nitrogen and end with the metals lead and bismuth. The oxides becomes increasingly basic on descending the group.

On moving diagonally across the periodic table the elements show certain similarities. These are usually weaker than the similarities within a group, but are quite pronounced in the following pairs of elements:

$$\begin{array}{cccc} \text{Li} & \text{Be} & \text{B} & \text{C} \\ & \diagdown & \diagdown & \diagdown \\ \text{Na} & \text{Mg} & \text{Al} & \text{Si} \end{array}$$

On moving across a period, the charge on the ions increases and the size decreases, causing the polarizing power to increase. On moving down a group, the size increases and the polarizing power decreases. On moving diagonally these two effects partly cancel each other, so that there is no marked change in properties. The type and strength of bond formed and the properties of the compounds are often similar, although the valency is different. Diagonal similarities are most important among the lighter elements, but the line separating the metals from the non-metals also runs diagonally.

Hydrogen

Position in the Periodic Table

Hydrogen, the first element in the periodic table, has the simplest atomic structure of all the elements, and consists of a nucleus of charge +1 and one orbital electron. The alkali metals (Group I) also have a single outer orbital electron, but they tend to lose this electron in reactions and form positive ions; by contrast, hydrogen has little tendency to lose this electron but a great tendency to pair the electron and form a covalent bond. The halogens (Group VII), like hydrogen, are one electron short of an inert gas structure. In many reactions the halogens gain an electron and so form negative ions, although hydrogen can only do this in reactions with highly electropositive metals. This behaviour is explained by the atomic structure, the extremely small size of hydrogen atoms and the low electronegativity value. These unique properties make it difficult to place hydrogen in the periodic table, since its properties differ from those of both Group I and Group VII elements, and although it is included in both groups in the tables in this book, it could well be put in a group on its own.

Isotopes of Hydrogen

If atoms of the same element have different mass numbers they are called isotopes. The difference in mass number arises because the nucleus contains a different number of neutrons. Three isotopes of hydrogen are known: ^1H, deuterium ^2H or ^2D and tritium ^3H or ^3T containing one proton and 0, 1 or 2 neutrons respectively in the nucleus. These isotopes have the same electronic configuration and have essentially the same chemical properties. Because of the enormous mass difference between these isotopes, they show much greater differences in physical properties than are found between the isotopes of other elements. The only differences in chemical properties are equilibrium constants and the rates of reactions; ^1H is more rapidly adsorbed on to surfaces than ^2D for example. Moreover, ^1H has a lower energy of activation than ^2D in reactions with the halogens, and therefore reacts faster. Some physical constants for ^1H and ^2D are given in Table 3.7.

TABLE 3.7

Physical Constant	H₂	D₂
Melting point	−259·2°C	−254·5°C
Boiling point	−252·6°C	−249·4°C
Latent heat of fusion	28·0 cal/mole	52·3 cal/mole
Latent heat of evaporation	216 cal/mole	293 cal/mole
Latent heat of sublimation*	245·7 cal/mole	340·8 cal/mole
Vapour pressure*	54 mmHg	5·8 mmHg

* At −259.1°C

Ordinary hydrogen contains 99·984% of the ^1H isotope and 0·016% of ^2D, and so its properties are essentially those of the lighter isotope. ^2D and compounds of deuterium are separated by electrolysis. If water is electrolysed, ^1H is liberated about six times more readily than ^2D; hence the deuterium content of the residual sample increases, and by repeated electrolyses, water enriched with D_2O or pure D_2O may be obtained. Deuterium oxide undergoes all of the reactions of ordinary water, and is useful in the preparation of other deuterium compounds. Because D_2O has a lower dielectric constant, ionic compounds are less soluble in it than in water. Some physical properties of H_2O and D_2O are compared in Table 3.8.

TABLE 3.8

Physical property	H₂O	D₂O
Specific gravity at 20°C	0·917 g/ml	1·017 g/ml
Freezing point	0°C	3·82°C
Boiling point	100°C	101·42°C
Temperature of maximum density	4°C	11·6°C
Dielectric constant at 20°C	82	80·5
Solubility g NaCl/100 g water at 25°C	35·9	30·5
Solubility g BaCl₂/100 g water at 25°C	35·7	28·9

Deuterium compounds are also prepared by 'exchange' reactions where under suitable conditions deuterium is exchanged for hydrogen in compounds. Thus deuterium reacts with hydrogen at high temperatures forming HD, and it also exchanges with NH_3 and CH_4. Exchange reactions occur readily when they involve ions in solution, for example

$$NaOH + D_2O \rightleftharpoons NaOD + HDO$$
$$NH_4Cl + D_2O \rightleftharpoons NH_3DCl + HDO$$

NH_3DCl may after successive treatments with D_2O be converted into ND_4Cl, which illustrates the equivalence of all four hydrogen atoms in the NH_4^+ ion.

Tritium is unstable, and only occurs to the extent of one part ^3T to 10^{17} parts ^1H. It is produced in nuclear transformations such as

$$^6_3Li + ^1_0n \rightarrow ^4_2He + ^3_1T \quad \text{(in a nuclear reactor)}$$
$$\text{and} \quad ^{14}_7N + ^1_0n \rightarrow ^{12}_6C + ^3_1T \quad \text{(occurs in nature)}$$

Nuclear reactions are explained in Chapter 9.

Ortho and Para Hydrogen

The hydrogen molecule H_2 exists in two different forms known as ortho and para hydrogen. The nuclear spins of the two atoms in the molecule are either in the same direction or in opposite directions and give rise to spin isomerism. This is also found in other symmetrical molecules whose nuclei have spin momenta, e.g. D_2, N_2, F_2, Cl_2.

parallel spins
(ortho)

opposite spins
(para)

There are considerable discrepancies between the physical properties (e.g. boiling points, specific heats and thermal conductivities) of the ortho and para forms, because of differences in their internal energy. This causes differences in the band spectrum of molecular hydrogen. The para form of hydrogen has the lower energy, and the equilibrium mixture between ortho and para forms at absolute zero contains 100% of the para form; but as the temperature is raised, the proportion of ortho hydrogen increases up to a limiting mixture containing 75% ortho hydrogen. Para hydrogen is usually prepared by passing normal hydrogen through a tube packed with charcoal and cooled to liquid air temperature. Para hydrogen prepared in this way can be kept for weeks at room temperature in a glass vessel, because the ortho-para conversion is slow in the absence of catalysts. Suitable catalysts include activated charcoal, atomic hydrogen, metals such as Fe, Ni, Pt and W and paramagnetic substances or ions (which contain unpaired electrons) such as O_2, NO, NO_2, Co^{2+} and Cr_2O_3.

Properties of Molecular Hydrogen

Hydrogen is the lightest gas known, and is colourless, odourless and almost insoluble in water. The abundance of molecular hydrogen on the earth is very small, but hydrogen in its compounds is very abundant for example water, carbohydrates and organic compounds, ammonia and acids. In fact hydrogen is present in more compounds than any other element. It is manufactured on a large scale by the electrolysis of water or sodium hydroxide, by the reaction between carbon and water (water gas), from the cracking of hydrocarbons, or from the reaction between salt-like hydrides with water. In the laboratory it is prepared by the action of dilute acids on metals such as zinc.

Hydrogen is not very reactive, although it burns in air and forms water; under certain conditions it explodes with oxygen and the halogens. Large quantities are used in the production of ammonia

$$N_2 + 3H_2 \rightarrow 2NH_3$$

and this reaction is favoured by high pressure, low temperature and the presence of a suitable catalyst. Hydrogen is also used commercially to reduce metal oxides to metals; the metals concerned are those below iron in the electrochemical series. Hydrogen plays an important part in the hardening of fats and oils, where unsaturated organic compounds are converted to saturated compounds. It also reacts with CO to form methyl alcohol, and with certain metals to form hydrides.

The hydrogen molecule is very stable, and has little tendency to dissociate at normal temperatures, since the reaction

$$H_2 \rightarrow 2H \qquad \Delta H = 103 \text{ kcal/mole}$$

is highly endothermic. However, at high temperatures, in an electric arc, or under ultraviolet light it does dissociate. The atomic hydrogen produced exists for less than half a second, after which it recombines to give molecular hydrogen and a large amount of heat. This reaction has been used in welding metals. Atomic hydrogen is a strong reducing agent, and is commonly prepared in solution by means of a zinc copper couple or a mercury aluminium couple.

Hydrides

Binary compounds of the elements with hydrogen are called hydrides. The type of hydride which an element forms depends on its electronegativity, and these types may be divided into three fairly distinct classes:

(1) ionic or salt-like hydrides
(2) covalent or molecular hydrides
(3) metallic or interstitial hydrides.

(1) *Ionic or Salt-like Hydrides*

Only elements with very low electronegativity values can transfer electrons to the hydrogen atom and form salt-like hydrides. These include the metals of Group I (alkali metals) and the heavier Group II (alkaline earth metals)

Ca, Sr and Ba and possibly others such as lanthanum. These are solids with ionic lattices, and have high melting points. They conduct electricity when fused, liberate hydrogen at the anode and thereby confirm that they contain the hydride ion H^-. They react with water and liberate hydrogen

$$LiH + H_2O \rightarrow LiOH + H_2.$$

They are powerful reducing agents especially at high temperatures; for example:

$$2CO + NaH \rightarrow H.COO\,Na + C$$
$$SiCl_4 + 4NaH \rightarrow SiH_4 + 4\,NaCl$$
$$PbSO_4 + 2Ca\,H_2 \rightarrow PbS + 2Ca(OH)_2$$

The density of this type of hydride is greater than that of the metal. They have high heats of formation, and are always stoichiometric.

(2) Covalent Hydrides

These are formed by elements of high electronegativity, since a small difference in electronegativity between atoms favours a sharing of electrons and hence covalent bonding. Thus the p-block elements share electrons with hydrogen and form covalent bonds. They have a molecular lattice made up of individual saturated covalent molecules, with only weak Van der Waals forces and in some cases hydrogen bonds, holding the molecules together. This accounts for their softness, low melting and boiling points, their volatility and lack of conductivity. The following elements form this sort of hydride, with a formula $XH_{(8-n)}$ where n is the group in the periodic table to which X belongs.

Group	III	IV	V	VI	VII
	B	C	N	O	F
	Al	Si	P	S	Cl
	Ga	Ge	As	Se	Br
	In	Sn	Sb	Te	I
		Pb	Bi	Po	

The Group III hydrides are unusual in that they are electron deficient and polymeric, although they do not contain direct bonds between the Group III elements. The simplest boron hydride is B_2H_6, and aluminium hydride is polymeric $(Al\,H_3)_n$. These are discussed under Group III in Chapter 5. In addition to simple hydrides, the rest of the lighter elements except the halogens, form polynuclear hydrides in which two or more of the non metal atoms are directly bonded to each other. This tendency is at a maximum with carbon, where an almost infinite number of compounds are formed.

Bonding between two different atoms is seldom completely covalent, because if the electronegativity values of the two atoms are different, then the bonding electrons are not equally shared, and hence the bond has some ionic character. Thus although the bonding in HF has some ionic character, it is not strictly ionic, and these hydrides are different from the salt-like hydrides.

(3) *Metallic or Interstitial Hydrides*

The remaining elements—the *d*-block or transition elements and Be and Mg from the *s*-block—form metallic hydrides if they react with hydrogen at all. They are less dense than the parent metal, and the hydrogen is often absorbed reversibly by the metal. The chemical composition is variable; that is, they are non stoichiometric. The hydrogen seems to occupy interstitial positions in the metal lattice and so forms a solid solution. In most cases these hydrides have properties which closely resemble those of the parent metals, and their strongly reducing properties suggest that the hydrogen is present in the atomic state.

The hydrides of the *f*-block elements (lanthanides and actinides) are more difficult to classify. Compositions such as $LaH_{2.76}$, $CeH_{2.69}$ and $ThH_{3.07}$ are found. The fact that they are less dense than the parent metal suggests a similarity to the interstitial hydrides. On the other hand, their electro-negativity values are fairly close to those of Group I and II metals, and they have fairly high heats of formation; they may be regarded as a transition between the salt-like and interstitial types.

The Hydrogen Ion

The energy required to remove the electron from a hydrogen atom (i.e. the ionization potential of hydrogen) is 13·6 eV or 313 kcal/mol. This is a very large amount of energy, and consequently the bonds formed by hydrogen are mainly covalent. Hydrogen fluoride is the compound most likely to contain H^+, since it has the greatest difference in electronegativity, but even here the bond is only 45% ionic. Thus hydrogen can only form the hydrogen ion if its compounds are dissolved in media which solvate protons, and where the solvation energy provides sufficient energy to offset the very high ionization potential of hydrogen. Thus in water, solvated hydrogen ions H_3O^+ occur, the heat of solvation being 256 kcal/mol. Compounds which form solvated hydrogen ions in a suitable solvent are acids. It is customary to write H^+ for a solvated hydrogen ion H_3O^+, though this is not strictly correct.

Acids and Bases

Arrhenius Theory

In the early stages of chemistry, acids were distinguished by their sour taste and their effect on certain plant pigments such as litmus. Bases were sub-stances which reacted with acids to form salts. Water was used almost exclusively for reactions in solution, and in 1884 Arrhenius suggested the theory of electrolytic dissociation and proposed the self-ionization of water

$$H_2O \rightleftharpoons H^+ + OH^-$$

Thus substances producing H^+ were called acids, and substances producing OH^- were called bases. In aqueous solutions the concentration of H^+ is often given in terms of pH, where

$$pH = \log_{10} \frac{1}{[H^+]}$$

where $[H^+]$ is the concentration, or more strictly the activity of the hydrogen ions.

Until the turn of the nineteenth century it was thought that water was the only solvent in which ionic reactions could occur. Studies made by Cady (1897) and by Franklin and Kraus (1898) on reactions in liquid ammonia, and by Walden (1899) on reactions in liquid sulphur dioxide revealed many analogies with reactions in water. These analogies suggested that the three media were ionizing solvents and could be used for ionic reactions, and that acids, bases and salts were common to all three systems.

Although water is still the most widely-used solvent, its exclusive use limited chemistry to those compounds which are stable in its presence. Non-aqueous solvents are now used increasingly in inorganic chemistry because many new compounds can be prepared which are unstable in water, and some anhydrous compounds can be prepared such as anhydrous copper nitrate, which differ markedly from the well-known hydrated form. The concepts of acids and bases based on the aqueous system need extending to cover non-aqueous solvents.

Bronsted Lowry Theory

In 1923, Bronsted and Lowry defined acids and bases in terms of the hydrogen ion or proton, in an attempt to extend the scope of acid base systems to cover all proton solvents. It should be emphasized that bases need not contain OH^- under this system. Acids were defined as proton donors, and bases as proton acceptors. This theory extends acids and bases to cover all proton solvents. Every acid has a conjugate base

$$\underset{\text{acid}}{A} \rightleftharpoons \underset{\substack{\text{conjugate} \\ \text{base}}}{B^-} + H^+$$

$$\underset{\text{acid}}{HCl} + H_2O \rightleftharpoons H_3O^+ + \underset{\substack{\text{conjugate} \\ \text{base}}}{Cl^-}$$

In the above reaction, HCl is an acid since it donates protons, and Cl^- is its conjugate base. Since H_2O accepts protons it is a base, and H_3O^+ is its conjugate acid.   A strong acid has a weak conjugate base and vice versa. The extent to which a dissolved substance can act as an acid or a base depends largely on the solvent.   The solute only shows acidic properties if its proton-donating properties exceed those of the solvent, and HF is forced to act as a base in liquid $HClO_4$ as solvent

$$HClO_4 + HF \rightleftharpoons H_2F^+ + ClO_4^-$$

Mineral acids in water as solvent all have a much stronger tendency to donate protons than does water.   The mineral acids all donate protons to the water, and ionize completely.   Such a solvent is called a levelling solvent, because it makes all the mineral acids of much the same strength.   Differentiating solvents such as glacial acetic acid emphasize the difference in acidic strength, and several mineral acids are only partially ionized in this solvent.   This is because acetic acid is a poor proton acceptor but a rather better proton donor. This behaviour also means that a solute which acts as a weak base in water behaves as a strong base in acetic acid; the solvent thus exerts a levelling effect on bases.

Lewis Theory

Lewis widened the definition of acids and bases so that they did not depend on the presence of protons, or involve reactions with the solvent.   He defined acids as materials which accept electron pairs, and bases as substances which donate electron pairs.   Thus a proton is a Lewis acid and ammonia a Lewis base since the lone pair of electrons on the nitrogn atom can be donated to a proton

$$H^+ + {\overset{x}{\underset{x}{\cdot}}}NH_3 \rightarrow [H \leftarrow NH_3]^+$$

Similarly hydrogen chloride is a Lewis acid because it can accept a lone pair from a base such as water though this is followed by ionization

$$H_2O + HCl \rightarrow [H_2O \rightarrow HCl] \rightarrow H_3O^+ + Cl^-$$

Though this is a more general approach than that involving protons, many substances not normally regarded as acids are Lewis acids, for example BF_3 and metal ions

$$NH_3 + BF_3 \rightarrow [H_3N{\overset{x}{\underset{x}{\cdot}}} \rightarrow BF_3]$$
$$NH_3 + Ag^+ \rightarrow [H_3N{\overset{x}{\underset{x}{\cdot}}} \rightarrow Ag]^+$$

Further there is no scale of acid or basic strength as these depend on the reaction, and almost all reactions become acid/base reactions under this system.

The Solvent System

Perhaps the most convenient general definition of acids and bases is due to Cady and Elsey (*J. Chem. Ed.* 5, 1425 (1928)).

Consider any solvent which undergoes self-ionization:

$$2H_2O \rightleftharpoons H_3O^+ + OH^-$$
$$2NH_3 \rightleftharpoons NH_4^+ + NH_2^-$$
$$2BrF_3 \rightleftharpoons BrF_2^+ + BrF_4^-$$
$$N_2O_4 \rightleftharpoons NO^+ + NO_3^-$$

Acids are substances which increase the concentration of the positive ions characteristic of the solvent, and bases are substances which increase the concentration of the negative ions characteristic of the solvent. Thus in water, substances providing protons are acids, and substances providing hydroxyl ions are bases. Similarly in liquid ammonia, ammonium salts are acids since they provide NH_4^+ ions, and sodamide $NaNH_2$ is a base since it provides NH_2^- ions. In N_2O_4 as solvent, NOCl is an acid and $NaNO_3$ is a base. Clearly this definition applies equally well to proton and non-proton systems.

PROBLEMS

1. (a) How does the size of atoms vary from left to right in a period, and on descending a group in the periodic table? What are the reasons for these changes?
   (b) Can you explain the large atomic radii of the inert gases?
   (c) Why is the decrease in size between Li and Be much greater than that between Na and Mg or K and Ca?

2. (a) What is the correlation between atomic size and ionization potential?
   (b) Account for the fact that there is a decrease in first I.P. from Be to B, and Mg to Al.
   (c) Suggest the reason for the decrease in first I.P. from N to O, and P to S.
   (d) Explain why the substantial decrease in first I.P. observed between Na and K, and Mg and Ca is not observed between Al and Ga.
   (e) What is the significance of the large increase in the third I.P. of Ca and the fifth I.P. of Si?
   (f) Why is the first I.P. of the transition elements reasonably constant?

3. (a) What is electronegativity, and how is it related to the type of bond formed?
   (b) What are Fajans' rules?
   (c) Predict the type of bonds formed in HCl, CsCl, NH_3, CS_2, $GeBr_4$.

4. Use a modified Born-Haber cycle suitable for the estimation of electrode potentials to explain:
   (a) why Li is as strong a reducing agent as Cs;
   (b) why Ag is a noble metal and K a highly reactive metal.

5. (a) What are the standard electrode potentials, and how are they related to the electrochemical series?
   (b) Explain the recovery of copper from solution using scrap iron.
   (c) How is it possible to preferentially deposit metals electrolytically, e.g. Cu Ni and Zn from a solution containing all three?
   (d) Why is it possible to obtain zinc by electrolysis of an aqueous solution even though the electrode potentials would suggest that the water should decompose first?

CHAPTER 4

s-BLOCK ELEMENTS

Group I—Alkali Metals (Table 4.1)

TABLE 4.1

Element	Symbol	Electronic structure
Lithium	Li	[He] $2s^1$
Sodium	Na	[Ne] $3s^1$
Potassium	K	[Ar] $4s^1$
Rubidium	Rb	[Kr] $5s^1$
Caesium	Cs	[Xe] $6s^1$
Francium	Fr	[Rn] $7s^1$

Electronic Structure

The elements of Group I all have one electron in their outer orbital—an *s* electron in a spherical orbital. Ignoring the filled inner shells the electronic structures may be written: $2s^1$, $3s^1$, $4s^1$, $5s^1$, $6s^1$ and $7s^1$. Because of similarities in the electronic structures of these elements, many similarities in chemical behaviour would be expected. The elements are typically soft, highly reactive, univalent metals, which form colourless ionic compounds.

General Properties

The atoms are the largest in their corresponding period in the periodic table, and when the outer electron is removed to give a positive ion, the positive charge on the nucleus is greater than the number of electrons so that the electrons are attracted towards the nucleus, and the ion is smaller than the corresponding atom. Even so, the ions are very large, and increase in size from Li to Fr when extra shells of electrons are added. Because of their large size, these elements have a low density. Because the outer orbital electrons are a long way from the nucleus, they are relatively easy to remove; hence the ionization potentials are low. As the size of the atom increases, the electrons are further away from the nucleus and are less strongly held, so the ionization potential decreases.

These elements may emit electrons when irradiated with light—hence the use of caesium and potassium in photo-electric cells. Electrons may also be excited to a higher energy level, for example, in the flame test. When the electron drops back to its original position it gives out the extra energy it obtained. In this case the amount of energy is small; hence it appears as visible light. This accounts for the characteristic flame colorations produced by these elements.

The electronegativity values for the elements in this group are very small. Thus when these elements react with other elements to form compounds, a large electronegativity difference between the two atoms is probable, hence ionic bonds are formed. The chemistry of the alkali metals is largely that of their ions.

TABLE 4.2

Symbol	Atomic radius Å	Ionic radius M^+ Å	Density g/cc	Ionization potential eV	Electro-negativity	M. Pt. °C	Abun-dance in earth's crust p.p.m.
Li	1·23	0·60	0·54	5·4	1·0	181	65
Na	1·57	0·95	0·97	5·1	0·9	98	28,300
K	2·03	1·33	0·86	4·3	0·8	63	25,900
Rb	2·16	1·48	1·53	4·2	0·8	39	310
Cs	2·35	1·69	1·87	3·9	0·7	29	7

The melting points and boiling points are very low and decrease as the size increases. The melting point of lithium is rather different from the others and, in general, the first element in each group differs appreciably from the rest of the group.

Sodium and potassium are the sixth and seventh most abundant elements in the earth's crust, but francium does not occur appreciably in nature because it is radioactive and has a short half-life period.

The metal ions all have inert gas configurations; thus they have no un-paired electrons and are diamagnetic and colourless. In fact, all the compounds formed by Group I metals are white, except those where the acid radical is coloured, e.g. chromates and permanganates.

Chemical Properties

Chemically these elements are very reactive and tarnish rapidly in air to form the oxide (or the nitride in the case of lithium). On descending the group from lithium to caesium, the reaction with water increases in violence, liberating hydrogen and forming hydroxides which are the strongest bases known. Sodium hydroxide is produced on a large scale by the electrolysis of brine (Nelson or Castner Kellner processes), or from Na_2CO_3 with lime or ferric oxide (Gossages and Ferrite processes). Oxides are formed when the metals are burnt in air; lithium forms the monoxide Li_2O; sodium forms the peroxide Na_2O_2 and the others form superoxides of the type MO_2. The monoxide is ionic $2Li^+$ and O^{2-}; the peroxide contains the $[-O-O-]^{2-}$ ion and the superoxide contains a three electron bond which makes it paramagnetic and coloured $\left[\; O \colon\colon O \; \right]^{-}$. The other oxides are prepared by dissolving the metal in liquid ammonia and causing it to react with the appropriate amount of oxygen. The typical oxides M_2O are strongly basic oxides, which react with water, forming strong bases. These caustic alkalis are the strongest bases known and, except for LiOH, they are all very soluble in water and are thermally stable, illustrating the strong electropositive nature of the metals. The peroxides and superoxides are oxidizing agents and react with water and acid giving H_2O_2 and O_2. The metals react with hydrogen with decreasing ease from $Li \rightarrow Cs$, forming ionic or salt-like hydrides M^+H^-. These contain the H^- ion and hydrogen is liberated at the anode on electrolysis. The hydrides react with water liberating hydrogen, and lithium hydride is a useful source of hydrogen, since it has a low molecular weight and evolves more hydrogen than is in the hydride itself.

$$LiH + H_2O \rightarrow LiOH + H_2.$$

Lithium aluminium hydride is a useful reducing agent in organic chemistry and is made from lithium hydride in ether solution.

$$4LiH + AlCl_3 \rightarrow Li[AlH_4] + 3LiCl.$$

Solubility and Hydration

All the simple salts are soluble in water, and whilst lithium, the smallest ion, should conduct electricity better than the other larger ions, conductivity measurements give results in the order $Cs^+ > Rb^+ > K^+ > Na^+ > Li^+$ in aqueous solution. This is due to the ions being hydrated in solution. Li^+ is heavily hydrated; hence it moves slowly, and Cs^+, the least hydrated, moves faster. The decrease in hydration $Li \rightarrow Cs$ is also shown in the crystalline salts, for nearly all lithium salts are hydrated, many sodium salts are, few potassium salts are and no rubidium salts or caesium salts are hydrated. Because the simple salts are all soluble in water, these metals are precipitated in qualitative analysis as less common salts such as potassium cobaltinitrite $K_3[Co(NO_2)_6]$, potassium perchlorate $KClO_4$ or sodium uranyl acetate $Na[UO_2(Ac)_3]$.

Stability of Carbonate and Bicarbonate

Because of the highly electropositive or basic nature of these metals, their compounds are quite stable; except for Li their carbonates are stable to heat, and they form the only stable solid bicarbonates known. (Once again Li is exceptional in that it does not form a bicarbonate.) The bicarbonates are converted to carbonates by gentle heat.

Halides

The alkali metal halides illustrate how the co-ordination number increases as the ions get larger. As discussed previously, a radius ratio greater than 0·73 allows a co-ordination number of eight; for ratios between 0·41 and 0·73 the co-ordination number is six and for ratios between 0·41 and 0·22 the co-ordination number is four. Consider the alkali metal chlorides (Table 4.3):

TABLE 4.3

Symbol	Radius ratio M^+/Cl^-	Predicted co-ordination number	Actual co-ordination number
Li	0·33	4	6
Na	0·52	6	6
K	0·73	6	6
Rb	0·82	8	6 or 8
Cs	0·93	8	8

The error in prediction for Li is due to the more favourable lattice energy if the co-ordination number is increased. Thus LiCl, NaCl and KCl have a face-centred cubic or sodium chloride type of structure. As the size of the metal ion increases it becomes possible to fit more halogen ions round the metal and RbCl may have either a co-ordination number of six (sodium chloride type structure) or it may be like CsCl with a co-ordination number of eight with a body-centred cubic structure.

Extraction of the Metals

The metals of this group are the strongest chemical reducing agents known, so are not prepared by reducing oxides. Since the metals are so electropositive they react with water, therefore attempted displacement of one element from solution by another higher in the electrochemical series will be unsuccessful. Electrolysis of aqueous solutions in order to obtain the metal is also unsuccessful unless a mercury cathode is used, when it is possible to obtain amalgams, but recovery of the pure metal from the amalgam is difficult. They are all isolated by electrolysis usually of the fused halide, with impurity added to lower the melting point. Thus sodium is made by the Downs process (electrolysis of NaCl with $CaCl_2$ added), or by the Castner process using fused sodium hydroxide.

Complexes

The alkali metals replace hydrogen in organic acids forming ionic salts such as sodium acetate and potassium benzoate. They also form covalent compounds such as the lithium and sodium alkyls $Li.CH_3$ and NaC_2H_5. The metal ions are too large to form complexes readily, but chelate compounds with organic molecules such as salicylaldehyde and acetylacetone are formed. The metal usually obtains a co-ordination number of four or six (see Fig. 4.1).

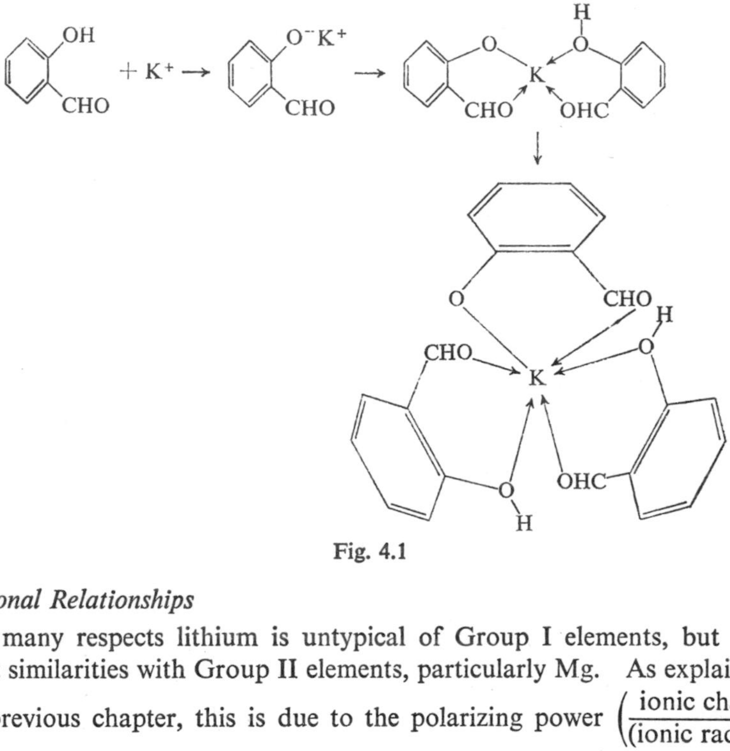

Fig. 4.1

Diagonal Relationships

In many respects lithium is untypical of Group I elements, but shows slight similarities with Group II elements, particularly Mg. As explained in the previous chapter, this is due to the polarizing power $\left(\dfrac{\text{ionic charge}}{(\text{ionic radius})^2}\right)$ being similar for these two elements. The following points illustrate the anomalous properties of lithium and the diagonal relationship:

1. The melting-point and boiling-point of Li are comparatively high.
2. Li is much harder than the other Group I metals.
3. Li reacts the least readily with oxygen forming the normal oxide, the higher oxides being unstable.
4. Li is much less electropositive; therefore many of its compounds are less stable—Li_2CO_3, $Li(NO_3)$ and LiOH all form the oxide on gentle heating and no solid bicarbonate is known.

5. Unlike Group I but like Group II, Li forms a nitride Li_3N.
6. Like the corresponding Mg salts Li_2CO_3, Li_3PO_4 and LiF are insoluble and LiOH is only sparingly soluble in water.
7. Due to their covalent nature, the halides and alkyls of Li and Mg are soluble in organic solvents.
8. The ion and its compounds are more heavily hydrated than those of the rest of the group.

Group II—Alkaline Earth Metals (Table 4.4)

TABLE 4.4

Element	Symbol	Electronic structure
Beryllium	Be	[He] $2s^2$
Magnesium	Mg	[Ne] $3s^2$
Calcium	Ca	[Ar] $4s^2$
Strontium	Sr	[Kr] $5s^2$
Barium	Ba	[Xe] $6s^2$
Radium	Ra	[Rn] $7s^2$

Electronic Structure

All Group II elements have two s electrons in their outer orbital; ignoring the filled inner orbitals, their electronic structures may be written $2s^2$, $3s^2$, $4s^2$, $5s^2$, $6s^2$ and $7s^2$. Being typically divalent, they form a well-graded series of highly reactive metals, generally forming colourless ionic compounds and being less basic than Group I. Beryllium shows considerable differences from the rest of the group and diagonal relationship similarities with aluminium in Group III.

General Properties

Beryllium is unfamiliar, partly because it is not very abundant and partly because it is difficult to extract. Magnesium and calcium are very abundant and are among the seven most common elements in the earth's crust. Strontium and barium are much less abundant, but are well known because they occur as concentrated ores and are easy to extract, while radium is extremely scarce and its radioactivity is more important than its chemistry.

The atoms are large, but are smaller than the corresponding Group I element since the extra charge on the nucleus draws the orbital electrons in. Similarly the ions are large, but are smaller than those of Group I, especially because removal of two orbital electrons increases the effective nuclear charge even further. Thus, these elements are denser and harder than Group I metals and have higher melting-points (see Table 4.5).

6—C.I.C.

TABLE 4.5

Symbol	Abundance in earth's crust p.p.m.	Atomic radius Å	Ionic radius M^{2+} Å	Density g/cc	Ionization potentials		Electro-negativity
					1st eV	2nd eV	
Be	6	0·89	0·31	1·8	9·3	18·2	1·5
Mg	20,900	1·36	0·65	1·7	7·6	15·0	1·2
Ca	36,300	1·74	0·99	1·6	6·1	11·9	1·0
Sr	300	1·91	1·13	2·6	5·7	11·0	1·0
Ba	250	1·98	1·35	3·5	5·2	10·0	0·9
Ra	$1·3 \times 10^{-6}$		1·50	5·0	5·3	10·1	

The compounds are always divalent and ionic. Since the atoms are smaller than those in Group I, the electrons are more tightly held, so that the energy needed to remove the first electron (first ionization potential) is greater than for Group I. Once one electron has been removed, the ratio of charges on the nucleus to orbital electrons is increased, so that the remaining electrons are more tightly held, and hence the energy needed to remove a second electron is nearly double that required for the first. The extra energy for removal of the second electron is offset by the lattice energy in crystals, or the solvation energy in solution. The compounds are more heavily hydrated than those in Group I, e.g. $MgCl_2.6H_2O$, $CaCl_2.6H_2O$, $BaCl_2.2H_2O$. The solubility of most salts decreases with increased atomic weight, though this trend is reversed with the fluorides and hydroxides. Since the divalent ions have an inert gas structure with no unpaired electrons, their compounds are diamagnetic and colourless, unless the acid radical is coloured.

Anomalous Behaviour of Beryllium

Beryllium differs from the rest of the group partly because it is extremely small and partly because of its comparatively high electronegativity. Thus when beryllium reacts with another atom, the difference in electronegativity is seldom large and beryllium is predominantly 2-covalent in its compounds. Its salts are extensively hydrolysed. Moreover, beryllium salts never have more than four molecules of water of crystallization, probably because there are only four orbitals available in the second shell of electrons, whereas magnesium can have a co-ordination number of six by using some $3d$ orbitals as well as $3s$ and $3p$.

Chemical Properties

The metals are less electropositive than those in Group I, but still react with water to form hydrogen and metal hydroxides. Beryllium is not typical and there is some doubt whether it reacts with steam to form the oxide BeO, or fails to react at all. Magnesium decomposes hot water and the other metals react with cold water. Beryllium hydroxide $(Be(OH)_2)$ is amphoteric; the others increase in basic strength in the order Mg to Ba. Solutions of calcium hydroxide and barium hydroxide are used as lime water and baryta water to detect carbon dioxide. The effect of excess CO_2 on these is to produce soluble bicarbonates, thus removing the turbidity.

$$Ca^{2+}(OH)_2^- + CO_2 \rightarrow \underset{\substack{\text{insoluble} \\ \text{white} \\ \text{precipitate}}}{CaCO_3} + H_2O \overset{\substack{\text{excess} \\ CO_2}}{\rightleftharpoons} \underset{\text{soluble}}{Ca^{2+}(HCO_3)_2^-}$$

These bicarbonates are only stable in solution and their decomposition to carbonates is the reason for stalactite and stalagmite formation.

All the elements in this group burn in oxygen to form ionic oxides MO (see Table 4.6). Thus all the oxides have a sodium chloride type of structure

TABLE 4.6

Oxide	Radius ratio M^{2+}/O^{2-}	Predicted co-ordination number	Co-ordination number found
BeO	0·22	4	4
MgO	0·44	6	6
CaO	0·56	6	6
SrO	0·81	8	6
BaO	0·96	8	6

except beryllium which has a zinc sulphide (wurtzite) arrangement. The failure of the radius ratio prediction for SrO and BaO shows that radius ratio is not the only factor involved. As the atoms get larger, the ionization potential decreases and the elements become more basic. Thus beryllium oxide is insoluble in water but dissolves in acids to give salts, and in alkalis to give beryllates, which on standing precipitate the hydroxide. It is therefore amphoteric. Magnesium oxide reacts with water-forming magnesium hydroxide $Mg(OH)_2$ which is weakly basic. Calcium oxide reacts very readily with water, and calcium hydroxide $(Ca(OH)_2)$ is a moderately strong base, while strontium and barium hydroxides are even stronger bases. The oxides are usually prepared by thermal decomposition of carbonates, nitrates or hydroxides. The increase in basic strength is illustrated by the temperatures at which the carbonates decompose: $BeCO_3 < 100°C$, $MgCO_3$ 540°C, $CaCO_3$ 900°C, $SrCO_3$ 1290°C, $BaCO_3$ 1360°C. Calcium oxide is prepared on a large scale by heating $CaCO_3$ in lime kilns and is used in the manufacture of Na_2CO_3, $NaOH$, CaC_2, bleaching powder, glass and cement. The ease with which the peroxides are formed increases with size. Barium peroxide BaO_2 is formed by passing air over BaO at 500°C. At high pressure and temperature, strontium peroxide can be formed. Calcium peroxide is not formed in this way, but can be made as the hydrate by treating calcium hydroxide with hydrogen peroxide and then dehydrating the product. Crude magnesium peroxide has been made using hydrogen peroxide, but no peroxide of beryllium is known. The peroxides are white ionic solids containing the $[O—O]^{2-}$ ion and can be regarded as salts of the very weak acid hydrogen peroxide. On treatment with acid, hydrogen peroxide is formed.

All the elements except beryllium form hydrides MH_2 by direct combination, and impure beryllium hydride has been made by reducing beryllium chloride with lithium aluminium hydride $Li[AlH_4]$. They are all reducing agents which react with water and liberate hydrogen; but beryllium and magnesium hydrides are probably covalent polymers (bridge structures) whilst calcium, strontium and barium hydrides are ionic (salt-like).

The metals all combine directly with the halogens at an appropriate temperature forming halides MX_2. These may also be formed by the action of halogen acid on the metal, or the carbonate. Beryllium halides are covalent, hygroscopic and fume in air due to hydrolysis. The fluorides MF_2 are all almost insoluble. The other metal halides are ionic and readily soluble in water. The solubility decreases somewhat with increasing atomic number, except among the fluorides. The halides are hygroscopic and form hydrates. $CaCl_2$ is a well-known drying agent, and anhydrous $MgCl_2$ is important in the electrolytic extraction of magnesium.

By contrast with elements in Group I, the alkaline earth elements burn in nitrogen and form nitrides M_3N_2. The beryllium compound is rather volatile; the others are not. They are all colourless crystalline solids which decompose on heating and react with water to liberate ammonia, and form either the metal oxide or hydroxide.

Ionic carbides MC_2 are formed by heating the metals Mg—Ba, or their oxides with carbon. These all have a sodium chloride type of structure with M^{2+} replacing Na^+ and $C≡C^{2-}$ replacing Cl^-. Calcium carbide is the best known; it reacts with water, liberates acetylene, and is thus called an acetylide.

$$CaC_2 + 2H_2O \rightarrow Ca(OH)_2 + C_2H_2$$

Beryllium forms Be_2C with C and BeC_2 with acetylene. The former is a methanide which liberates methane with water. MgC_2 on heating forms Mg_2C_3 which is an allylide since water liberates allylene (methyl acetylene).

The metals all liberate hydrogen from acids, although beryllium reacts slowly. Sodium hydroxide also gives hydrogen when treated with beryllium but has no effect on the other metals. This illustrates the increase in basic properties from amphoteric to basic on descending the group.

Most of the salts are soluble. The sulphates of calcium, strontium and barium are insoluble, and the carbonates, oxalates, chromates and fluorides of the whole group are insoluble. This is a useful factor in qualitative analysis.

Complexes

Group II metals are not noted for their ability to form complexes. Complex formation is favoured by small highly-charged ions with suitable empty orbitals of approximately the right energy. Thus beryllium forms many complexes and barium very few. Beryllium fluoride BeF_2 readily co-ordinates extra fluoride ions forming $[BeF_3]^-$ or $[BeF_4]^{2-}$; the tetra-fluoroberyllates $M_2[BeF_4]^{2-}$ are well known and resemble the sulphates in properties. In most cases beryllium is four co-ordinate in complexes and the tetrahedral arrangement adopted correlates with the orbitals available for complex formation.

	$1s$	$2s$	$2p$	
Electronic structure of Beryllium atom— ground state	[↑↓]	[↑↓]	[ ][ ][ ]	no unpaired electrons so no covalent bonds
Electronic structure of Beryllium atom— excited state	[↑↓]	[↑]	[↑][ ][ ]	two unpaired electrons can form two covalent bonds
Electronic structure of Beryllium in gaseous BeF_2	[↑↓]	[↑↓]	[↑↓][ ][ ]	
Electronic structure of Beryllium in $[BeF_4]^{2-}$ (Fig. 4.2)	[↑↓]	[↑↓]	[↑↓][↑↓][↑↓]	two F^- ions each donate an electron pair into an empty orbital forming a co-ordinate bond

sp^3 hybridization tetrahedral

In a similar way $BeCl_2 . D_2$ (where D is an ether, aldehyde or ketone with an oxygen atom with a lone pair of electrons which can be donated) and $[Be(H_2O)_4]^{2+}$ are tetrahedral. Many stable chelate compounds of beryllium are known, for example if beryllium hydroxide is evaporated with acetic acid, basic beryllium acetate $Be_4O(CH_3COO)_6$ is formed. This is covalent and a central oxygen atom is surrounded by four beryllium atoms, the six acetate groups being arranged along the six edges of the tetrahedron (see Fig. 4.3).

This complex is useful in the extraction of beryllium. Other chelate complexes include beryllium oxalate, catechol and acetyl acetone and in all of these the beryllium ion is tetrahedrally surrounded (see Fig. 4.4). The extreme toxicity of beryllium compounds is probably due to their very high solubility and their ease of complex formation.

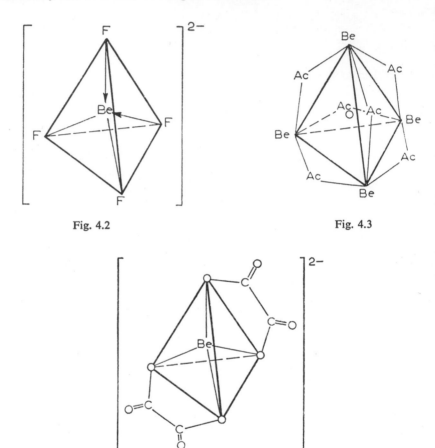

Fig. 4.2

Fig. 4.3

Fig. 4.4. Beryllium oxalate ion complex

The most important complex formed by magnesium is chlorophyll, the green plant-pigment which can produce sugars and on which all life ultimately depends. The magnesium is at the centre of a flat organic ring system called a porphyrin, in which four heterocyclic nitrogen atoms are bonded to the magnesium (see Fig. 4.5). Calcium and the rest of the group only form complexes with strong complexing agents such as acetyl acetone, $CH_3.CO.CH_2.CO.CH_3$ (which has two functional oxygen atoms) and ethylenediaminetetraacetic acid, EDTA, which has four functional oxygen atoms and two donor nitrogen atoms in each molecule.

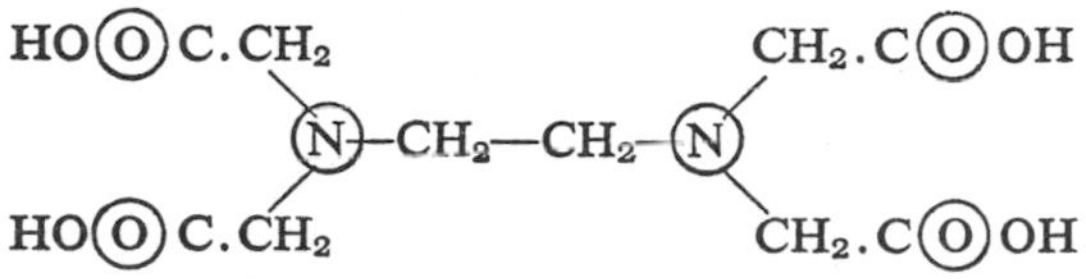

HO Ⓞ C.CH₂   CH₂.C Ⓞ OH
        Ⓝ—CH₂—CH₂—Ⓝ
HO Ⓞ C.CH₂   CH₂.C Ⓞ OH

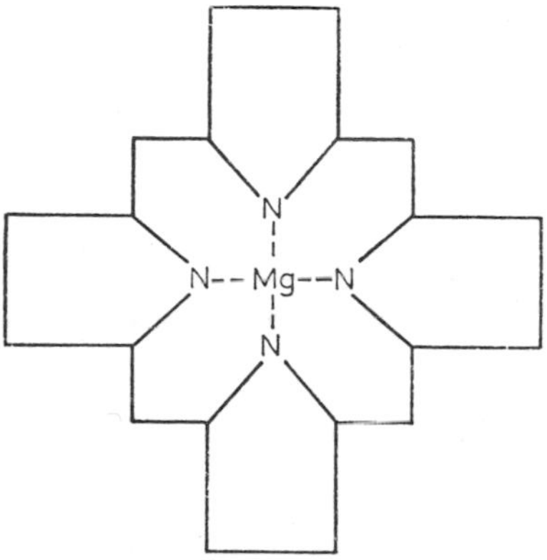

Fig. 4.5.   Skeleton of chlorophyll molecule (double bonds omitted)

Extraction of the Metals

The metals of this group are not easy to produce by chemical reduction because they are strong reducing agents and they form carbides. They are strongly electropositive and so aqueous solutions cannot be used for displacing one metal by another, or for electrolysis, because of the reaction of the metal with water. A mercury cathode can be employed in electrolysis, but recovery of the metal from the amalgam is difficult. All the metals can be obtained by electrolysis of the fused chloride, with sodium chloride added to lower the melting point, although strontium and barium tend to form a colloidal suspension. Beryllium is often extracted as its complex, sodium tetra fluoro beryllate, $Na_2[BeF_4]$, and converted to the hydroxide and then to the oxide. Older processes for extracting beryllium from the unreactive silicate mineral beryl involve heat treatment or fusion with alkali, followed by treatment with sulphuric acid, which yields the soluble $BeSO_4$. Very pure beryllium and beryllium oxide have been used in nuclear reactors, the basic acetate being made, distilled under reduced pressure and then decomposed by heating. Beryllium is also used in alloys. Magnesium is an important structural metal. It forms many alloys and also Grignard reagents such as C_2H_5MgBr. It was formerly prepared by heating magnesium oxide and carbon to 2000°C and shock-cooling the gas to avoid a state of equilibrium,

$$MgO + C \rightleftharpoons Mg + CO.$$

It is now prepared commercially by the Pidgeon process by reduction of magnesium oxide with ferrosilicon and aluminium. Strontium and barium are obtained from their oxides by reduction with aluminium (a thermite reaction).

Diagonal Relationships

Beryllium is anomalous in many of its properties and shows a diagonal relationship to aluminium in Group III:

1. Be is very small and has a high charge density so by Fajans' rules it should have a strong tendency to covalency. Thus the melting point of its compounds is lower (BeF_2 m.p. 800°C, rest of group about 1300°C) and they are all soluble in organic solvents and hydrolyse in water rather like the compounds of aluminium.
2. Be forms many complexes—not typical of Groups I and II.
3. Be like Al is rendered passive by nitric acid.
4. Be is amphoteric, liberating H_2 with NaOH and forming beryllates. Al forms aluminates.
5. Be salts are among the most soluble known.
6. Be_2C, like Al_4C_3, yields methane on hydrolysis.

PROBLEMS

1. Why are Group I elements:
   (a) univalent;
   (b) largely ionic;
   (c) strong reducing agents;
   (d) poor complexing agents;
   (e) why have they the lowest I.P. in their periods?
2. Lithium is the smallest ion in Group I, and would be expected to have a higher ionic mobility and thus conduct electricity better than caesium. Explain why this is not so.
3. Group I elements generally form very soluble compounds. How are they detected and confirmed in qualitative analysis?
4. Why and in what ways does Li resemble Group II metals?
5. What chemicals are obtained industrially from sodium chloride? Outline the processes.
6. Compare the extent of hydration of Group I and Group II halides. Why do Be salts seldom contain more than four molecules of water of crystallization?
7. Compare the reaction of Group I and Group II metals with water. How does the basic strength of Group II hydroxides vary within the group? Is this trend typical of the rest of the periodic table?
8. The four general methods of extracting metals are thermal decomposition, displacement of one element by another, chemical reduction, and electrolytic reduction. How are Group I and Group II metals obtained, and why are the other methods unsuitable?

CHAPTER 5

p-BLOCK ELEMENTS

Group III (Table 5.1)

TABLE 5.1

Element	Symbol	Electronic configuration		Oxidation states*	
Boron	B	[He]	$2s^2 2p^1$		**3**
Aluminium	Al	[Ne]	$3s^2 3p^1$	(1)	**3**
Gallium	Ga	[Ar]	$3d^{10} 4s^2 4p^1$	1	**3**
Indium	In	[Kr]	$4d^{10} 5s^2 5p^1$	1	**3**
Thallium	Tl	[Xe]	$4f^{14} 5d^{10} 6s^2 6p^1$	**1**	3

* In all the tables of oxidation states in this book, the most important states are in bold print. These are generally the most abundant and most stable. Well-characterized, but slightly less important states are in ordinary print. Oxidation states which are unstable, or in doubt, are given in brackets.

General Properties

Boron is a non-metal, but the other elements in this group (Table 5.1) are fairly reactive metals. Aluminium is the third most abundant element in the earth's crust and is the most abundant metal, but the other elements are much less common.

The elements all show an oxidation state of $+3$. The small size of the ions, their high charge, and the large values for the sum of the first three ionization potentials, suggest that the elements are largely covalent. Boron is always covalent and many simple compounds like $AlCl_3$ and $GaCl_3$ are covalent when anhydrous. However, in solution, the large amount of hydration energy evolved, offsets the high ionization potential and all the metal ions exist in a hydrated state.

Unlike the s-block elements, some of the elements of this group show lower valency states in addition to the group valency. The heavier elements show an increased tendency to form univalent compounds, and in

TABLE 5.2

Symbol	Abundance in earth's crust	Ionic radius M^{3+}	Sum of first three ionization potentials $M \rightarrow M^{3+}$	Electro- negativity
	p.p.m.	Å	eV	
B	3	0·20	70·1	2·0
Al	81,300	0·52	53·0	1·5
Ga	15	0·60	57·0	1·6
In	0·1	0·81	52·5	1·7
Tl	~2	0·95	56·1	1·8

fact univalent thallium (thallous) compounds are the most stable. Mono-valency is explained by the *s* electrons in the outer shell remaining paired, and not participating in bonding because the energy to unpair them is too great. This occurs particularly among heavy elements in the *p*-block and is called the inert pair effect. Gallium is apparently divalent in a few compounds, such as $GaCl_2$, but the structure has been shown to be $Ga^+[GaCl_4]^-$ which contains $Ga(+1)$ and $Ga(+3)$.

Finely divided amorphous boron is usually impure and burns in air to form the oxide and nitride, and in the halogens to form trihalides. It reduces nitric and sulphuric acids and liberates hydrogen with sodium hydroxide. Pure crystalline boron is, in contrast, unreactive except at very high temperatures or with reagents such as hot, concentrated sulphuric acid, or sodium peroxide.

The metals Al, Ga, In and Tl are silvery white. Aluminium is stable in air because it develops an oxide film which protects the metal from further attack. If the oxide covering the metal is removed and not allowed to protect the metal, for example by amalgamating with mercury, the metal is rapidly oxidized and decomposes cold water. Gallium and indium are stable in air and are not attacked by water except when free oxygen is present. Thallium is a little more reactive and is superficially oxidized in air.

Electropositive Character

The electropositive nature of the elements increases from boron to aluminium and then decreases from aluminium to thallium. The increase in electropositivity from B to Al is the usual trend associated with increased size. However, B and Al follow immediately after the *s*-block elements, while Ga, In and Tl follow after the *d*-block. These extra *d* electrons do not shield the nuclear charge very effectively, so that the orbital electrons are more firmly held, and the metals are less electropositive. This is illustrated by the increase in ionization potential between Al and Ga even though the larger atom would be expected to have a lower value.

Boron Sesquioxide and the Borates

Sesquioxides M_2O_3 of all the elements can be made by heating the elements in oxygen, though B_2O_3 is more usually made by dehydrating boric acid:

$$H_3BO_3 \xrightarrow{\ 100°C\ } HBO_2 \xrightarrow{\ \text{red heat}\ } B_2O_3$$

ortho boric acid   meta boric acid

As might be expected of a non-metallic oxide, boron sesquioxide is acidic in its properties and is the anhydride of orthoboric acid. On heating with metal oxides it gives metaborates which often have characteristic colours. This is the basis of the borax bead test:

$$CoO + B_2O_3 \rightarrow Co(BO_2)_2$$

Boron sesquioxide can react with very strongly acidic oxides such as phosphorous or arsenic pentoxides, forming a phosphate and an arsenate, and in these particular reactions it is being forced to behave as a base.

$$B_2O_3 + P_2O_5 \rightarrow 2BPO_4$$

Orthoboric acid H_3BO_3 behaves as a weak monobasic acid.

$$H_3BO_3 \rightleftharpoons H^+ + H_2BO_3^-$$
$$H_2BO_3^- \rightleftharpoons H_2O + BO_2^-$$

Thus on titration with NaOH:

$$H_3BO_3 + NaOH \rightarrow NaBO_2 + 2H_2O$$

sodium metaborate

The addition of certain organic polyhydroxy compounds such as glycerol, mannitol or sugars makes the orthoboric acid a stronger monobasic acid, and the end point of the titration is then easier to detect.

In the borates, each B atom is bonded to three oxygen atoms, arranged at the corners of an equilateral triangle. This would be predicted from hybridization of the available orbitals.

                   $1s$ $2s$ $2p$

Boron atom—excited state   [↑↓]   [↑]   [↑ ↑]

Three singly occupied orbitals form bonds with three oxygen atoms—sp^2 hybridization—plane triangle.

Thus orthoboric acid contains triangular BO_3^{3-} units, hydrogen bonded together into two dimensional sheets (Fig. 5.1). The orthoborates contain discrete BO_3^{3-} ions, but in the metaborates these units are joined together forming a variety of polymeric chain and ring structures (see Fig. 5.2).

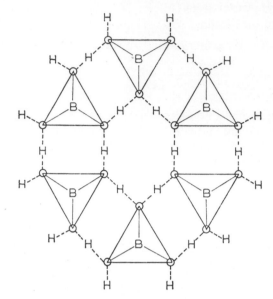

Fig. 5.1. Hydrogen bonded structure of orthoboric acid

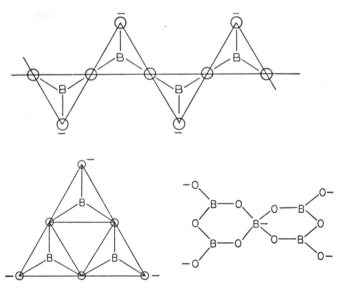

Fig. 5.2. Metaborate chain (CaB_2O_4), metaborate ring ($K_3B_3O_6$) and
complex metaborate ($KH_4B_5O_{10}.2H_2O$)

In many complex borates there are BO_4 tetrahedra in addition to BO_3 tri-
angles.

The most common metaborate is borax $Na_2B_4O_7.10H_2O$, which is a useful primary standard for titrating with acids.

$$Na_2B_4O_7.10H_2O + 2HCl \rightarrow 2NaCl + 4H_3BO_3 + 5H_2O$$

Other elements form polymeric compounds of this sort, notably silicon in the silicates and phosphorus in the phosphates.   Since the borates are based on a triangular BO_3 unit, borates are two-dimensional sheet structures, whilst SiO_4 and PO_4 units, being tetrahedral, can form three-dimensional structures. Further, the complex borate structures are broken up when dissolved in water, whilst the silicates and phosphates are not.

The Other Group III Oxides

Alumina Al_2O_3 can be made by dehydrating $Al(OH)_3$, or from the elements.   Aluminium has a very strong affinity for oxygen, and the heat of formation of Al_2O_3 is over 400 kcal/mole.   This is used in the thermite reduction of metal oxides.

$$3Mn_3O_4 + 8Al \rightarrow 4Al_2O_3 + 9Mn.$$

Aluminium hydroxide is precipitated as a white gelatinous substance in qualitative analysis.   It is amphoteric, though it principally acts as a base, giving salts with acids, which contain the $[Al(H_2O)_6]^{3+}$ ion.

$$Al(OH)_3 \rightleftharpoons Al^{3+} + 3OH^-$$

As an acid it gives rise to salts called aluminates, which contain AlO_2^- or AlO_3^{3-}

$$Al(OH)_3 \rightleftharpoons H^+ + AlO_2^- + H_2O$$
$$Al(OH)_3 \rightleftharpoons 3H^+ + AlO_3^{3-}$$

The aluminate ions are hydrated and $AlO_2^-.2H_2O$ and $AlO_3^{3-}.3H_2O$ are better formulated $[Al(OH)_4]^-$ or $[Al(OH)_6]^{3-}$.   Thus $Al(OH)_3$ dissolves in NaOH forming sodium aluminate, but is reprecipitated by the addition of carbon dioxide, or a trace of acid, since the acidic properties are very weak.

Gallium, like aluminium, forms an amphoteric oxide and hydroxide. The latter is white and gelatinous and dissolves in alkali forming gallates. Thallium and indium sesquioxides are completely basic, and form neither hydrates nor hydroxides.   Thallous hydroxide TlOH is a strong base, is soluble in water, and thus differs from the trivalent hydroxides, although it resembles the Group I hydroxides.   Where an element can exist in more than one valency state, there is a general tendency for the lower valency state to be the most basic.

Hydrides

None of the Group III elements react directly with hydrogen, but a number of interesting hydrides are known.   The boron hydrides are sometimes called boranes by analogy with the alkanes (hydrocarbons). There are eight well characterized boranes which fall into two series: B_nH_{n+4} and a less stable series B_nH_{n+6}.

diborane	B_2H_6	
tetraborane	B_4H_{10}	
pentaborane	B_5H_9	(stable)
pentaborane	B_5H_{11}	(unstable)
hexaborane	B_6H_{10}	
enneaborane	B_9H_{15}	
decaborane	$B_{10}H_{14}$	
decaborane	$B_{10}H_{16}$	

Diborane has been studied more than the other boranes and it may be prepared by a variety of methods:

(1) $\quad\quad\quad$ $Mg_3B_2 + H_3PO_4 \rightarrow$ mixture of boranes $\xrightarrow{\text{heat}} B_2H_6$
$\quad\quad\quad\quad$ magnesium $\quad\quad\quad\quad\quad\quad$ mainly B_4H_{10}
$\quad\quad\quad\quad$ boride

(2) $\quad\quad\quad\quad\quad$ $2BCl_3 + 6H_2 \xrightarrow[\substack{\text{electric} \\ \text{discharge}}]{\text{silent}} B_2H_6 + 6HCl$

(3) $\quad\quad\quad\quad$ $4BCl_3 + 3LiAlH_4 \rightarrow 2B_2H_6 + 3AlCl_3 + 3LiCl$

The method using lithium aluminium hydride gives a quantitative yield.

The boranes are of great interest since there are not enough valency electrons to form the expected number of covalent bonds, that is, they are electron deficient. Thus in diborane there are twelve valency electrons, three from each boron atom and six from the hydrogens. Electron diffraction results indicate the structure:

$$
\begin{array}{ccccc}
H & & H \; {\scriptstyle 1\cdot33\text{\AA}} \; H & & \\
\diagdown & \diagup & \diagdown & \diagup & {\scriptstyle 1\cdot19\text{\AA}} \\
& B & & B & \\
\diagup & \diagdown & \diagup & \diagdown & {\scriptstyle 1\cdot19\text{\AA}} \\
H & & H \; {\scriptstyle 1\cdot33\text{\AA}} \; H & &
\end{array}
$$

The two bridge hydrogen atoms are in a plane perpendicular to the rest of the molecule and prevent rotation between the two boron atoms. Specific heat measurements confirm that rotation is hindered. Four of the hydrogen atoms are in a different environment from the other two. This is confirmed by Raman spectra and by the fact that diborane cannot be methylated beyond $Me_4B_2H_2$ without breaking the molecule into BMe_3. The terminal B—H distances are the same as the bond lengths measured in non-electron deficient compounds, so the electron deficiency must be associated with the bridge groups. The nature of the bonds in the hydrogen bridges is now well established. Clearly they are abnormal bonds since the two bridges involve only one electron from each boron atom and one from each hydrogen atom, making a total of four electrons. An sp^3 hybrid orbital from each boron atom overlaps with the $1s$ orbital of the hydrogen, giving a delocalized orbital covering all three nuclei, containing one pair of electrons and making up one of the bridges (see Fig. 5.3).

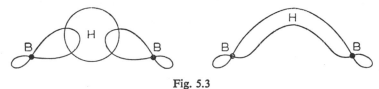

Fig. 5.3

The molecule may be represented as in Fig. 5.4.

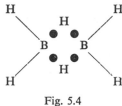

Fig. 5.4

The higher boranes are also electron deficient and have the same type of hydrogen bridges.

The boranes are volatile and decompose to boron and hydrogen at red heat.   They burn or explode in air and are decomposed by water or aqueous alkali:

$$B_2H_6 + 6H_2O \rightarrow 2H_3BO_3 + 6H_2.$$

All the boranes react with ammonia, but the products depend on the conditions:

$$B_2H_6 + NH_3 \xrightarrow[\text{low temperature}]{\text{excess NH}_3} B_2H_6.2NH_3$$

$$\xrightarrow[\text{higher temperature}]{\text{excess NH}_3} (BN)_x \text{ Boron nitride}$$

$$\xrightarrow[\text{higher temperature}]{\text{ratio 2NH}_3 : 1B_2H_6} B_3N_3H_6 \text{ Borazole.}$$

The compound $B_2H_6.2NH_3$ is ionic, $[H_3N \rightarrow BH_2 \leftarrow NH_3]^+[BH_4]^-$ and on heating it forms borazole.   A boron and a nitrogen atom bonded together have the same number of valency electrons as two carbon atoms.   Thus boron nitride has almost the same structure as graphite (Fig. 5.5).

Borazole $B_3N_3H_6$ has been called 'inorganic benzene' and the similarity in structure and properties is very close (see Fig. 5.6).

In addition to the boranes, rather more stable complex borohydrides containing the group BH_4^- are known.   Sodium borohydride can be made:

$$4NaH + B(OCH_3)_3 \rightarrow NaBH_4 + 3NaOCH_3.$$

Other metal borohydrides are made from the sodium salt.   The alkali metal

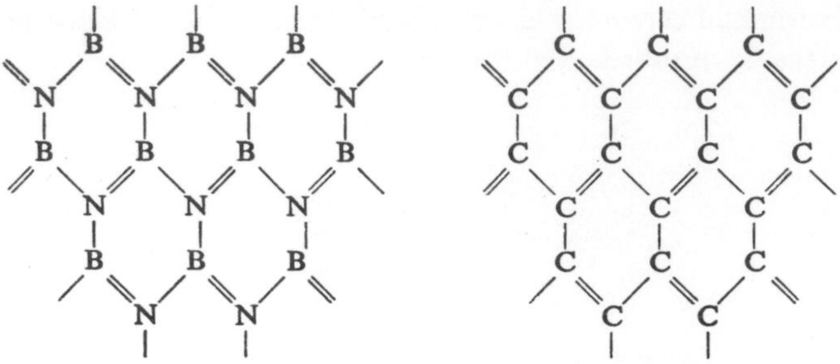

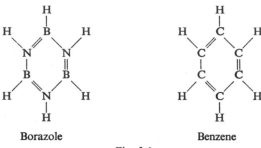

Boron nitride   Graphite

Fig. 5.5

Borazole   Benzene

Fig. 5.6

borohydrides are white ionic solids, but the beryllium, aluminium and transition metal borohydrides become increasingly covalent and volatile. The borohydride ion is tetrahedral and reacts with water with varying ease. Thus $LiBH_4$ reacts violently with water; $NaBH_4$ may be recrystallized from cold water with only slight decomposition, and KBH_4 is quite stable.

$$LiBH_4 + H_2O \rightarrow LiBO_2 + 4H_2$$

The alkali metal borohydrides are valuable reducing agents in inorganic chemistry. The stability of $NaBH_4$ in alcoholic and aqueous solutions makes it a useful reagent in the reduction of carbonyl compounds to alcohols and certain other organic reductions.

The other elements in the group also form electron deficient hydrides. Thus $(AlH_3)_n$ exists as a white polymer of unknown structure, but it may contain aluminium atoms joined together by hydrogen bridges rather like diborane. Aluminium hydride can be made from LiH and $AlCl_3$ in ether solution, but with excess LiH, lithium aluminium hydride $LiAlH_4$ is formed.

$$LiH + AlCl_3 \rightarrow (AlH_3)_n$$
$$\rightarrow Li[AlH_4]$$

$Li[AlH_4]$ is a most useful organic reducing agent because it will reduce functional groups, but not, in general, double bonds. It is analogous to the borohydrides but cannot be used in aqueous solutions.

Gallium forms compounds analogous to the borohydrides, e.g. $Li[GaH_4]$. Indium forms a polymeric hydride $(InH_3)_n$, but there is some doubt about the existence of a hydride of thallium.

Halides

All the elements form trihalides. The boron halides BX_3 are covalent and gaseous. Hybridization of one s and two p orbitals used for bonding, gives a planar triangular molecule. The boron halides are all hydrolysed by water, the fluoride forming fluoborates and the other halides giving boric acid.

$$BF_3 + H_2O \rightarrow H[BF_3OH] \quad \text{(this is a derivative of } HBF_4\text{)}$$
$$BCl_3 + 3H_2O \rightarrow H_3BO_3 + 3HCl$$

Since there are only six electrons in the outer shell of the B atom in the BX_3 molecule, it can readily accept a lone pair of electrons from a donor atom such as O, N, P or S. It is this tendency which makes BF_3 a useful organic catalyst for Friedel-Crafts reactions such as alkylations and acylations, esterifications and the polymerization of olefines.

The fluorides of Al, Ga, In and Tl are ionic and have high melting points. The other halides are largely covalent when anhydrous. $AlCl_3$, $AlBr_3$ and $GaCl_3$ exist as dimers, thus attaining an octet of electrons.

The dimeric formula is retained when the halides dissolve in non-polar solvents such as benzene, but because of high heat of hydration when the halides dissolve in water, the covalent dimer is broken into $[M.6H_2O]^{3+}$ and $3X^-$ ions.

Dihalides

In addition to the trihalides, boron forms halides of formula B_2X_4. These are thought to be

Gallium and indium form dihalides,

$$GaCl_3 + Ga \rightarrow GaCl_2$$
$$In + HCl_{gas} \rightarrow InCl_2$$

These are more properly written $Ga^+[GaCl_4]^-$ and contain $Ga(+1)$ and $Ga(+3)$ rather than divalent gallium. Thallium forms univalent thallous halides which are more stable than the trihalides.

Complexes

Group III elements form complexes much more readily than the *s*-block elements, on account of their smaller size and increased charge. In addition to the tetrahedral hydride and halide complexes $Li[AlH_4]$ and $H[BF_4]$ already mentioned, many octahedral complexes such as $[GaCl_6]^{3-}$, $[InCl_6]^{3-}$ and $[TlCl_6]^{3-}$ are known. The most important octahedral complexes are those with chelate groups, for example, acetylacetone, oxalates and 8-hydroxyquinoline. The latter complex is commonly used in the gravimetric determination of aluminium (see Fig. 5.7).

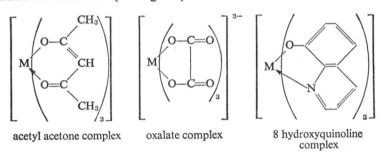

acetyl acetone complex   oxalate complex   8 hydroxyquinoline complex

Fig. 5.7

Extraction of the Elements

Boron is obtained by the reduction of B_2O_3 with magnesium or sodium, or by using a tungsten filament in the reduction of BCl_3 with hydrogen. Very pure boron is obtained by the van Arkel method (pyrolysis of BI_3), and is used to increase the hardenability of steels (depth to which steels will harden). Boric acid and borax are used extensively. Aluminium is obtained from the ore, bauxite Al_2O_3. Sodium hydroxide is added to the ore, forming sodium aluminate which dissolves, thus separating Al from iron oxide. Aluminium hydroxide is re-precipitated with CO_2 calcined to Al_2O_3, fused with cryolite Na_3AlF_6 and electrolysed. Aluminium is produced on a large scale and is used widely in alloys, paint, pyrotechnics and cooking utensils. Gallium, indium and thallium occur only in minute quantities, and are usually obtained by electrolysing aqueous solutions of their salts.

The large differences between boron (non-metal, always covalent, acidic, high melting point) and aluminium are to be expected since Al^{3+} is 2·5 times the size of B^{3+}.

Group IV (Table 5.3)

TABLE 5.3

Element	Symbol	Electronic structure	Oxidation states*	
Carbon	C	[He] $\qquad 2s^2\,2p^2$	(2)	4
Silicon	Si	[Ne] $\qquad 3s^2\,3p^2$	(2)	4
Germanium	Ge	[Ar] $\quad 3d^{10}\,4s^2\,4p^2$	2	4
Tin	Sn	[Kr] $\quad 4d^{10}\,5s^2\,5p^2$	2	4
Lead	Pb	[Xe] $\quad 4f^{14}\,5d^{10}\,6s^2\,6p^2$	2	4

* See page 77.

Metallic and Non-Metallic Character

The change from non-metal to metal with increasing atomic number is well illustrated in Group IV, where carbon and silicon are non-metals, germanium has some metallic properties and tin and lead are metals.

Differences Between Carbon, Silicon and the Remaining Elements

In general, the first element in a group differs from the rest of the group because of its smaller size, higher electronegativity and the non-availability of d orbitals. Carbon differs from the other elements in its limitation to a co-ordination number of four (because there are no d orbitals in the second shell), in its unique ability to form multiple bonds, such as C=C, C≡C, C=O, C=S and C≡N and in its marked ability to form chains (catenation). The tendency to catenation is related to the strength of the bond (see Table 5.4).

TABLE 5.4

Bond	Bond energy kcals/mole	Remarks
C—C	83	Forms many chains
Si—Si	53	Forms a few chains
Ge—Ge	40	Very little tendency to form chains

Carbon and silicon have only s and p electrons, but the other elements follow a completed transition series with ten d electrons. Thus some differences are expected, and carbon and silicon differ both from one another and from the rest of the group, while germanium, tin and lead form a graded series.

General Properties

The elements are all tetravalent. The ionization potentials are very high and the existence of simple 4^+ ions is unlikely. The electronegativity values do not decrease in a completely regular way in the group (C = 2·5, Si = 1·8, Ge = 1·8, Sn = 1·8, Pb = 1·8), possibly due to the filling of d and later f orbitals. The electronegativity values are low and 4^- ions do not normally exist, though carbon does form C_2^{2-} ions in salt-like carbides with electropositive metals such as $Ca^{2+}C_2^{2-}$. The elements all show a covalency of four, which necessitates promotion of electrons from the ground state to an excited state, and sp^3 hybridization of the orbitals results in a tetrahedral structure.

Electronic structure of
Carbon atom—ground state

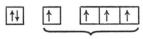

(two unpaired electrons thus can form two covalent bonds.)

Carbon atom—excited state

(four unpaired electrons thus forms four covalent bonds and sp^3 hybridization results in a tetrahedral structure.)

Inert Pair Effect

The inert pair effect shows itself increasingly in the heavier members of the group. There is a decrease in stability of the $+4$ oxidation state and an increase in the stability of the $+2$ state on descending the group. Thus Ge($+2$) exists as a strong reducing agent and Ge($+4$) is stable. Sn($+2$) exists as simple ions but is strongly reducing and Sn($+4$) is covalent. Pb($+2$) is ionic, stable and more common than Pb($+4$) which is oxidizing. The lower valencies are more ionic because the radius of M^{2+} is greater than M^{4+} and according to Fajans' rules, the smaller the ion the greater the tendency to covalency.

Complexes

The ability to form complexes is favoured by a high charge, small size and availability of empty orbitals of the right energy. Carbon is in the second period and has a maximum of eight electrons in its outer shell. In four covalent compounds of carbon, the second shell contains the maximum of eight electrons. Because this structure resembles that of an inert gas, these compounds are stable, and carbon does not form complexes. Four-covalent compounds of the subsequent elements can form complexes due to the availability of *d* orbitals, and they generally increase their co-ordination number from four to six.

$$SiF_4 + 2F^- \rightarrow [SiF_6]^{2-}$$
$$GeF_4 + 2NMe_3 \rightarrow [GeF_4.(NMe_3)_2]$$
$$SnCl_4 + 2Cl^- \rightarrow [SnCl_6]^{2-}$$

In these cases, four covalent and two co-ordinate bonds are formed and sp^3d^2 hybridization gives an octahedral structure. For example, $[SiF_6]^{2-}$:

	3*s*	3*p*	3*d*
Electronic structure of Silicon atom—ground state	[↑↓]	[↑][↑][ ]	[ ][ ][ ][ ][ ]
Silicon—excited state	[↑]	[↑][↑][↑]	[ ][ ][ ][ ][ ]
Silicon atom—having gained share in 4*e* in SiF_4 molecule	[↑↓]	[↑↓][↑↓][↑↓]	[ ][ ][ ][ ][ ]
$[SiF_6]^{2-}$ where two F^- each donate share in electron pair, forming two co-ordinate bonds	[↑↓]	[↑↓][↑↓][↑↓]	[*X*][*X*][ ][ ][ ]

sp^3d^2 hybridization—octahedral structure.

Hydrides

All the elements form covalent hydrides, but the number formed and the ease with which they form differs greatly. Carbon forms a vast number of chain and ring compounds including the alkanes (paraffins) C_nH_{2n+2}, alkenes (olefines) C_nH_{2n}, alkynes (acetylenes) C_nH_{2n-2} and aromatic compounds. These are the basis of organic chemistry. The strong tendency to catenation has been related to the strength of the C—C bond. Silicon forms a limited number of saturated hydrides, Si_nH_{2n+2}, called the silanes. A mixture of silanes was originally prepared by hydrolysing magnesium silicide, Mg_2Si, with sulphuric or phosphoric acid.

$$2Mg + Si \xrightarrow[\text{of air}]{\text{Heat in absence}} Mg_2Si + H_2SO_4 \rightarrow \begin{cases} SiH_4\ (40\%) \\ Si_2H_6\ (30\%) \\ Si_3H_8\ (15\%) \\ Si_4H_{10}\ (10\%) \\ \left.\begin{matrix} Si_5H_{12} \\ Si_6H_{14} \end{matrix}\right\}(5\%) \end{cases}$$

More recently monosilane has been prepared by using lithium aluminium hydride.

$$SiCl_4 + LiAlH_4 \rightarrow SiH_4$$

Unlike the alkanes, the silanes are strong reducing agents, burn in air, explode in Cl_2 and are readily hydrolysed by alkaline solutions.

$$Si_2H_6 + H_2O \xrightarrow{\text{trace of alkali}} 2SiO_2.nH_2O + 7H_2$$

The difference in behaviour between alkanes and silanes is probably due to the difference in electronegativity between C and Si. This results in an uneven sharing of the bonding electrons leaving a $\delta-$ charge on C and a $\delta+$ charge on Si.

$$\overset{\delta-}{C}\!-\!\overset{\delta+}{H} \qquad\qquad \overset{\delta+}{Si}\!-\!\overset{\delta-}{H}$$

The germanium hydrides or germanes are similar to the silanes, but are less inflammable and less readily hydrolysed. Stannane SnH_4 and plumbane PbH_4 are the only hydrides of tin and lead. They are difficult to prepare and are made by $LiAlH_4$ and cathodic reduction, respectively.

Halides

Tetrahalides of all the elements are known and are all tetrahedral and covalent. CF_4 is unreactive and very stable, and fluorocarbons are useful lubricants, solvents and insulators. Mixed chlorofluorohydrocarbons are known as Freons. They are unreactive and non-toxic and are widely used as refrigeration fluids and as the propellant in aerosols. In contrast SiF_4 is readily hydrolysed by alkali.

$$SiF_4 + 8OH^- \rightarrow SiO_4^{4-} + 4F^- + 4H_2O$$

The silicon halides are rapidly hydrolysed by water, to give silicic acid.

$$SiCl_4 + 4H_2O \rightarrow Si(OH)_4 + 4HCl$$

In the case of the tetrafluoride, a secondary reaction occurs between the resultant HF and the unchanged SiF_4.

$$SiF_4 + 2HF \rightarrow 2H^+ + [SiF_6]^{2-}$$

$GeCl_4$ and $GeBr_4$ are hydrolysed less readily and $SnCl_4$ and $PbCl_4$ hydrolyse in dilute solutions, but hydrolysis is often incomplete and can be repressed by the addition of the appropriate halogen acid. The carbon halides are not hydrolysed because they cannot increase their co-ordination number, but because of the availability of the $3d$ orbitals in silicon, OH^- ions may be co-ordinated as a first step in hydrolysis. In the presence of excess acid, the halides of Si, Ge, Sn and Pb increase their co-ordination number from four to six, and form complex ions, such as $[SiF_6]^{2-}$, $[GeF_6]^{2-}$, $[SnCl_6]^{2-}$ and $[SnCl_5]^-$. $PbBr_4$ and PbI_4 are not known, probably because of the oxidizing power of $Pb(+4)$ and the reducing power of Br^- and I^-, which results in the divalent compounds always being formed.

Carbon forms a number of catenated halides, perhaps the best known being Teflon or polytetrafluoroethylene. Silicon forms a limited series up to Si_6Cl_{14}, and germanium forms the dimer Ge_2Cl_6, whilst no catenated halides are known for tin and lead.

Oxygen Compounds

Five oxides of carbon are known: CO, CO_2, C_3O_2, C_5O_2 and $C_{12}O_9$. Carbon monoxide is a poisonous gas, sparingly soluble in water and a neutral oxide. It is formed when carbon is burned in a limited amount of air. It is prepared by dehydrating formic acid with concentrated sulphuric acid.

$$H.COOH + H_2SO_4 \rightarrow CO + H_2O$$

The gas burns in air and evolves a considerable amount of heat; hence carbon monoxide is an important fuel.

$$2CO + O_2 \rightarrow 2CO_2 + 135 \text{ kcal}$$

Water gas, an equimolecular mixture of CO and H_2, producer gas, a mixture of CO and N_2 and coal gas, a mixture of CO, H_2, CH_4 and CO_2 are all important industrial fuels.

$$C + H_2O \xrightarrow{\text{red heat}} CO + H_2 \quad \text{(water gas)}$$
$$C + \underbrace{O_2 + 4N_2}_{\text{air}} \rightarrow CO_2 + 4N_2$$
$$\downarrow +C$$
$$2CO + 4N_2 \quad \text{(producer gas)}$$

Carbon monoxide is a good reducing agent and can reduce many metal oxides to the metal.

$$Fe_2O_3 + 3CO \xrightarrow{\text{Blast furnace}} 2Fe + 3CO_2$$
$$CuO + CO \rightarrow Cu + CO_2$$

Carbon monoxide is an important ligand which can donate a share in a lone pair of electrons, that is it can form a co-ordinate bond with many transition metals and form carbonyl compounds. The number of carbon monoxide molecules bonded to the metal in this way is generally in accordance with the effective atomic number rule (see Chapter 8). Nickel carbonyl $Ni(CO)_4$ is important in the Mond process for extracting nickel. The electronic structure of CO has been debated, but it may be represented:

$$:\overset{\cdot}{\underset{\cdot}{C}}:O: \quad \text{or} \quad C \overset{\leftarrow}{=} O$$

The metal-carbon bond in carbonyls may be represented $M \leftarrow C \equiv O$, though there is probably some back bonding or dative π bonding from sideways overlap of full d orbitals on the metal and empty p *orbitals* of the carbon, giving $M \rightleftharpoons C = O$.   The bond length M—C is shorter than a single bond and C—O is longer than a triple bond.

Carbon dioxide, CO_2 is obtained by the action of dilute acids on carbonates, or by burning carbon in excess of air.   The gas is detected by its action on lime water $Ca(OH)_2$ or baryta water $Ba(OH)_2$, since a white insoluble precipitate of $CaCO_3$ or $BaCO_3$ is formed, but if more CO_2 is passed through the mixture, the cloudiness disappears as the soluble bicarbonate is formed.

$$Ca(OH)_2 + CO_2 \rightarrow CaCO_3 + H_2O$$
$$\downarrow \ + CO_2$$
$$Ca(HCO_3)_2$$

Carbon dioxide is an acidic oxide and is the anhydride of carbonic acid H_2CO_3.

$$CO_2 + H_2O \rightarrow H_2CO_3$$

The acid is unstable and has never been isolated, but it gives rise to two series of salts, namely bicarbonates and carbonates.

$$NaOH + H_2CO_3 \Big\langle \begin{array}{l} \nearrow \quad NaHCO_3 \quad \text{sodium bicarbonate} \\ \qquad\qquad\qquad \text{(acid salt)} \\ \searrow \quad Na_2CO_3 \quad \text{sodium carbonate} \\ \qquad\qquad\qquad \text{(normal salt)} \end{array}$$

The structure of CO_2 is:

$$O = C = O \leftrightarrow O^+ \equiv C - O^- \leftrightarrow \bar{O} - C \equiv O^+$$

The carbon atom thus forms four bonds, but in determining the hybridization and shape of the molecule double bonds are not included.

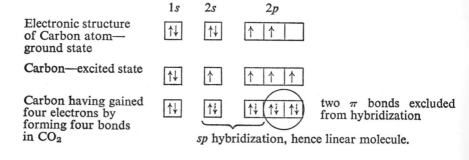

	$1s$	$2s$	$2p$	
Electronic structure of Carbon atom— ground state	↑↓	↑↓	↑ ↑ ☐	
Carbon—excited state	↑↓	↑	↑ ↑ ↑	
Carbon having gained four electrons by forming four bonds in CO_2	↑↓	↑↓	↑↓ (↑↓ ↑↓)	two π bonds excluded from hybridization

sp hybridization, hence linear molecule.

In a similar way, carbonic acid may be represented:

$$\begin{array}{c} H-O \\ \diagdown \\ C=O \\ \diagup \\ H-O \end{array}$$

and the structure of the CO_3^{2-} ion:

Electronic structure of carbon having gained four electrons by forming four bonds in CO_3^{2-}

$1s$ $\boxed{\uparrow\downarrow}$ $2s$ $\boxed{\uparrow\downarrow}$ $2p$ $\boxed{\uparrow\downarrow}\,\boxed{\uparrow\downarrow}\,(\uparrow\downarrow)$

sp^2 hybridization, hence ion has plane triangular shape.

π bond excluded from hybridization

Biologically, carbon dioxide is important in the processes of photosynthesis,

$$6CO_2 + 6H_2O \xrightarrow{\text{sunlight}} \underset{\text{glucose}}{C_6H_{12}O_6} + 6O_2$$

respiration,

$$C_6H_{12}O_6 + 6O_2 \rightarrow 6CO_2 + 6H_2O + \text{energy}$$

and fermentation

$$C_6H_{12}O_6 \rightarrow 2\underset{\text{ethyl alcohol}}{C_2H_5OH} + 2CO_2$$

Carbon suboxide C_3O_2, is made by dehydrating malonic acid with P_2O_5 and its structure is probably a resonance hybrid between:

$$O{=}C{=}C{=}C{=}O \leftrightarrow \overset{+}{O}{=}C{-}C{\equiv}C{-}\overset{-}{O} \leftrightarrow \overset{-}{O}{-}C{\equiv}C{-}C{=}\overset{+}{O}.$$

The existence of C_5O_2 is uncertain, but it could also be resonance stabilized $C_{12}O_9$ is the anhydride of mellitic acid $C_6(COOH)_6$.

Two oxides of silicon SiO and SiO_2 have been reported. Silicon monoxide is thought to be formed by high temperature reduction of SiO_2 with Si, but its existence at room temperature is in doubt.

$$SiO_2 + Si \rightarrow 2SiO$$

Silicon dioxide SiO_2, is commonly called silica. Whereas carbon can form double bonds and CO_2 is a discrete molecule, silicon cannot form double bonds hence SiO_2 forms an infinite three-dimensional structure. Thus CO_2 is a gas, but SiO_2 a high melting solid, which exists in three forms: quartz, tridymite and cristobalite. Each of these forms has a different structure at high and low temperatures.

(low temp. forms)   α quartz   α tridymite   α cristobalite

$$\Big\Updownarrow 573°C \qquad \Big\Updownarrow 120\text{--}160° \qquad \Big\Updownarrow 200\text{--}275°$$

(high temp. forms) β quartz $\overset{870°}{\rightleftharpoons}$ β tridymite $\overset{1470°}{\rightleftharpoons}$ β cristobalite $\overset{1710°}{\rightleftharpoons}$ liquid SiO_2

In all of these forms each silicon is bonded tetrahedrally to four oxygen atoms and each oxygen atom is common to two tetrahedra. The difference between these structures is the arrangement of the tetrahedral SiO_4 units. The relation between tridymite and cristobalite is the same as that between wurtzite and zinc blende. Quartz has a helical arrangement and since the screw may be left- or right-handed it has optical isomers too.

Silica in any form is unreactive, but it does react with fluorine, hydrofluoric acid and alkalies. The last reaction indicates that SiO_2 is an acidic oxide. The reaction with HF is used in qualitative analysis to detect silicates, since the resultant volatile silicon tetrafluoride is hydrolysed by water to silicic acid.

$$H_2SO_4 + CaF_2 \rightarrow HF \xrightarrow{+SiO_2} SiF_4 \xrightarrow{+H_2O} HF + \begin{cases} Si(OH)_4 & \text{or} \\ SiO_2.2H_2O \end{cases}$$

Reaction with alkali yields silicates which will be discussed later.

$$SiO_2 + NaOH \rightarrow (Na_2SiO_3)_n \quad \text{and} \quad Na_4SiO_4$$

Silica is useful in the manufacture of optical components such as lenses and prisms since it is very transparent to visible and u.v. light. It is also used for laboratory glassware. Silical gel which is obtained by dehydrating silicic acid contains about 4% water, and is employed as a drying agent and as a catalyst. Silicon is used in transistors.

The dioxides GeO_2, SnO_2 and PbO_2 decrease in acidity. Thus GeO_2 is not as strongly acidic as SiO_2, and SnO_2 and PbO_2 are amphoteric. All three oxides dissolve in alkali to form germanates, stannates and plumbates respectively. The germanates have complicated structures similar to the silicates, but the stannates and plumbates contain $[Sn(OH)_6]^{2-}$ and $[Pb(OH)_6]^{2-}$ complex ions. There is no evidence of the existence of $Ge(OH)_4$, $Sn(OH)_4$ and $Pb(OH)_4$ and these are better represented $MO_2(H_2O)_n$, where n is about two. All three oxides are insoluble in acids except when a complexing agent such as F^- and Cl^- is present, when complex ions such as $[GeF_6]^{2-}$ and $[SnCl_6]^{2-}$ are formed.

The lower oxides GeO, SnO and PbO are slightly more basic and ionic than the corresponding higher oxides. GeO is distinctly acidic, whilst SnO and PbO are amphoteric. The increased stability of lower valent states on descending a group is illustrated by the fact that Ge^{2+} and Sn^{2+} are quite strong reducing agents while Pb^{2+} is stable.

Lead also forms a mixed oxide Pb_3O_4. This is called red lead and may be represented as $2PbO.PbO_2$, and thus contains Pb^{2+} and Pb^{4+}. PbO is used in ceramics, Pb_3O_4 in paint, and PbO_2 in lead accumulators.

Silicates

A large percentage of the earth's crust consists of silicate minerals or aluminosilicate clays. Silicates can be prepared by fusing an alkali metal carbonate with silica.

$$Na_2CO_3 \xrightarrow{1500°C} CO_2 + Na_2O \xrightarrow{SiO_2} Na_4SiO_4, (Na_2SiO_3)_n \quad \text{and others.}$$

Sodium silicate or waterglass is the only common soluble silicate, the majority being very insoluble because of the strength of the Si—O bond, which is only broken by such reagents as HF. The insolubility of these minerals made it difficult to study their structure, and physical properties such as cleavage were studied. The development of X-ray diffraction techniques led to an understanding of the wide variety of silicate structures.

The electronegativity difference between O and Si, $3.5 - 1.8 = 1.7$, suggests that the bond is covalent but with a large degree of ionic character. The structure may therefore be considered theoretically by both ionic and covalent methods. The radius ratio $Si^{4+}:O^{2-}$ is 0.29, which suggests that these minerals are based on four co-ordinate silicon, that is, on the $(SiO_4)^{4-}$ tetrahedron. This can also be predicted from hybridization of the orbitals used for bonding.

Electronic structure of Silicon atom—excited state

	$1s$	$2s$	$2p$			$3s$	$3p$		
	↑↓	↑↓	↑↓	↑↓	↑↓	↑	↑	↑	↑

four unpaired electrons form four bonds with oxygen atoms—sp^3 hybridization—tetrahedral structure.

The way in which the $(SiO_4)^{4-}$ tetrahedral units are linked together provides a convenient classification.

1. *Orthosilicates*. These contain discrete $(SiO_4)^{4-}$ tetrahedra. The oxygen atoms form co-ordinate bonds to the associated metal ions (see Fig. 5.8). Various structures are formed, depending on how many co-ordinate bonds are formed, that is on the co-ordination number of the metal. Thus in willemite Zn_2SiO_4, and phenacite Be_2SiO_4, the zinc and beryllium ions are tetrahedrally surrounded by four oxygen atoms. In forsterite, Mg_2SiO_4, the magnesium is surrounded octahedrally by six oxygen atoms, and in zircon, $ZrSiO_4$, the co-ordination number of zirconium is eight.

If silicate minerals are regarded as a hexagonal close-packed arrangement of oxide ions, two tetrahedral holes are formed for every one octahedral hole.

These may be filled by cations (Si^{4+} or metal ions), or left empty. The type of hole occupied by a particular metal ion may be predicted from the radius ratio with the exception of Al^{3+}, which can occupy either type of hole (see

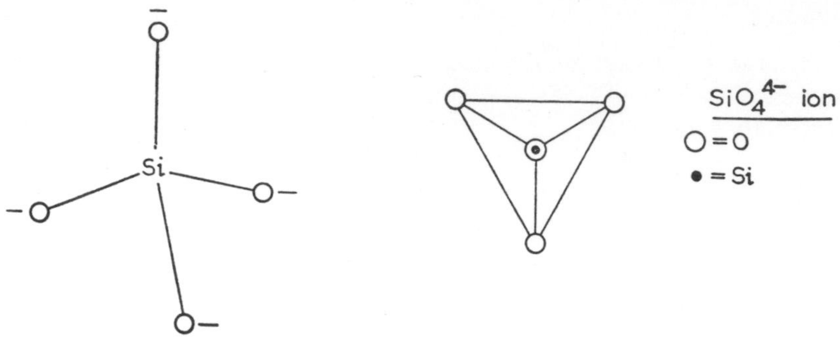

Fig. 5.8. (After T. Moeller)

Table 5.5). Although the radius ratio principle is a useful guide, it is only strictly applicable to ionic compounds, and silicates are partly covalent.

TABLE 5.5

Oxide	Radius ratio	Co-ordination number	Type of hole occupied
$Be^{2+}:O^{2-}$	0·25	4	Tetrahedral
$Si^{4+}:O^{2-}$	0·29	4	Tetrahedral
$Al^{3+}:O^{2-}$	0·42	4 or 6	Tetrahedral or Octahedral
$Mg^{2+}:O^{2-}$	0·59	6	Octahedral
$Fe^{2+}:O^{2-}$	0·68	6	Octahedral

The mineral olivine $(\overline{Mg, Fe})_2SiO_4$ has the same structure as forsterite, but about one tenth of the Mg^{2+} ions in forsterite are replaced by Fe^{2+} ions. Since the ions have similar radii, Mg^{2+} 0·65Å, Fe^{2+} 0·75Å, and occupy the same type of hole, substitution of one ion for another does not change the structure. This is known as isomorphous replacement. In certain minerals Al^{3+} replaces Si^{4+} in tetrahedral holes since these ions have similar sizes, but an extra positive ion must also be added to maintain electrical neutrality.

2. *Pyrosilicates.* Two tetrahedral units are joined by one oxygen giving the $(Si_2O_7)^{6-}$ ion (see Fig. 5.9).

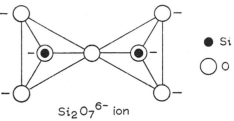

$Si_2O_7^{6-}$ ion

Fig. 5.9. (After T. Moeller)

This is the simplest of the condensed silicate ions but is uncommon. The only two known examples are thorteveitite $Sc_2(Si_2O_7)$ and hemimorphite $Zn_4(OH)_2(Si_2O_7).H_2O$.

3. *Cyclic silicates.* If two oxygens per tetrahedron are shared, ring structures may be formed of general formula $(SiO_3)_n^{2n-}$ (see Fig. 5.10).

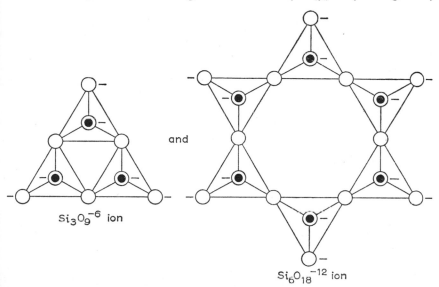

$Si_3O_9^{-6}$ ion   and $Si_6O_{18}^{-12}$ ion

Fig. 5.10. (After T. Moeller)

The cyclic ion $Si_3O_9^{6-}$ occurs in wollastonite, $Ca_3(Si_3O_9)$, and benitoite, $BaTi(Si_3O_9)$, and $Si_6O_{18}^{12-}$ occurs in beryl, $Be_3Al_2(Si_6O_{18})$. In beryl the Si_6O_{18} units are superimposed one above the other leaving channels, hence the mineral is permeable to gases which have small molecules, e.g. helium.

4. *Chain silicates.* The sharing of two oxygens by each tetrahedron may result in simple chains (pyroxenes) of formula $(SiO_3)_n^{2n-}$ (see Fig. 5.11). Examples include enstatite $MgSiO_3$ and spodumene $LiAl(SiO_3)_2$. Double chains (amphiboles) of formula $(Si_4O_{11})_n^{6n-}$ are well known (see Fig. 5.12),

where two simple chains are joined together by shared oxygens. Thus some tetrahedra share two oxygens, others three.

A typical amphibole is tremolite, $Ca_2Mg_5Si_4O_{11}.(OH)_2$. Amphiboles always contain hydroxyl groups, which are attached to the metal ions. The

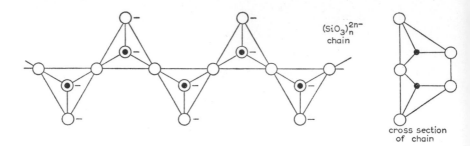

$(SiO_3)_n^{2n-}$
chain

cross section
of chain

Fig. 5.11.   (After T. Moeller)

metal ions hold the parallel chains of both pyroxenes and amphiboles together. Since the Si—O bonds in the chains are strong and directional, pyroxenes and amphiboles cleave readily parallel to the chains and form

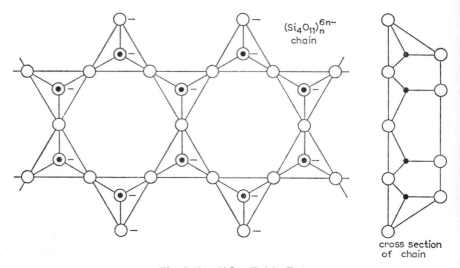

$(Si_4O_{11})_n^{6n-}$
chain

cross section
of chain

Fig. 5.12.   (After T. Moeller)

fibres. The characteristic cleavage angles of 89° for pyroxenes and 56° for amphiboles are related to the size of the cross-sectional trapezium of the chains and the way in which they are packed together (see Fig. 5.13). The term asbestos minerals was originally confined to fibrous amphiboles derived from tremolite or crocidolite by isomorphous replacement of metals or silicon. The name asbestos is also applied to derivatives of the sheet

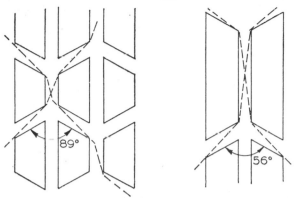

Fig. 5.13

silicates. Commercial asbestos is mostly chrysotile which is the magnesium analogue of kaolin, a sheet silicate:

$$\text{kaolin; } Al_2(OH)_4Si_2O_5 \qquad \text{chrysotile; } Mg_3(OH)_4Si_2O_5$$

5. Sheet silicates. The sharing of three oxygen atoms per tetrahedron results in an infinite two-dimensional sheet, of empirical formula $(Si_2O_5)_n^{2n-}$

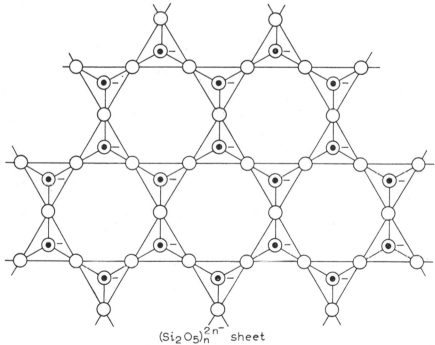

$(Si_2O_5)_n^{2n-}$ sheet

Fig. 5.14.   (After T. Moeller)

(see Fig. 5.14).   Individual layers are held together by the electrostatic forces of the metal ions present.   These forces are not as strong as the bonds in the Si—O sheet, and so the minerals cleave into thin sheets.   Minerals in this group include aluminosilicate clays and the micas.   The sheets are not simple silicate layers, but usually contain sub-layers made up of a combination of SiO_4 and AlO_4 tetrahedra and MgO_6 and AlO_6 octahedra held together by shared oxygen atoms.   Two common examples of clay minerals are talc, $Mg_3(OH)_2(Si_4O_{10})$, and kaolin, $Al_2(OH)_4(Si_2O_5)$.   If Si is replaced by Al and an alkali metal, much harder micas are formed, e.g. muscovite $KAl_2(OH)_2$ (Si_3AlO_{10}).

6. *Three-dimensional silicates.*   If all four oxygens of a SiO_4 tetrahedron are shared with other tetrahedra, a three-dimensional lattice is formed, and if there is no replacement of Si by metals, the formula is SiO_2 (quartz, tridymite or cristobalite).   Isomorphous replacement of Si^{4+} by Al^{3+} in tetrahedral positions in the SiO_2 lattice requires the presence of additional metal ions in the lattice, to preserve electrical neutrality.   Such replacement results in groups of minerals called feldspars, zeolites and ultramarines.

The feldspars are the most important rock forming minerals and constitute two-thirds of the igneous rocks.   Feldspars are divided into two groups according to the symmetry of their structure.

Orthoclase feldspars		*Plagioclase feldspars*	
orthoclase	$KAlSi_3O_8$	albite	$NaAlSi_3O_8$
celsian	$BaAl_2Si_2O_8$	anorthite	$CaAl_2Si_2O_8$

Orthoclase are more symmetrical than plagioclase since K^+ and Ba^{2+} are just the right size to fit into the lattice whilst Na^+ and Ca^{2+}, being smaller, allow distortion.

Zeolites are the most important of the three-dimensional silicates.   They have a much more open structure than the feldspars, which permits them to take up or lose water quite readily from the channels in the honeycomb-like structure.   A variety of other molecules such as CO_2, NH_3 and EtOH may also be absorbed instead of water; zeolites act as molecular sieves by absorbing molecules small enough to enter the cavities, but not those which are too big to enter.   Zeolites also act as natural ion exchangers.   For example, Permutit water-softeners are sodium zeolites.   They take Ca^{2+} ions from hard water and replace them by Na^+, thereby softening the water.   The Permutit softener is regenerated by treatment with brine, when the reverse process takes place.   Many synthetic zeolites have been made in addition to naturally occurring minerals, such as natrolite, $Na_2(Al_2Si_3O_{10})2H_2O$, heulandite, $Ca(Al_2Si_7O_{18}).6H_2O$, and analcite $Na(AlSi_2O_6).H_2O$.

The ultramarines are synthetically produced.   Many are coloured and are used as pigments, although some are colourless.   In contrast to the zeolites, ultramarines contain no water, but, apart from the metal ions which are introduced to balance the charges when Al^{3+} replaces Si^{4+}, extra anions and cations (e.g. Cl^-, SO_4^{2-} and S_2^{2-}) are situated in the cavities.   Exchange of these ions and the metal ions is possible as with the zeolites, and sodalite is converted to nosean by heating with fused sodium sulphate.   Some examples of ultramarines are: ultramarine $Na_8(Al_6Si_6O_{24})S_2$, sodalite $Na_8(Al_6Si_6O_{24})Cl_2$ and nosean $Na_8(Al_6Si_6O_{24})SO_4$.

Silicates are the most important compounds of silicon because the glass, ceramic and cement industries are based on their chemistry.   The metal-lurgical industries are also concerned with silicates because many minerals are silicates and because of their presence in slags.   Further information may be obtained from:

BARRER, R. M., *Quarterly Reviews of the Chemical Society*, 3, 239, 1949.
EMELÉUS, H. J. and ANDERSON, J. S., *Modern Aspects of Inorganic Chemistry*, Routledge & Kegan Paul, 1960.
PAULING, L., *The Nature of the Chemical Bond*, 3rd Edn., Oxford University Press, 1960.

Silicones

The complete hydrolysis of $SiCl_4$ yields silica SiO_2, which has a very stable three-dimensional structure.   The fundamental research of F. S. Kipping on the hydrolysis of alkyl-substituted chlorosilanes led, not to the expected silicon compound analogous to a ketone, but to long chain polymers called silicones.

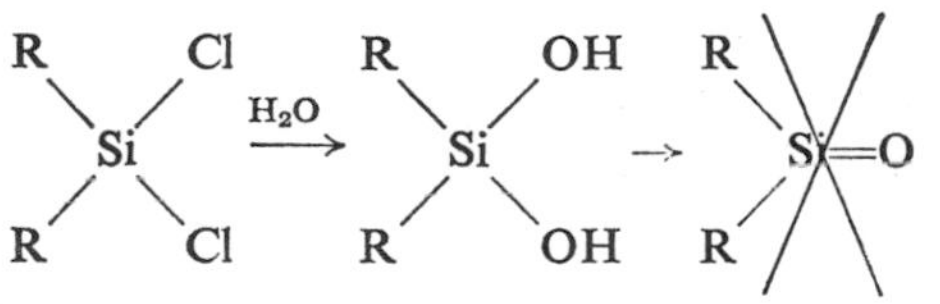

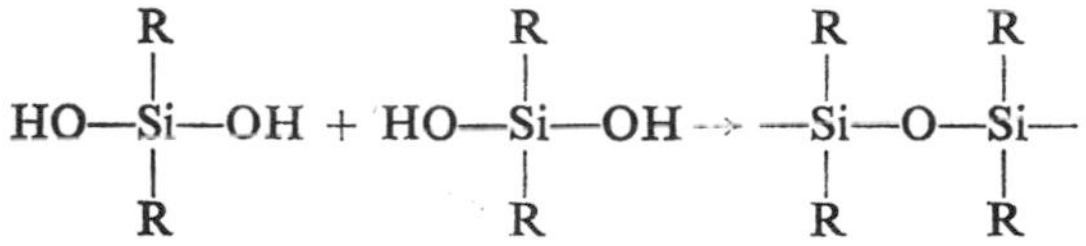

The starting materials for the manufacture of silicones are alkyl-substituted chlorosilanes.   Thus the hydrolysis of trialkylmonochlorosilane, R_3SiCl, yields hexa-alkylsiloxane.

$$
\begin{array}{ccc}
\text{R} & & \text{R} \\
| & & | \\
\text{R—Si—O—Si—R} \\
| & & | \\
\text{R} & & \text{R}
\end{array}
$$

The dialkyldichlorosilane, R_2SiCl_2 on hydrolysis gives rise to straight chain polymers and since an active OH group is left at each end of the chain, polymerization continues and the chain increases in length.

$$
\begin{array}{cccc}
\text{R} & \text{R} & \text{R} & \text{R} \\
| & | & | & | \\
\text{HO—Si—O—Si—O—Si—O—Si—OH} \\
| & | & | & | \\
\text{R} & \text{R} & \text{R} & \text{R}
\end{array}
$$

The hydrolysis of alkyl trichlorosilane $RSiCl_3$ gives a very complex cross-linked polymer.

$$
\begin{array}{cc}
| & \\
\text{O} & \text{R} \\
| & | \\
\text{R—Si—O—Si—O—} \\
| & | \\
\text{O} & \text{O} \\
| & | \\
\text{R—Si—O—Si—R} \\
| & | \\
\text{O} & \text{O} \\
| & |
\end{array}
$$

If some R_3SiCl is mixed with the R_2SiCl_2 and hydrolysed, the R_3SiCl will block the end of the chain produced by R_2SiCl_2, since it has only one functional —OH group and will thus limit the chain size. Similarly, the addition of $RSiCl_3$ to the hydrolysis mixture produces cross-linking. By controlled mixing of the reactants, any given type of polymer can be produced.

Alkyl chlorosilanes are prepared by a Grignard reaction.

$$SiCl_4 + CH_3MgCl \rightarrow CH_3.Si.Cl_3 + MgCl_2,$$

$$CH_3.SiCl_3 + CH_3MgCl \rightarrow (CH_3)_2SiCl_2 + MgCl_2,$$

and by the 'Direct Process', where chlorinated hydrocarbons react with silicon in the presence of a metal catalyst, probably by a free radical mechanism:

$$Si + 2CH_3Cl \xrightarrow{\text{Cu catalyst}} (CH_3)_2SiCl_2$$

Both methods yield a mixture of products, and careful fractionation is important. The products are highly reactive and inflammable and the reaction with water is strongly exothermic.

Silicones are fairly expensive but have many desirable properties. Their durability and inertness is related to their stable silica-like arrangement of Si—O—Si—O—Si.

Straight chain polymers of two to several thousand units are used as silicone fluids and rubbers. The boiling point and viscosity increase with chain length. These fluids are water repellent because of the organic side groups. Most of the polymers are stable to heat, up to a temperature of at least 200°C; the most heat-stable side groups are phenyl groups, followed by the methyl, ethyl, and propyl groups in descending order of stability. On heating in air to 350–400°C, silicones are rapidly oxidized and cross-links are formed. The polymer becomes brittle and cracks, and low molecular weight polymers and cyclic structures are evolved. Strong heating in the absence of air causes silicones to soften and form volatile products, but oxidation and cross-linking do not occur. These polymers are used in waterproofing textiles, in glassware, as lubricants and releasing agents and as polish and anti-foaming agents. Silicone rubbers are useful since they retain their elasticity from −90 to +250°C and because they are good electrical insulators.

Silicone resins have branched chains and are used in paints and varnish, in structural resins similar to bakelite, and as water repellents for treating masonry.

Two good reviews on the history, manufacture, structure and properties of silicones are given in *School Science Review*, by BAKER, C. J., **142**, 414, 1959 and HART, S. J., **141**, 256, 1959.

Allotropy of Carbon

Carbon exists in two crystalline forms, diamond and graphite. The black powder formed by the thermal decomposition of carbon compounds was once thought to be amorphous carbon, but is now regarded as finely divided graphite.

In diamond, which is colourless, each carbon atom utilizes sp^3 hybrid orbitals to form four bonds. Thus each carbon atom is tetrahedrally bonded to four other carbon atoms and a three-dimensional polymer is formed. Melting diamond involves breaking the strong covalent bonds which extend in all directions; hence the melting point is abnormally high (about 3600°C) and the structure is very hard (see Fig. 5.15).

Graphite forms a two-dimensional sheet-like polymeric structure. Each sheet may be regarded as a fused system of benzene rings, and illustrates the ability of carbon to form multiple bonds. The layers are held together by relatively weak van der Waals forces and are about 3·35 Å apart, which is more than twice the covalent radius of carbon (1·54Å). The wide separation accounts for the density of graphite (2·22 g/cc) being much lower than diamond (3·51 g/cc). Graphite is quite soft and cleaves easily between the layers; hence it has lubricating properties which contrast with the abrasive properties of diamond (see Fig. 5.16). Only three of the valency electrons of each carbon atom are involved in forming sp^2 hybrid bonds, the fourth electron forming a π bond. Because π electrons are mobile, graphite can conduct electricity. Graphite is the thermodynamically stable form of

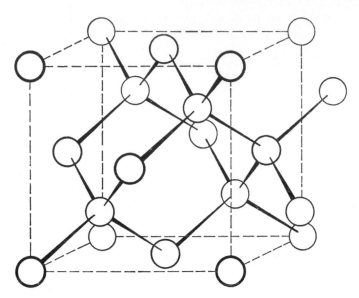

Fig. 5.15. The crystal structure of diamond (WELLS, A. F., *Structural Inorganic Chemistry*, Clarendon Press, Oxford)

carbon by 0·45 kcal/mole at room temperature and ordinary pressure; it can be converted to diamond at 1600°C by a pressure of 50–60,000 atmospheres.

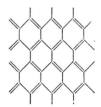

Fig. 5.16. The crystal structure of a graphite sheet

Graphitic Compounds

The π electrons in graphite are shared by a whole layer of carbon atoms and they can react with other elements without breaking either the rings or the layers. The reacting atoms, molecules or ions go in between the layers and thus greatly increase the distance between layers. Some of these lamellar compounds have a higher electrical conductivity than graphite whilst others are non-conducting. These are considered in turn.

When graphite reacts with metallic potassium, rubidium or caesium, a bronze-coloured compound is formed. This may have the formula C_8M, but the composition depends on the concentration of the invading species and the number of layers invaded. The halogens Cl_2 and Br_2, many halides $FeCl_3$, oxides MoO_3, sulphides FeS_2 and ammonia may penetrate the structure in this way. Their presence increases the conductivity of graphite either by adding electrons to the π system, $(K \rightarrow K^+ + e)$ or by removing π electrons $(Cl + e \rightarrow Cl^-)$ thus leaving a 'positive hole' in the sheet which can migrate, and therefore carry current. The exact nature of these mechanisms has not yet been definitely settled.

If graphite is oxidized with strong reagents such as concentrated nitric acid, perchloric acid or potassium permanganate, graphite oxide is obtained as a non-stoichiometric compound where the O:C ratio approaches 1:2, but is often short of oxygen and frequently contains hydrogen. The interlayer spacing is increased to 6–7 Å, but the oxide absorbs a variety of molecules such as water, alcohols and acetone when the spacing may increase to 19 Å. The oxygen is thought to form ether-like linkages C—O—C and possibly keto and enol forms as well $\diagup C = O$ $\diagup C—OH$. Since all four electrons on a carbon atom are now involved in σ bonding, there are now no mobile π electrons, hence the loss of electrical conductivity. The layers should become buckled, but this remains to be proved. Graphite fluoride with a ratio F:C of up to 0·99:1 is formed by direct combination and has a layer spacing of about 8 Å. The tetrahedral bonding should result in buckled sheets and graphite fluoride is non-conducting.

Carbides

Compounds of carbon and a less electronegative element are called carbides. This excludes compounds with nitrogen, phosphorous, oxygen, sulphur and the halogens from this section. Carbides are of three main types: ionic or salt-like, interstitial or metallic and covalent. All three types are prepared by heating the metal or its oxide with carbon or a hydrocarbon at temperatures of 2000°C.

Salt-like carbides are formed mainly by the elements in Groups I, II and III, the coinage metals, zinc and cadmium and some of the lanthanides. They contain the carbide ion $(—C \equiv C—)^{2-}$. Since these react with water liberating acetylene they are called acetylides.

$$CaC_2 + 2H_2O \rightarrow Ca(OH)_2 + HC \equiv CH$$

Beryllium carbide Be_2C and aluminium carbide Al_4C_3 yield methane on hydrolysis, and one of the two carbides of magnesium Mg_2C_3 yields methyl acetylene CH_3—$C \equiv CH$. The acetylides have a NaCl type of lattice, but the shape of the $(C \equiv C)^{2-}$ ion elongates the unit cell in one direction in CaC_2.

Interstitial carbides are formed mostly by transition elements, particularly the chromium, manganese and iron groups. They are typically very high-melting (TaC m.p. 3900°C) and very hard (9–10 on Moh's scale of hardness), and WC is used for cutting tools. The carbon atoms occupy octahedral holes in the close-packed metal lattice, and do not affect the electrical conductivity of the metal. Provided that the radius of the metal atoms is greater than about 1·3 Å, the carbon atoms can enter the metal lattice without distorting it. The metals Cr, Mn, Fe, Co and Ni have radii below 1·3 Å, hence the metal lattice is distorted and these carbides are intermediate in properties between ionic and interstitial. They are hydrolysed by water and acids, giving a mixture of hydrocarbons and hydrogen. These carbides have chains of carbon atoms running through a distorted metal structure.

Of the covalent carbides, SiC and B_4C are the most important. Silicon carbide is hard, infusible and chemically inert and occurs in three forms. It is widely used as an abrasive called carborundum. It has a three-dimensional structure of Si and C atoms, each tetrahedrally surrounded by four of the other kind. Boron carbide is even harder than silicon carbide and is used both as an abrasive and as a shield from radiation.

Cyanides

The alkali metal cyanides particularly NaCN, are made in quantity by high temperature reactions from sodamide or sodium carbonate.

$$NaNH_2 + C \rightarrow H_2 + NaCN$$

$$Na_2CO_3 + 4C + N_2 \rightarrow 3CO + 2NaCN$$

The cyanide ion is important in forming stable complexes, particularly with the metals of the Cr, Mn, Fe, Co, Ni, Cu and Zn groups. Two common complexes are ferrocyanides $[Fe(CN)_6]^{4-}$ and ferricyanides $[Fe(CN)_6]^{3-}$. The reason why the later transition elements form such stable cyanide complexes is because these elements have more filled d orbitals, so that there is a greater chance that the original co-ordinate bond $M \leftarrow (CN)^-$ may be supplemented by dative π back-bonding as in the carbonyls. The extreme toxicity of cyanides is due to the cyanide ion complexing with metals in enzymes and haemoglobin in the body, thus preventing normal metabolism. Besides forming many complexes analogous to halide complexes, the cyanide ion often brings out the maximum co-ordination number of a metal. Thus Fe^{3+} gives $[FeCl_4]^-$ with chloride ions, but $[Fe(CN)_6]^{3-}$ with cyanide ions. Many metal ions such as Cu^+, Ni^+, Mn^+, Au^+ and Mn^{3+}, which are too unstable to exist in solution, are quite stable when complexed with cyanide ions. The formation of complexes is important in the extraction of silver and gold, since the metals dissolve in a solution of sodium cyanide in the presence of air, and form sodium argentocyanide, from which the metal is recovered by reduction with zinc.

$$2Ag + 4NaCN + H_2O + O \rightarrow 2Na[Ag(CN)_2] + 2NaOH$$

Cyanide ions may act both as complexing and reducing agents

$$2Cu^{2+} + 4CN^- \rightarrow (CN)_2 + 2CuCN \xrightarrow{CN^-} [Cu(CN)_4]^{3-}$$

In this reaction the cyanide ion is itself oxidized to cyanogen $(CN)_2$ in much the same way as I^- is oxidized to I_2 by Cu^{2+}. In alkaline solution, cyanogen disproportionates into cyanide and cyanate ions.

$$(CN)_2 + 2OH^- \rightarrow H_2O + CN^- + NCO^-$$

The cyanate ion is isoelectronic with carbon dioxide; hence they have similar structures and are both linear.

$$O{=}C{=}O \qquad {}^-N{=}C{=}O$$

Hydrogen cyanide HCN is prepared either by acidification of ionic cyanides, or by dehydrating ammonium formate $H.COO.NH_4$ or formamide $H.CONH_2$. Its boiling point, 26°C, is abnormally high because of hydrogen bonding and it is one of the weakest acids known. HCN has been used as a non-aqueous ionizing solvent.

Group V

TABLE 5.6

Element	Symbol	Electronic structure		Oxidation states*
Nitrogen	N	[He]	$2s^2\,2p^3$	1, 2, **3**, 4, **5**
Phosphorus	P	[Ne]	$3s^2\,3p^3$	**3**, (4), **5**
Arsenic	As	[Ar]	$3d^{10}\,4s^2\,4p^3$	**3**, **5**
Antimony	Sb	[Kr]	$4d^{10}\,5s^2\,5p^3$	**3**, **5**
Bismuth	Bi	[Xe]	$4f^{14}\,5d^{10}\,6s^2\,6p^3$	**3**, **5**

*See page 77.

Electronic Structure and Oxidation States

The elements of this group all have five electrons in their outer shell. They exhibit a maximum oxidation state of five towards oxygen by using all five outer electrons in forming bonds. The tendency of the pair of s electrons to remain inert (the inert pair effect), increases with increasing atomic weight. Thus, only the p electrons are used in bonding and trivalency results. Valencies of 3 and 5 are shown with the halogens and with sulphur, and the hydrides are trivalent. In the case of nitrogen, a very wide range of oxidation states exists from $+1$ in N_2O to $+5$ in HNO_3 and N_2O_5.

Bond Type

High ionization potentials prevent the formation of highly charged ions. Except with F, the difference in electronegativity is not sufficient to permit an ionic bond, though in a few cases Sb and Bi lose electrons and form M^{3+}; these ions, however, are rapidly hydrolysed to SbO^+ and BiO^+ in water. The tendency to gain three electrons and give M^{3-} occurs only with N. In the majority of cases, the bonds are covalent and this tendency increases with increased oxidation number.

Metallic and Non-Metallic Character

Within the group there is an increase in electropositive (metallic) character. N and P are non-metals, As and Sb are metalloids which show many metallic properties and Bi is a true metal. Thus the normal oxides of N and P are strongly acidic, whilst As and Sb are amphoteric and Bi is largely basic.

Differences between N *and the Other Elements*

As in the previous groups, the first element differs from the rest. Thus nitrogen is gaseous and diatomic. This involves triply bonded nitrogen

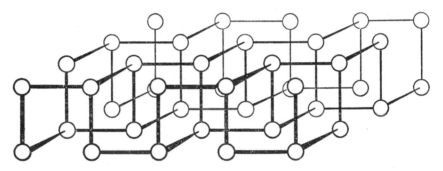

Fig. 5.17. The arrangement of atoms in the corrugated planes found in crystalline black phosphorus (VAN WAZER, J. R., *Phosphorus and Its Compounds*, Vol. I, Interscience, New York–London, 1958, p. 121)

$N\equiv N$ which in this case is very stable. The other elements are solids and have allotropic forms, including tetra-atomic forms such as P_4 and As_4, and more complicated arrangements such as red and black phosphorus (see Fig. 5.17).

Except for NF_3 the nitrogen halides are unstable and often explode, whilst the halides of the other elements are stable. Many oxides and oxy ions such as, N_2O_3, N_2O_5, NO_2^+, NO_3^- are monomeric, whilst the trioxides and pentoxides of the other elements are dimeric. Because the second shell of electrons is limited to an octet, N cannot form complexes by accepting electron pairs. The subsequent elements have suitable vacant *d* orbitals and can form such complexes, thus increasing their maximum co-ordination number to six. Further, N forms several oxides (N_2O, NO and N_2O_4) which have no counterparts in the other elements.

Occurrence and Extraction

Nitrogen comprises 78% of the earth's atmosphere; it is important as an essential constituent of proteins, and is also used in fertilizers and explosives. It is obtained commercially by the fractional distillation of liquid air, but when it is obtained in this way it contains a trace of oxygen. Nitrogen obtained by removing the other constituents from air contains traces of the inert gases. In the laboratory it is made by warming ammonium nitrite or by oxidizing ammonia with hypochlorite.

$$NH_4Cl + NaNO_2 \rightarrow NaCl + NH_4NO_2 \rightarrow N_2 + 2H_2O$$

$$4NH_3 + 3Ca(OCl)_2 \rightarrow 3CaCl_2 + 6H_2O + 2N_2$$

Very pure nitrogen is obtained by carefully warming NaN_3, sodium azide.

Phosphorus is the tenth most abundant element in the earth's crust and is important in biological metabolism, since it occurs in nucleic acids, in bones as $Ca_3(PO_4)_2$ and in fertilizers; it also has a variety of other uses. It is obtained by the reduction of calcium phosphate with carbon in an electric furnace. Arsenic, antimony and bismuth are not very abundant, but are well known because they are obtained as metallurgical by-products, and are easily extracted by reduction of the oxides with carbon.

Hydrides

All the elements form volatile hydrides of formula $M\mathrm{H_3}$. The ease of formation, stability, ability to use the lone pair of electrons for co-ordinate bond formation and the ease of replacing the hydrogens by other groups decreases from NH_3 to BiH_3.

Ammonia is prepared in the laboratory by heating an ammonium salt with sodium hydroxide:

$$NH_4Cl + NaOH \rightarrow NaCl + NH_3 + H_2O$$

Commercially, ammonia may be obtained from the distillation of coal, or from the hydrolysis of calcium cyanamide, $CaCN_2$, which is also used as a fertilizer:

$$CaC_2 + N_2 \xrightarrow{1100°C} CaCN_2 + C$$

$$CaCN_2 + 5H_2O \rightarrow CaCO_3 + 2NH_4OH$$

The most important commercial process is the Haber process, in which nitrogen and hydrogen combine directly:

$$N_2 + 3H_2 \rightleftharpoons 2NH_3 + \text{heat.}$$

High pressure and low temperature are indicated by Le Chatelier's principle.

but in practice 200 atmospheres, 550°C and a catalyst of iron and molybdenum are used to attain a reasonable conversion at a reasonable rate.

Arsine, AsH_3, and stibine, SbH_3, are formed in Marsh's test by the reduction of a trivalent arsenic or antimony compound with zinc and acid. Arsine, stibine and bismuthine, BiH_3, can be prepared from binary metal compounds such as Na_3P, Zn_3As_2, Mg_3Sb_2 or Mg_3Bi_2 by the action of water or dilute acid.

The structure of these trihydrides is described as pyramidal, or tetrahedral with one position occupied by a lone pair (Fig. 5.18).

	1s	2s	2p
Electronic structure of nitrogen atom—ground state	↑↓	↑↓	↑ ↑ ↑
Nitrogen having gained a share in three electrons from three hydrogen atoms in NH_3 molecule	↑↓	↑↓	↑↓ ↑↓ ↑↓

sp^3 hybridization.

TABLE 5.7

Electronegativity	Bond angle	Bond energy kcal/mole
N = 3·0 P = 2·1 As = 2·0 Sb = 1·9	H—N—H = 106° 45′ H—P—H = 94° H—As—H = 91° 30′ H—Sb—H = 91° 30′	N—H = 93 P—H = 76 As—H = 59 Sb—H = 61

Since the repulsion between a lone pair and a bond pair of electrons always exceeds that between two bond pairs, the regular tetrahedral shape is distorted. As the electronegativity of the central atom decreases, the bond pairs become further away from the central atom, hence the lone pair causes even greater distortion (Table 5.7).

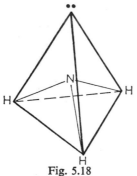

Fig. 5.18

The stability of the hydrides decreases on descending the group, as indicated by their bond energies. Consequently, SbH_3 and BiH_3 may be obtained in small amounts only. In Marsh's test, the hydrides formed are passed through a glass tube heated with a burner. SbH_3 decomposes and gives a metallic mirror before the flame, but AsH_3 gives a mirror after the flame.

Ammonia is a weak base, and is hydrogenbonded in the liquid state. Phosphine is a very much weaker base, and like AsH_3, SbH_3 and BiH_3 does not form hydrogen bonds. These hydrides are strong reducing agents and react with solutions of metal ions to give phosphides, arsenides and stibnides. They are inflammable and extremely poisonous.

Ammonia forms ammonium NH_4^+ salts very readily, and utilizes the lone pair of electrons to form a co-ordinate bond. Phosphine forms salts with HCl and HI only under anhydrous conditions, whilst the other hydrides do not form co-ordinate bonds. Ammonia also forms co-ordination complexes with metal ions from the Co, Ni, Cu and Zn groups, which accords with its strong donor properties.

Nitrogen forms several hydrides (see Table 5.8).

TABLE 5.8

Formula	Name	Oxidation state
NH_3	Ammonia	-3
N_2H_4	Hydrazine	-2
NH_2OH	Hydroxylamine	-1

Hydrazine has recently attracted attention as a rocket fuel. It is basic and forms two series of salts.

$$N_2H_4 + HX \rightarrow N_2H_5^+ + X^-$$
$$N_2H_4 + 2HX \rightarrow N_2H_6^{2+} + 2X^-.$$

Hydrazine is still manufactured by the Raschig process, where ammonia is oxidized by sodium hypochlorite in aqueous solution:

$$NH_3 + NaOCl \rightleftharpoons NH_2Cl + NaOH$$
$$2NH_3 + NH_2Cl \rightleftharpoons NH_2NH_2 + NH_4Cl.$$

A side reaction which decreases the yield is inhibited by the addition of glue or gelatin as a negative catalyst.

$$N_2H_4 + 2NH_2Cl \rightarrow N_2 + 2NH_4Cl.$$

The structure of hydrazine is similar to that of hydrogen peroxide and the chemistry of the two are related:

$$\begin{array}{cc} H & H \\ \diagdown \quad \diagup \\ N-N \\ \diagup \quad \diagdown \\ H & H \end{array} \qquad H-O-O-H$$

The fact that two nitrogen atoms are joined together, indicates that the N—N bond is stable. Hydrazine is a powerful reducing agent in alkaline solution:

$$N_2H_4 + 2I_2 \rightarrow 4HI + N_2$$
$$N_2H_4 + 2O_2 \rightarrow 2H_2O_2 + N_2.$$

When there are powerful reducing agents in acidic solution, it is forced to react as an oxidizing agent.

$$N_2H_4 + Zn + 2HCl \rightarrow 2NH_3 + ZnCl_2$$

The nitrogen atoms of hydrazine have a lone pair of electrons, which can form co-ordinate bonds to metal ions such as Ni^{2+} and Co^{2+}, and phenyl hydrazine characterizes carbonyl compounds and sugars. Phosphorus forms an unstable hydride P_2H_4, which has little chemical similarity to N_2H_4.

Hydroxylamine, like hydrazine, is a weaker base than ammonia.

$$NH_2OH + HCl \rightarrow [NH_3OH]^+Cl^-.$$

It is used mainly as a reducing agent, though it can act as an oxidizing agent too. It is prepared by reduction of nitrates or nitrites either by SO_2 or electrolytically. It can form co-ordinate bonds, and complexes with metals.

Liquid Ammonia as a Solvent

Liquid ammonia is the most studied non-aqueous solvent and it resembles the aqueous system quite closely. Both water and ammonia undergo self-ionization:

$$2H_2O \rightleftharpoons H_3O^+ + OH^-$$
$$2NH_3 \rightleftharpoons NH_4^+ + NH_2^-.$$

Thus, substances producing H_3O^+ ions in water are acids, and ammonium salts are acids in liquid ammonia. Similarly, substances producing OH^- in water or NH_2^- in liquid ammonia are bases in that solvent.

Thus acid base neutralization reactions occur in both solvents, and phenolphthalein may be used to detect the end-point in either:

$$\underset{\text{acid}}{HCl} + \underset{\text{base}}{NaOH} \rightarrow \underset{\text{salt}}{NaCl} + \underset{\text{solvent}}{H_2O} \quad \text{(in water)}$$
$$NH_4Cl + NaNH_2 \rightarrow NaCl + 2NH_3 \quad \text{(in ammonia)}$$

In a similar way, precipitation reactions occur in both solvents. However, the direction of the reaction is a function of the solvent:

$$(NH_4)_2S + Cu^{2+} \rightarrow Cu_2S \downarrow \quad \text{(in water)}$$
$$(NH_4)_2S + Cu^{2+} \rightarrow Cu_2S \downarrow \quad \text{(in ammonia)}$$
$$BaCl_2 + 2AgNO_3 \rightarrow Ba(NO_3)_2 + 2AgCl \downarrow \quad \text{(in water)}$$
$$BaCl_2 \downarrow + 2Ag(NO_3) \leftarrow Ba(NO_3)_2 + 2AgCl \quad \text{(in ammonia)}$$

Amphoteric behaviour is observed in both solvents, for example, $Zn(OH)_2$ is amphoteric in water and $Zn(NH_2)_2$ is amphoteric in ammonia:

$$Zn^{2+} + NaOH \rightarrow \underset{\text{insoluble}}{Zn(OH)_2} + \overset{\text{excess}}{NaOH} \rightarrow \underset{\text{soluble}}{Na_2[Zn(OH)_4]} \quad \text{in water}$$
$$Zn^{2+} + KNH_2 \rightarrow \underset{\text{insoluble}}{Zn(NH_2)_2} + \overset{\text{excess}}{KNH_2} \rightarrow \underset{\text{soluble}}{K_2[Zn(NH_2)_4]} \quad \text{in ammonia}$$

Liquid ammonia is an extremely good solvent for the alkali metals and Ca, Sr and Ba. The metals are very soluble and have a conductivity comparable to that of pure metals. The ammonia solvates the metal ions, but is resistant to reduction by the free electrons. These solutions of metals in liquid ammonia are very good reducing agents either because they add electrons or produce nascent hydrogen:

$$Na \xrightarrow{\text{liquid ammonia}} Na^+ + e$$
$$\text{or } NH_4^+ + e \rightarrow NH_3 + H$$

Liquid sodium is used in the cooling of nuclear reactors. The cooling system needs cleaning periodically. Liquid ammonia is a good solvent for metals, but it leaves a trace of finely-divided sodium which is pyrophoric. Thus it is necessary to destroy the sodium by using an acid and liquid ammonia:

$$2NH_4Br + 2Na \xrightarrow{\text{in } NH_3} 2NaBr + H_2 + 2NH_3$$

Because liquid ammonia accepts protons readily, it enhances the ionization of so-called weak acids such as acetic acid.

$$CH_3.COOH \rightleftharpoons CH_3.COO^- + H^+$$

Removal of H^+ by NH_3 causes the reaction to proceed in the forward direction. Thus acetic acid has a pK value of 5 in water but is almost completely ionized in liquid ammonia. Ammonia thus reduces the difference between the strengths of acids, and is called a levelling solvent.

A review of inorganic reactions in liquid ammonia has been written by FOWLES, G. W. A. and NICHOLLS, D., *Quarterly Reviews*, **16**, 1, 19, 1962.

Azides

Hydrazoic acid HN_3 is explosive when pure, but stable in aqueous solution. It is a weak acid and its salts are called azides. Sodium azide can be made by reaction between nitrous oxide and sodamide under anhydrous conditions:

$$N_2O + NaNH_2 \rightarrow Na^+(N_3)^-$$

Lead azide $Pb(N_3)_2$ has been used as a detonator and cyanuric trazide is a powerful explosive (Fig. 5.19). On the other hand, azides are used as organic

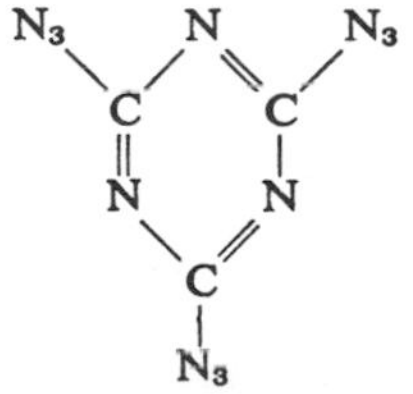

Fig. 5.19.   Cyanuric triazide

intermediates and dyestuffs.   Covalent azides are usually much less stable than ionic azides.   For the $(N_3)^-$ ion, three resonance structures may be drawn:

$$\overset{-}{:}\underset{..}{N}\!\!=\!\!\overset{+}{N}\!\!=\!\!\overset{-}{\underset{..}{N}}:\qquad\qquad \overset{2-}{:}\underset{..}{N}\!\!-\!\!\overset{+}{N}\!\!\equiv\!\!N:\qquad\qquad :N\!\!\equiv\!\!\overset{+}{N}\!\!-\!\!\overset{2-}{\underset{..}{N}}:$$

For the acid HN_3 which is largely covalent, three resonance structures may also be drawn, but, according to Pauling's adjacent charge rule, one structure is excluded, since two adjacent atoms have the same charge.

$$H\!\!-\!\!\overset{+}{\underset{..}{N}}\!\!=\!\!\underset{..}{N}\!\!=\!\!\overset{-}{\underset{..}{N}}:\qquad\qquad H\!\!-\!\!\overset{-}{\underset{..}{N}}\!\!-\!\!\overset{+}{N}\!\!\equiv\!\!N:\qquad\qquad H\!\!-\!\!\overset{+}{N}\!\!=\!\!\overset{+}{N}\!\!-\!\!\overset{2-}{\underset{..}{N}}:$$

The increased stability of the ionic azides may be due to the increased number of permissible resonance forms.   Analysis of N_3^- is by oxidation of H_2S.

$$NaN_3 + H_2S + H_2O \rightarrow NH_3 + N_2 + S + NaOH$$

Halides

Nitrogen forms two main types of halides: those derived from hydrazoic acid, and those regarded as substitution products of ammonia.   Fluorazide FN_3, chlorazide ClN_3, bromazide BrN_3 and iodazide IN_3 resemble the covalent azides in that they are extremely unstable and explosive.

All the possible trihalides of N, P, As, Sb and Bi are known except NBr_3 and NI_3, which have only been obtained as ammoniates $NBr_3.6NH_3$. These halides are predominantly covalent and, like NH_3, have a tetrahedral structure with one position occupied by a lone pair. BiF_3 is, however, ionic and the other halides of Bi and SbF_3 are intermediate in character. NF_3 is an extremely stable gas; in contrast, NCl_3 is explosive and readily hydrolysed:

$$NCl_3 + 3H_2O \rightarrow NH_3 + 3HOCl$$

NCl_3 was formerly sold as 'agene' to bleach flour, but this use declined when it was suspected that bread made from flour bleached in this way sent dogs mad.

Since NF_3 and NCl_3 are both covalent, it might be expected that they would hydrolyse similarly.   This is not so, because during the first stage in hydrolysis an extra bond is formed, and whilst Cl can expand its octet by using *d* orbitals, F and N cannot.   Since P, As and Sb can expand their octets, their trihalides all hydrolyse readily, yielding the appropriate -ous acid:

$$PCl_3 + H_2O \rightarrow H_3PO_3 + 3HCl$$

$BiCl_3$ and $BiBr_3$ are much more ionic, but give the BiO^+ ion, not Bi^{3+} on dissolving in water. NF_3 has little tendency to form co-ordinate bonds with its lone pair of electrons, but the phosphorous trihalides (and to a lesser degree the antimony trihalides) can co-ordinate in this way.

$$Ni(CO)_4 + 4PCl_3 \rightarrow Ni(PCl_3)_4 + 4CO$$

Nitrogen is unable to form pentahalides owing to the absence of suitable d orbitals, but the subsequent elements can do so and PF_5, PCl_5, PBr_5, AsF_5, SbF_5 and $SbCl_5$ are known. These molecules have a trigonal bipyramid shape in the gas phase (see Fig. 5.20).

	3s	3p	3d

Electronic structure of Phosphorus atom—ground state

Excited state

five singly-filled orbitals, can form five bonds—sp^3d hybridization.

A trigonal bipyramid is not a regular structure since some bond angles are 90° and others 120°. It is not very stable, and whilst the gaseous halides have this structure, they may accept an additional halide ion which forms a co-ordinate bond by donating a lone pair into an empty d orbital. Thus an $[MX_6]^-$ ion is formed which has a more stable octahedral structure. In the solid state, PCl_5 splits into $[PCl_6]^-$ and $[PCl_4]^+$ which have octahedral and tetrahedral structures respectively. PBr_5 splits into $[PBr_4]^+$ and Br^-. Complete hydrolysis of the pentahalides yields the appropriate -ic acid.

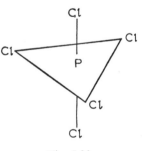

Fig. 5.20

$$PCl_5 + 4H_2O \rightarrow H_3PO_4 + 5HCl$$

Oxides

Nitrogen forms a very wide range of oxides, the lower ones being neutral, and the higher ones acidic (Table 5.9).

Nitrous oxide is a stable, relatively unreactive gas and is prepared by gently heating ammonium nitrate. It is used as an anaesthetic, as a propellant for whipped ice-cream and in the preparation of azides:

$$NH_4NO_3 \rightarrow N_2O + 2H_2O$$

$$N_2O + NaNH_2 \rightarrow NaN_3 + H_2O$$

TABLE 5.9

Formula	Oxidation number	Name
N_2O	+1	Nitrous oxide
NO	+2	Nitric oxide
N_2O_3	+3	Nitrogen sesquioxide
NO_2, N_2O_4	+4	Nitrogen dioxide, dinitrogen tetroxide
N_2O_5	+5	Dinitrogen pentoxide
(NO_3, N_2O_6) very unstable	+6	Nitrogen trioxide, dinitrogen hexoxide

The molecule is linear and there is resonance between two extreme structures:

$$\overset{-}{:}\text{N}::\text{N}::\overset{+}{\text{O}}: \leftrightarrow :\text{N}\overset{+}{:}\text{N}:\overset{-}{\overset{..}{\text{O}}}:$$

Nitrous oxide is a neutral oxide and does not form hyponitrous acid $H_2N_2O_2$ with water nor hyponitrites with alkali.   Nitric oxide is a colourless gas and is commercially important in the manufacture of nitric acid by oxidizing ammonia (Haber process) and in the obsolete Birkeland and Eyde process by sparking nitrogen and oxygen.   It is prepared in the laboratory by the reduction of dilute nitric acid with copper, or nitrous acid with iodide ions:

$$3Cu + 8HNO_3 \rightarrow 2NO + 3Cu(NO_3)_2 + 4H_2O$$

$$2HNO_2 + 2I^- + 2H^+ \rightarrow 2NO + I_2 + 2H_2O.$$

Nitric oxide has eleven valency electrons.   It is impossible for them all to be paired, hence this is an odd electron molecule and the gas is paramagnetic. However, the liquid and solid states are diamagnetic, because loose dimers are formed and the magnetic effect of unpaired electrons cancels out (Fig. 5.21).

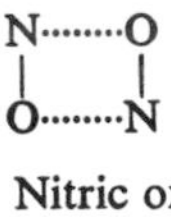

Fig. 5.21.   Nitric oxide dimer

The electronic structure of NO may be written:

$$:\text{N}\overset{...}{::}\text{O}:$$

with a double bond and a three-electron bond between N and O.   Three-electron bonds are only formed between atoms of similar electronegativity and this type of bond may be considered as a resonance hybrid between the two extreme structures:

$$\text{A}\cdot :\text{B} \leftrightarrow \text{A}: \cdot\text{B}$$

Thus NO is a resonance hybrid between:

$$\overset{-}{:N::\overset{\bullet\bullet}{O}:} \leftrightarrow \overset{+}{:\overset{\bullet\bullet}{N}::\overset{\bullet}{O}:}$$

A three-electron bond is about half as strong as a covalent bond, thus the bond length in NO is in between that of double and triple bonds. Three-electron bonds are described in terms of the molecular orbital theory on pages 129–130. Odd electron molecules are usually extremely reactive and tend to dimerize. NO is unusually stable for an odd electron molecule, but nevertheless it is quite reactive. NO reacts instantly with oxygen and gives NO_2, and with the halogens it gives nitrosyl halides NOCl. NO can also act as a ligand and form co-ordination compounds with metal ions, called nitrosyls. In these, it donates three electrons, rather than the usual two. These are fully discussed in the following articles:

ADDISON, C. C. and LEWIS, J., *Quarterly Reviews*, **9**, 115, 1955.
MOELLER, T., *J. Chem. Ed.*, **23**, 441, 542, 1946 and **24**, 149, 1947.

One such complex between Fe^{2+} and NO is responsible for the colour in the 'brown-ring test' for nitrates. NO is a neutral oxide and is not an acid anhydride.

Nitrogen sesquioxide is unstable and can be obtained by condensing NO and NO_2 together. It is an acidic oxide and is the anhydride of nitrous acid HONO. The structure of the oxide is not known, but the nitrite ion $NO_2{}^-$ has a plane triangular structure, in which one position is occupied by a lone pair.

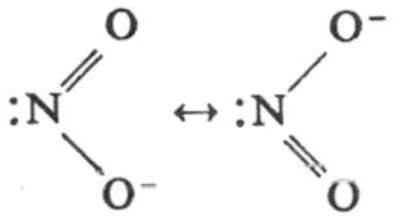

		1s	2s	2p		

Electronic structure of nitrogen atom—ground state

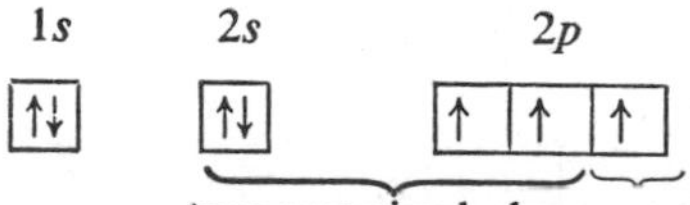

two unpaired elec- used to form
trons to form 2σ double bond
bonds to O,

sp^2 hybridization—plane triangle structure with one position occupied by a lone pair.

Nitrous acid is unstable, but it is easily made in solution by acidifying a nitrite. Nitrous acid and nitrites may act as oxidizing agents with the formation of N_2O or NO, although powerful oxidizing agents such as $KMnO_4$ and Cl_2 oxidize nitrite to nitrate $NO_3{}^-$. The nitrite ion is a good co-ordinating agent and because lone pairs of electrons are present in both N and O atoms, either can form a co-ordinate bond, so that isomerism occurs between $M \leftarrow NO_2$ and $M \leftarrow ONO$. This is discussed in Chapter 8. Treatment of a solution of Co^{2+} ions with NO_2^- ions results first in oxidation $Co^{2+} \rightarrow Co^{3+}$, then in complex formation giving $[Co(NO_2)_6]^{3-}$ ions. Precipitation of potassium cobaltinitrite $K_3[Co(NO_2)_6]$ is used to detect K^+ in qualitative analysis.

Nitrogen dioxide is a red-brown poisonous gas and is produced on a large scale by oxidizing NO in the manufacture of nitric acid. In the laboratory it is prepared by heating lead nitrate:

$$2Pb(NO_3)_2 \rightarrow 2PbO + 4NO_2 + O_2$$

The gas condenses to a brown liquid which turns paler on cooling, and eventually becomes a colourless solid. This is due to the dimerization of the dioxide to the colourless dinitrogen tetroxide:

$$2NO_2 \rightleftharpoons N_2O_4$$

The dioxide molecule is angular with an O—N—O angle of 132°. The bond length O—N of 1·20 Å is intermediate between a single and a double bond. It is suggested that the structure contains a double bond, a single bond and a three-electron bond, and that resonance occurs between the two structures:

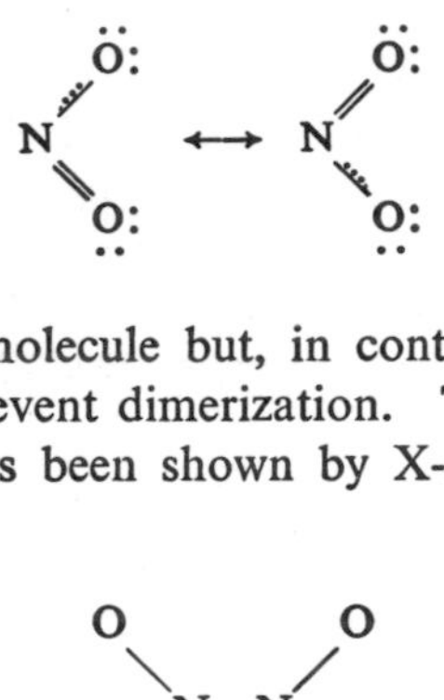

NO_2 is an odd electron molecule but, in contrast to NO, the resonance energy is insufficient to prevent dimerization. The dimer has no unpaired electrons and the solid has been shown by X-ray diffraction to have the structure

The N—N bond is very long, and is therefore weak. N_2O_4 has been extensively studied as a non-aqueous solvent which ionizes:

$$N_2O_4 \rightleftharpoons \underset{\text{acid}}{NO^+} + \underset{\text{base}}{NO_3^-}$$

Further details of this system are given in the following Royal Institute of Chemistry monographs:

GRAY, P., 'The Chemistry of N_2O_4', 1958, 4.
ADDISON, C. C., 'Use of Non-aqueous Solvents in Inorganic Chemistry', 1960, 2.

N_2O_4 is a mixed anhydride, because it reacts with water to give a mixture of nitric and nitrous acids:

$$N_2O_4 + H_2O \rightarrow HNO_3 + HNO_2$$

Some NO is also formed from decomposition of the HNO_2:

$$2HNO_2 \rightarrow NO + NO_2 + H_2O$$

The NO_2—N_2O_4 system is a strong oxidizing agent.

N_2O_5 is prepared by dehydrating HNO_3 with P_2O_5 and probably has the structure in the gas:

$$\begin{array}{ccc}
O & & O \\
\diagdown & & \diagup \\
& N\!-\!O\!-\!N & \\
\diagup & & \diagdown \\
O & & O
\end{array}$$

In the solid it exists as $NO_2{}^+NO_3{}^-$. It is the anhydride of HNO_3. Nitric acid is an excellent oxidizing agent when hot and concentrated, and is now produced in vast quantities by the Haber-Bosch process. The earlier Birkeland-Eyde process is now obsolete.

Haber-Bosch $N_2 + 3H_2 \xrightarrow[\text{Fe catalyst}]{\text{200 atmos. 500°C}} 2NH_3 + O_2 \rightarrow NO \rightarrow NO_2 \rightarrow HNO_3$

Birkeland-Eyde $N_2 + O_2 \nearrow^{\text{spark}}$

The nitrate ion may be represented as a resonance hybrid.

$$\begin{array}{ccccccccccc}
O & & O & & O & & O- & & O & & O- \\
\uparrow & & \uparrow & & \| & & | & & \| & & | \\
N & \leftrightarrow & N & \leftrightarrow & N & \leftrightarrow & N & \leftrightarrow & N & \leftrightarrow & N \\
\end{array}$$

Excluding the π bonds, one s and two p orbitals are used for bonding, and sp^2 hybridization gives a plane triangle, hence the bond angles are 120°. Reduction of nitrates in acid solution gives either NO_2 or NO, but in alkaline solutions with metals such as Devarda's alloy, ammonia is produced.

The oxides of the rest of the group are listed in Table 5.10. Fewer oxides

TABLE 5.10

Oxide	Oxidation state	Oxide	Oxidation state	Oxide	Oxidation state	Oxide	Oxidation state
P_4O_6	+3	As_4O_6	+3	Sb_4O_6	+3	Bi_2O_3	+3
$(PO_2)_n$	+4(?)			$(SbO_2)_n$	+3, +5		
P_4O_{10}	+5	As_4O_{10}	+5	Sb_4O_{10}	+5		

are formed than are found with nitrogen, presumably because of the inability of these elements to form double bonds. Phosphorus trioxide is dimeric and

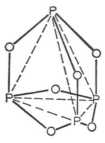

Fig. 5.21

should be written P_4O_6, not P_2O_3. Like the trioxides of As and Sb, the structure is based on an arrangement of four P, As or Sb atoms at the corners of a tetrahedron, with six oxygen atoms along the edges (Fig. 5.21).

Because yellow P is more reactive than N_2, phosphorus oxides (unlike N oxides) can all be obtained by burning phosphorus in air. P_4O_6 is formed by burning P in a limited supply of air, whilst As_4O_6 and Sb_4O_6 are obtained by direct reaction in air or oxygen. Bi_2O_3 is not dimeric like the others. The basicity increases on descending the group; the trioxides of P and As are acidic, Sb is amphoteric and Bi wholly basic. The hydrolysis of P_4O_6 to phosphorous acid is considered later.

$$P_4O_6 + 6H_2O \rightarrow 4H_3PO_3$$

The dioxide $(PO_2)_n$ is probably polymeric, though the vapour density gives a molecular weight corresponding to P_8O_{16}. It reacts with water and yields phosphoric and phosphorous acids, and could be a mixed oxide $P_4O_{10}.P_4O_6$.

$$2PO_2 + 3H_2O \rightarrow \underset{\substack{\text{ortho phosphoric}\\\text{acid}}}{H_3PO_4} + \underset{\substack{\text{ortho phosphorous}\\\text{acid}}}{H_3PO_3}$$

Phosphorus pentoxide is dimeric and has the formula P_4O_{10}, not P_2O_5. Its structure is well known and it is assumed that As_4O_{10} and Sb_4O_{10} are similar. In P_4O_6, each P atom forms three bonds to oxygen atoms. There are five outer electrons round a P atom, so the lone pair not used in bonding will be situated on the outside of the tetrahedral unit. In P_4O_{10}, each P forms an additional co-ordinate bond by donating this lone pair to an oxygen atom (Fig. 5.22). Measurement of the P—O bond lengths shows that the co-ordinate bonds are shorter than a single bond. This is explained by $p\pi$—$d\pi$ back-bonding, because of the lateral overlap of full p orbitals on the oxygen with empty d orbitals on the phosphorus. This back-bonding is similar to that of the carbonyls. P_4O_{10} is formed by burning P in an excess of air or oxygen, but As and Sb require more drastic oxidation by concentrated HNO_3 to form the pentoxides. As_4O_{10} and Sb_4O_{10} lose oxygen when they are heated, and form the trioxide. The pentoxides dissolve in water and form phosphoric acid and arsenic acid, but Sb_4O_{10} is insoluble. Antimonic acid is not known, but antimonates containing $[Sb(OH)_6]^-$ are known.

$$P_4O_{10} + 6H_2O \rightarrow 4H_3PO_4$$

Thus the stability of the highest oxidation states decreases on descending the

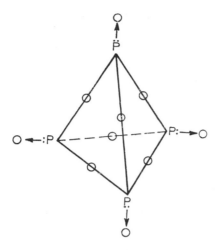

Fig. 5.22

group, and Bi does not form a pentoxide. The usual trend that higher oxidation states are more acidic is also observed.

Oxy-Acids of Phosphorus

Phosphorus forms two series of oxyacids: the phosphoric and phosphorous series. In all of these, P is four-co-ordinate and tetrahedrally surrounded wherever possible, and there is some degree of $p\pi$—$d\pi$ back bonding in P→O bonds as mentioned previously. The hydrogen atoms in − OH groups are ionizable and therefore acidic, but the P—H bonds found in phosphorous acids have reducing, not acidic, properties.

The simplest phosphoric acid is H_3PO_4, orthophosphoric acid. This may be prepared by complete hydrolysis of P_4O_{10}, or by the action of concentrated nitric acid on phosphorus:

$$\left.\begin{array}{l} P_4O_{10} + H_2O \\ P + HNO_3 \end{array}\right\} \longrightarrow H_3PO_4 \xrightarrow[\text{heat}]{\text{gentle}} H_4P_2O_7 \xrightarrow[\text{heat}]{\text{strong}} (HPO_3)_n$$

pyrophos-   metaphosphoric acid   phoric acid

The hydrolysis proceeds in stages, and an understanding of these stages leads to an understanding of the wide range of phosphoric acids (Fig. 5.23).

Polyphosphates are straight chain compounds $(PO_3)_n . PO_4$, whilst metaphosphates are ring compounds $(PO_3)_n$. Orthophosphoric acid is tribasic, pyrophosphoric acid is tetrabasic, tetrapolyphosphoric acid is hexabasic and tetrametaphosphoric acid is tetrabasic.

$$P_4O_{10} + 6H_2O \rightarrow 4H_3PO_4 \quad \text{(overall reaction)}$$

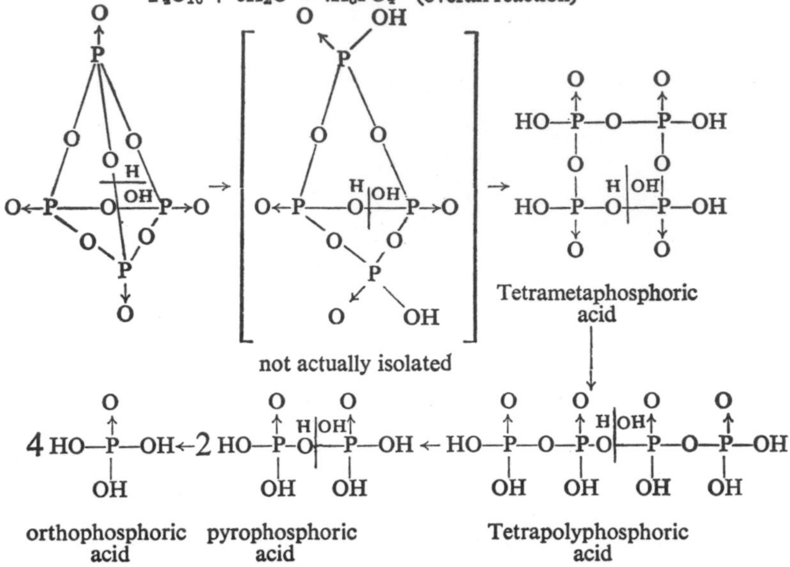

Fig. 5.23

Many polyphosphates are known, and have chains of different lengths. The first four are well known.

H_3PO_4 (mono) orthophosphoric acid

$H_4P_2O_7$ dipolyphosphoric acid (pyrophosphoric acid)

$H_5P_3O_{10}$ tripolyphosphoric acid

$H_6P_4O_{13}$ tetrapolyphosphoric acid

Sodium tripolyphosphate is sometimes present up to 40% in industrial detergents, and is used for softening water. It can be prepared in the following ways:

(1) By fusing Na_2O and P_4O_{10} and controlling the cooling so that the pyrophosphate which crystallizes out is converted into $Na_5P_3O_{10}$:

$$10Na_2O + 3P_4O_{10} \xrightarrow[\text{cool slowly}]{1000°C} 4Na_5P_3O_{10}$$

(2) By fusing the correct quantities of sodium phosphate and sodium dihydrogen phosphate. Recrystallization from water gives the pure hexahydrate $Na_5P_3O_{10}.6H_2O$:

$$2Na_2HPO_4 + NaH_2PO_4 \xrightarrow{450°C} Na_5P_3O_{10} + 2H_2O$$

(3) By hydrolysis of a trimetaphosphate:

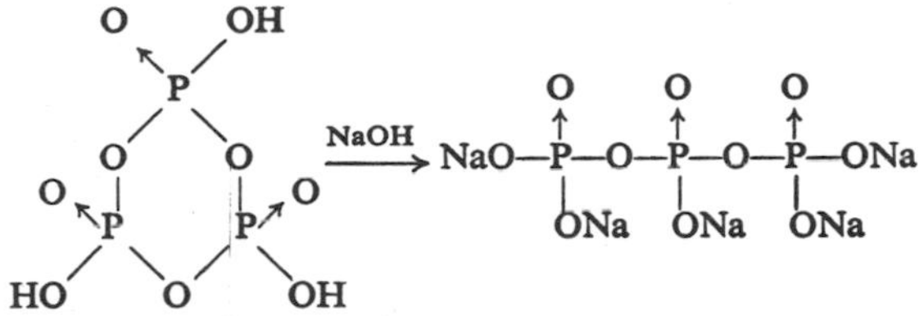

The orthophosphates of Group I metals and NH_4^+ are soluble in water. Most of the other metal orthophosphates are soluble in dilute acetic or hydrochloric acids; but titanium, zirconium and thorium phosphates are insoluble even in acids, and are commonly used to remove phosphates in qualitative analysis.

The metaphosphates form a family of ring compounds and are prepared by heating orthophosphates:

$$H_3PO_4 \xrightarrow{\text{heat}} HPO_3 + H_2O$$

Free PO_3^- ions do not occur and there is no complete evidence for the existence of a dimetaphosphate ion, but tri- and tetrametaphosphates are well known:

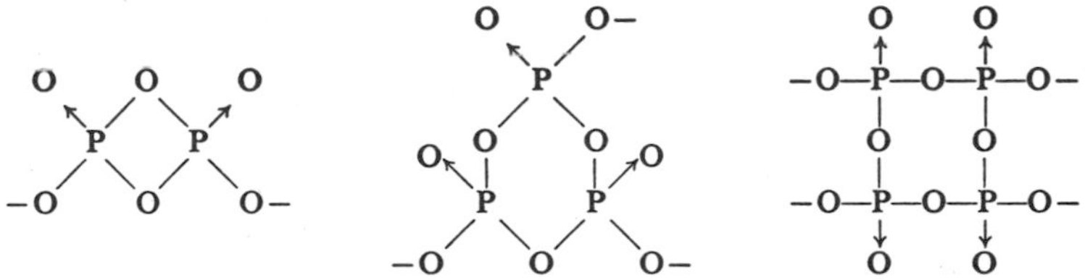

Dimetaphosphate ion   Trimetaphosphate ion   Tetrametaphosphate ion

By cross linking of rings, polymers of high molecular weight are formed. The precise mixture obtained and hence its physical properties depend on the method of preparation (Fig. 5.24).

All forms of sodium metaphosphate revert to trimetaphosphate near 630°C, presumably because this has the greatest stability. Graham's salt is miscalled sodium hexametaphosphate, because it does not contain six P units and is a high polymer $(NaPO_3)_n$. It is sold commercially as calgon, which is used for softening water, since Ca^{2+} and Mg^{2+} are soluble in it. Many of these sodium metaphosphates are used for water softening without precipitation, and descaling boilers and pipes. The structure is probably that of many rings which are liked by cross chains.

Hypophosphoric acid $H_4P_2O_6$ has one less oxygen atom than pyrophosphoric acid $H_4P_2O_7$. It is prepared by hydrolysis and oxidation of red phosphorus by NaOCl, or yellow phosphorus by water and air.

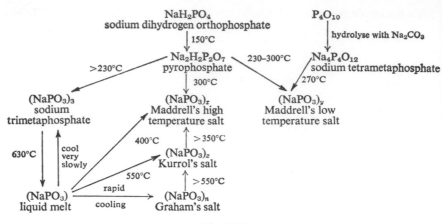

Fig. 5.24

There are no P—H bonds, and so this acid is not a reducing agent. There are four acidic hydrogens, hence the acid is tetrabasic and can form four

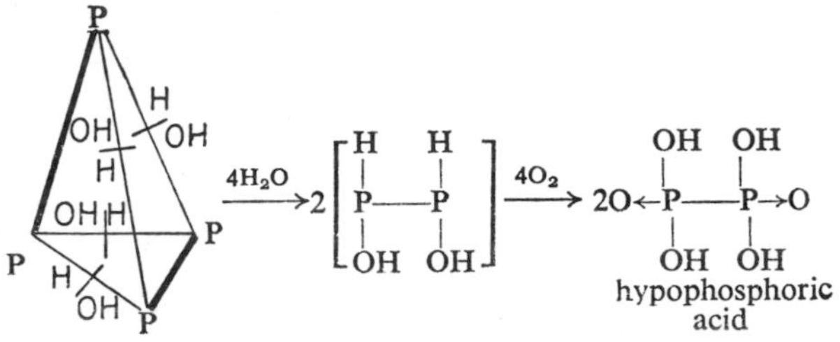

Fig. 5.25

series of salts, though usually two hydrogens are replaced. The P—P bond is much stronger than the P—O—P bonds, so that hydrolysis is slow.

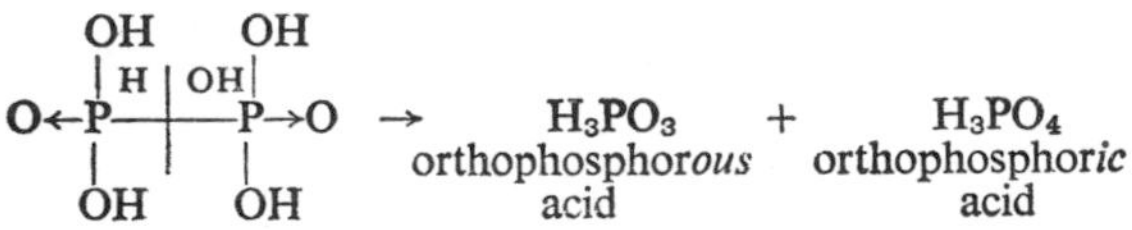

$$O{\leftarrow}P{\underset{\text{OH}}{\overset{\text{OH}}{|}}}{\underset{\text{OH}}{\overset{\text{H|OH|}}{|}}}P{\rightarrow}O \quad \rightarrow \qquad H_3PO_3 \quad + \quad H_3PO_4$$

orthophosphor*ous*   orthophosphor*ic* acid   acid

The phosphorous acids are less well known. They all contain P—H bonds and are therefore reducing agents. Hydrolysis of P_4O_6 in a manner analogous to the hydrolysis of P_4O_{10} already described, yields pyro- and ortho-phosphorous acids, which are both dibasic and reducing agents

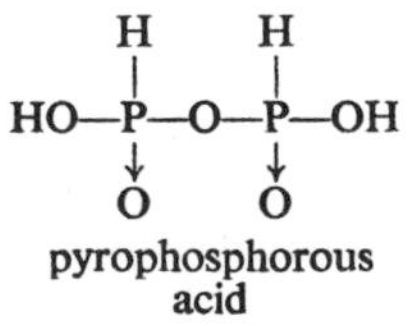

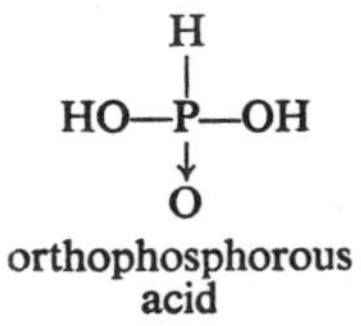

pyrophosphorous acid

orthophosphorous acid

Metaphosphorous acid $(HPO_2)_n$ is prepared from phosphine at low pressure.

$$PH_3 + O_2 \xrightarrow{\text{25 mm. Hg}} H_2 + HPO_2$$

If the formula were HPO_2, the P atom would only form three bonds or else form double bonds. In fact, it polymerizes rather than forms double bonds. The structure is not known, but by analogy with metaphosphoric acid it may well be a ring structure.

Hypophosphorous acid H_3PO_2 has one oxygen atom less than the ortho-phosphorous acid. It is prepared by alkaline hydrolysis of phosphorus.

$$P_4 + 3OH^- + 3H_2O \to PH_3 + 3H_2PO_2^-$$

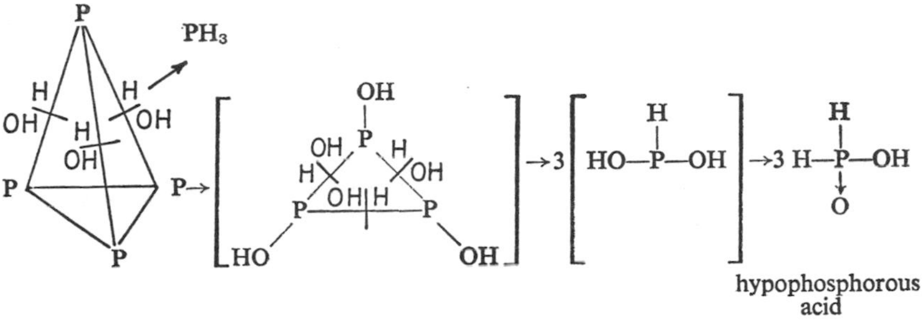

hypophosphorous acid

Fig. 5.26

The acid is monobasic and a very strong reducing agent. Salts of this acid are called hypophosphites and are used industrially to bleach wood and to make paper.

The tendency of the acidic ions of P to condense and give isopoly acids is quite strong. The phosphates and phosphites are similar to the arsenates and arsenites. Condensed As anions are much less stable than the corresponding P poly anions and they are rapidly hydrolysed in water. Antimonates and antimonites are known; but because Sb has a co-ordination number of six, these probably resemble silicates more closely than phosphates in structure.

Group VI (Table 5.11)

TABLE 5.11

Elements	Symbol	Electronic structure	Oxidation states*
Oxygen	O	[He] $\quad 2s^2\, 2p^4$	**2**
Sulphur	S	[Ne] $\quad 3s^2\, 3p^4$	2, **4**, **6**
Selenium	Se	[Ar] $\quad 3d^{10}\, 4s^2\, 4p^4$	2, **4**, **6**
Tellurium	Te	[Kr] $\quad 4d^{10}\, 5s^2\, 5p^4$	2, **4**, **6**
Polonium	Po	[Xe] $\; 4f^{14}\, 5d^{10}\, 6s^2\, 6p^4$	2, **4**, 6

* See page 77.

Metallic and Non-Metallic Character

The first four elements are non-metallic in character and are called collectively the chalcogens or ore-forming elements, because many metal ores are oxides or sulphides. Non-metallic character is strongest in O and S, weaker in Se and Te, whilst Po which is radioactive and short-lived, is markedly metallic.

Electronic Structure and Oxidation States

The elements all have the electronic structure s^2p^4 and tend to attain an inert gas configuration by gaining or sharing two electrons. The electronegativity of oxygen suggests that most metal oxides will be ionic and contain O^{2-} ions, thus giving an oxidation state of -2. Even with the most electropositive elements, S, Se and Te form few compounds which are more than 50% ionic, hence S^{2-}, Se^{2-} and Te^{2-} are less probable (Table 5.12).

TABLE 5.12

Symbol	Electronegativity
O	3·5
S	2·5
Se	2·4
Te	2·1

The elements also form compounds containing two electron pair (covalent) bonds such as H_2O, Cl_2O, H_2S, SCl_2. Where the chalcogen atom is the least electronegative atom in the molecule, it shows an oxidation state of $+2$.

Oxygen is never more than divalent because the second shell is limited to eight electrons and it requires too much energy to excite an electron into a higher shell. However, the elements S, Se, Te and Po have d orbitals available for bonding, and they can form four or six bonds by unpairing electrons.

Ground state

two unpaired electrons therefore can form two bonds—sp^3 hybridization—tetrahedral structure with two positions occupied by lone pairs.

Excited state

four unpaired electrons therefore can form four bonds—sp^3d hybridization—trigonal bipyramid with one position occupied by lone pair.

Further excited
state

six unpaired electrons therefore can form six bonds—sp^3d^2
hybridization—octahedral structure.

Compounds of S, Se and Te with oxygen are typically tetravalent, but
fluorine brings out the maximum oxidation state of $+6$. The higher oxidation states become less stable on descending the group. The $+4$ state shows
both oxidizing and reducing properties, but in the $+6$ state the compounds
are only oxidizing. These compounds are typically volatile because they are
covalent.

Bond Lengths

The bonds between S and O, or Se and O are
much shorter than might be expected for a single
bond, and may be formulated as double bonds.
These arise by the sideways overlap of a p orbital
on the oxygen with a d orbital on the sulphur,
giving a $p\pi$—$d\pi$ interaction in addition to the
original σ bond. The $p\pi$—$d\pi$ interaction is in contrast to the $p\pi$—$p\pi$ interactions in ethylene, and
accounts for the short bond length (Fig. 5.27).

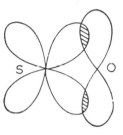

Fig. 5.27

Differences between O and the Other Elements

Oxygen differs from the rest of the group in that it is more electronegative
and therefore more ionic in its compounds. Hydrogen bonding is very
important for oxygen compounds, but it is only recently that weak hydrogen
bonds involving S have been proved to exist. Other differences, such as the
absence of higher valency states and the limitation to a co-ordination number
of four, are a consequence of the limitation of the second shell to eight
electrons, whereas the other elements can have a co-ordination number of
six by using d orbitals.

Uses of the Elements

Practically all the elements except the inert gases react with oxygen, the
reactions generally being strongly exothermic. Oxygen is essential to respiration, and hence to life. S, Se and Te are moderately reactive and burn in
air to form dioxides. They combine with many metals and non-metals, but
are not attacked by acids except those which are oxidizing agents. This is
in accordance with their non-metallic character. Polonium dissolves in
H_2SO_4, HF, HCl and HNO_3, which is further evidence of its increased
metallic character. Sulphur and selenium will dehydrogenate saturated
hydrocarbons. Sulphur reacts with olefins and forms sulphur cross-links,
which is important in the vulcanizing of rubber. Sulphur is also used in

large amounts in the manufacture of H_2SO_4, and other uses include fungicides and gunpowder.

Abundance and Extraction

Oxygen, the most abundant of all elements, exists in the free form and makes up 20·9% by volume of the atmosphere. As ores it makes up 46·6% of the earth's crust and as water it comprises 89% of the oceans. Sulphur, which occurs in sulphides and sulphates and naturally as an element, constitutes 0·05% of the earth's crust. The other elements are very scarce.

Oxygen is manufactured either by electrolysis of water, when it contains a trace of sulphuric acid, or by the fractional distillation of liquid air. It is prepared in the laboratory by thermal decomposition of oxidizing agents such as $KClO_4$ (with MnO_2 as catalyst), $KMnO_4$, PbO_2, HgO, H_2O_2 or nitrates.

Sulphur deposits are found in Sicily and Louisiana, U.S.A. Elementary sulphur is obtained as a by-product in the production of coal gas, and sulphur dioxide is obtained as a by-product in the extraction of metals from sulphide ores.

Selenium and tellurium occur among sulphide ores and are obtained in concentrated form from anode sludge after the electrolytic refining of copper, and from flue dust produced during the roasting of FeS_2.

Polymorphism

All the elements exist in more than one allotropic form: that is, they are polymorphic. Oxygen occurs as two non-metallic forms, O_2 and ozone O_3. Sulphur has two common crystalline forms, α or rhombic which is stable at room temperature, and β or monoclinic which is stable above 95·5°C. A third modification known as Engel's sulphur is unstable and is made by pouring $Na_2S_2O_3$ solution into concentrated HCl and extracting with toluene. Plastic or amorphous sulphur is obtained by pouring liquid sulphur into water. All these forms are non-metallic. Selenium exists as a red non-metallic form and a grey metallic form; and in the case of tellurium, the metallic form is more stable than the non-metallic. Polonium exists as α and β metallic forms. Thus there is an increase in metallic character within the group.

Molecular Structure

Oxygen is stable as a diatomic molecule, which accounts for its being a gas. However, S, Se, Te and Po are solids at normal temperatures and have more complex molecules. Sulphur and selenium occur as S_8 and Se_8 molecules at room temperature and these have a puckered ring structure (Fig. 5.28).

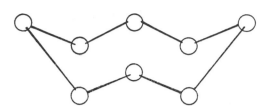

Fig. 5.28. Structure of S_8 molecule (HESLOP and ROBINSON, *Inorganic Chemistry*
Elsevier, Amsterdam, 1963)

The bonding in the O_2 molecule is not as simple as might appear at first.
If the molecule had two covalent bonds:

$$\ddot{O}::\overset{..}{O}\cdot \qquad O{=}O$$

then all the electrons would be paired and the molecule should be diamagnetic.
Oxygen is paramagnetic and therefore contains unpaired electrons. The
explanation of this phenomenon was one of the early successes of the molecular orbital theory. The electrons of the two oxygen atoms are fed into the
molecular orbitals in order of increasing energy (see Chapter 2). Thus the
structure of O_2 may be written:

$$K,K, \; \sigma 2s^2 \; \sigma^* 2s^2 \; \sigma 2px^2 \begin{Bmatrix} \pi 2py^2 \\ \pi 2pz^2 \end{Bmatrix} \begin{Bmatrix} \pi^* 2py^1 \\ \pi^* 2pz^1 \end{Bmatrix}$$

K,K represents the completed K shell of electrons which is non-bonding.
$\sigma 2s^2$ represents a σ bond formed by two electrons in the $2s$ molecular orbital.
This bonding effect is cancelled by $\sigma^* 2s^2$ which represents two electrons in
an antibonding $2s$ molecular orbital. $\sigma 2px^2$ represents two bonding electrons
in the $2px$ orbital. The $\pi 2py$ and $\pi 2pz$ orbitals have the same energy and both
contain two electrons; thus both form π bonds. $\pi^* 2py$ and $\pi^* 2pz$ are antibonding orbitals and have the same energy. According to Hund's rule,
which states that the number of unpaired electrons in a given energy level is
a maximum, each orbital contains one electron. Thus the molecule O_2
contains two unpaired electrons, which accounts for the paramagnetism.
The two antibonding π^* electrons cancel out one of the π bonds, so that the
net result is one σ and one π bond between the two atoms.

This may be represented by the valence bond structure,

$$:O\text{⫶}O:$$

in which the oxygen atoms are joined by one electron pair (covalent) bond
and two three-electron bonds.

A similar molecular orbital explanation may be applied to the other three electron bonds already discussed (NO and NO_2), though in these cases there is one unpaired electron occupying the antibonding π^*p orbitals.

Ozone, O_3, the other allotropic form of oxygen is prepared by the action of a silent electric discharge upon oxygen. Concentrations of up to 10% of O_3 are obtained in this way. Higher concentrations, or pure O_3 can be obtained by fractional liquefaction of the mixture, although pure liquid O_3 is explosive. Ozone decomposes slowly to oxygen. It is an extremely powerful oxidizing agent, second only to F_2 in oxidizing power, and reacts much more readily than oxygen.

The structure of O_3 is:

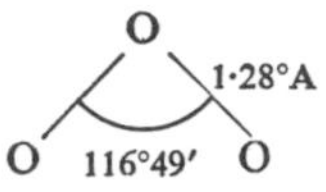

The bond length of 1·28 Å is intermediate between that which characterizes single and double bonds (1·48 and 1·21 Å respectively); ozone is thought to be a resonance hybrid, in which the first two structures predominate (Fig. 5.29). Each atom may be regarded as roughly sp^2 hybridized, the end atoms having two lone pairs and the central atom one lone pair, with a delocalized π orbital over all three atoms.

Fig. 5.29

Hydrides

The elements all form volatile bivalent hydrides H_2O, H_2S, H_2Se, H_2Te and H_2Po. Hydrogen sulphide, selenide and telluride are obtained by the action of acids on metal sulphides, selenides and tellurides, whilst hydrogen polonide has only been obtained in trace amounts from a mixture of Mg, Po and dilute acid.

$$FeS + H_2SO_4 \rightarrow H_2S + FeSO_4$$

These compounds are poisonous and have unpleasant odours. The volatility increases markedly from H_2O to H_2S and then declines. Water has an abnormally low volatility because it is associated by means of hydrogen bonds in the solid and liquid states.

The hydrides dissociate to a varying degree and give H^+. They are all very weak acids and there is an increase in acidic strength from H_2O to H_2Te. This would not be expected from the electronegativity differences. However, by inference from Fajans' rules, the larger the negative ion, the greater the tendency to an ionic bond. Further, Te is larger than O, hence the energy to remove H^+ from a large Te atom will be less than from a small O atom. The more acidic the hydrogen atom in the hydrides, the more stable will be the salts derived from them, i.e. oxides, sulphides, selenides and tellurides.

Oxygen, and to a greater extent sulphur, differ from the remainder in their ability to catenate and form polyoxides and polysulphides, which are less stable than the normal salts.

$$H_2O_2 \quad H—O—O—H \qquad H_2S_2 \quad H—S—S—H$$
$$H_2S_3 \quad H—S—S—S—H$$
$$H_2S_4 \quad H—S—S—S—S—H$$

H_2O_2 and H_2S_2 have similar structures and are prepared by the addition of acid to a peroxide or a persulphide salt.

$$BaO_2 + HCl \rightarrow H_2O_2$$
$$Na_2S_2 + HCl \rightarrow H_2S_2 \quad \text{(also } H_2S_3\text{)}$$

Hydrogen peroxide is an important rocket fuel and is obtained by electrolysis involving the formation and hydrolysis of a peroxydisulphuric acid.

$$2SO_4^- \xrightarrow{\text{electrolysis}} S_2O_8^{2-} + 2e$$

$$\underset{\substack{\text{peroxydisulphuric} \\ \text{acid}}}{H_2S_2O_8} + H_2O \rightarrow \underset{\substack{\text{peroxymonosulphuric} \\ \text{acid}}}{H_2SO_5} + H_2SO_4$$

$$H_2SO_5 + H_2O \rightarrow H_2SO_4 + H_2O_2$$

Hydrogen peroxide is also produced on a large scale by a cyclic process (Fig. 5.30) involving a quinol/quinone system such as:

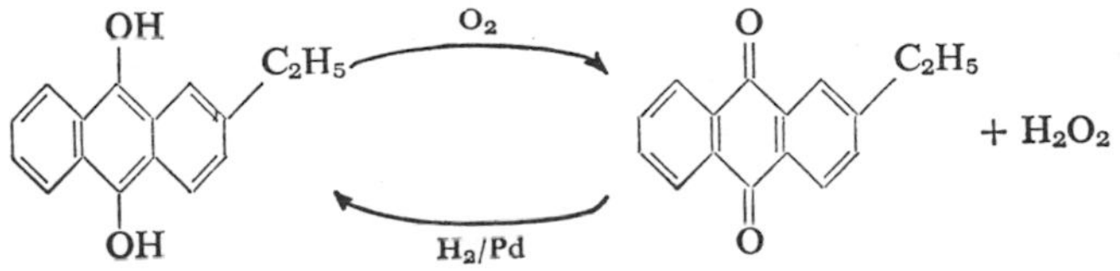

Fig. 5.30

H_2O_2 acts as a strong oxidizing agent but H_2S_2 does not. Whereas H_2O_2 is fairly stable, except in the presence of certain metal impurities such as Cu, H_2S_2 is not very stable because the decomposition is accelerated by the presence of hydroxyl ions.

$$H_2S_2 \rightarrow H_2S + S$$

Although hydrogen polyselenides and polytellurides do not exist, the metal salts do.

Halides (Table 5.13)

TABLE 5.13

	F	Cl	Br	I
O	F_2O_2, F_2O	Cl_2O, ClO_2, Cl_2O_6, Cl_2O_7	Br_2O, BrO_2, BrO_3	I_2O_4, I_4O_9, I_2O_5
S	S_2F_2, SF_4, SF_6, S_2F_{10}	S_2Cl_2, SCl_2, SCl_4	S_2Br_2	
Se	Se_2F_2, SeF_4, SeF_6	Se_2Cl_2, $SeCl_4$	Se_2Br_2, $SeBr_4$	
Te	TeF_4, Te_2F_{10}, TeF_6	$TeCl_2$, $TeCl_4$	$TeBr_2$, $TeBr_4$	TeI_4
Po		$PoCl_2$, $PoCl_4$	$PoBr_2$, $PoBr_4$	PoI_4

Fluorine brings out the maximum valency of six with S, Se and Te; and SF_6, SeF_6 and TeF_6 are all formed by direct combination. They are all colourless gases and have an octahedral structure with sp^3d^2 hybridization.

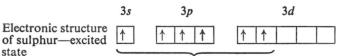

Electronic structure of sulphur—excited state

six unpaired electrons can form bonds with six fluorine atoms—sp^3d^2 hybridization.

The low boiling point indicates a high degree of covalency. SF_6 is extremely inert, SeF_6 is slightly more reactive and TeF_6 is hydrolysed by water. This is possibly due to the larger size of Te which permits the larger co-ordination number necessary in the first stage of hydrolysis.

$$TeF_6 + 6H_2O \rightarrow 6HF + H_6TeO_6$$

Many tetrahalides are known. It is difficult to prepare tetrafluorides by direct combination even with diluted F_2, because they readily change to hexafluorides. SF_4 is gaseous, SeF_4 liquid and TeF_4 solid. They have been prepared:

$$S + 4CoF_3 \rightarrow SF_4 + 4CoF_2$$
$$SeCl_4 + 4AgF \rightarrow SeF_4 + 4AgCl$$
$$TeO_2 + 2SeF_4 \rightarrow TeF_4 + 2SeOF_2$$

They are highly reactive fluorinating agents. S, Se, Te and Po form tetrachlorides by direct reaction with chlorine. SCl_4 is a rather unstable liquid, but the other tetrachlorides are solids. The structure of $TeCl_4$ is known (Fig. 5.31) and it is assumed that the other tetrahalides are similar.

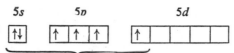

Electronic structure of tellurium atom —excited state.

four unpaired electrons can form bonds with four chlorine atoms—sp^3d hybridization giving trigonal bipyramid with one position occupied by a lone pair.

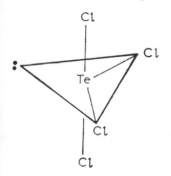

Fig. 5.31

$TeCl_4$ reacts with hydrochloric acid and gives the complex ion $[TeCl_6]^{2-}$, which is isomorphous with $[SiF_6]^{2-}$ and $[SnCl_6]^{2-}$

$$TeCl_4 + 2HCl \rightarrow H_2[TeCl_6]$$

Po also forms complex halide ions and a series of compounds $(NH_4)_2[PoX_6]$ and $Cs_2[PoX_6]$ are known where X is Cl, Br or I.

Tetrabromides of Se, Te and Po are known, but $SeBr_4$ is unstable and hydrolyses readily.

$$2SeBr_4 \rightarrow Se_2Br_2 + 3Br_2$$
$$SeBr_4 + 4H_2O \rightarrow [Se(OH)_4] + 4HBr$$
$$\text{unstable}$$
$$\downarrow$$
$$H_2SeO_3 + H_2O$$

Te and Po are the only elements which form tetraiodides.

SCl_2 is the best known dihalide, and it may be prepared by saturating S_2Cl_2 with chlorine. The dihalides form angular molecules, due to sp^3 hybridization, and the tetrahedral angle of 109° 28′ is distorted by the presence of two lone pairs of electrons.

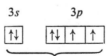

Electronic structure of sulphur atom—ground state

two unpaired electrons can form bonds with two chlorine atoms—sp^3 hybridization—tetrahedral with two lone pairs.

The bond angle is 103° in SCl_2, 101·5° in F_2O and 98° in $TeBr_2$.

Dimeric monohalides such as S_2F_2, Se_2Cl_2 and Se_2Br_2 are formed by S and Se. These monohalides are hydrolysed slowly and tend to disproportionate.

$$2S_2F_2 + 2H_2O \rightarrow 4HF + SO_2 + 3S$$
$$2SeCl_2 \rightarrow SeCl_4 + 3Se$$

Their structure is similar to hydrogen peroxide and the bond angle of 104° may be due to sp^3 hybridization distorted by two lone pairs.

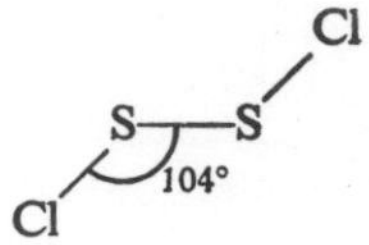

Oxides (Table 5.14)

TABLE 5.14

Element	Oxide					
S	S_2O		(S_2O_3)	SO_2	SO_3	SO_4
Se				SeO_2	SeO_3	
Te		TeO		TeO_2	TeO_3	
Po		PoO		PoO_2		

S_2O is formed when S and SO_2 are subjected to a silent electric discharge. It is very reactive, attacks metals and KOH, and will polymerize. Until recently it was incorrectly formulated SO.

TeO and PoO are obtained by thermal decomposition of a sulphite:

$$TeSO_3 \rightarrow TeO + SO_2$$

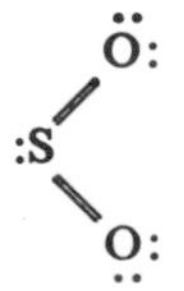

The dioxides SO_2, SeO_2, TeO_2 and PoO_2 are made by burning the element in air. There is a considerable difference in structure between the dioxides. SO_2 is a gas, and forms discrete molecules even in the solid state. The structure is shown in Fig. 5.32. The S—O double bonds arise from $p\pi$—$d\pi$ bonding, due to the lateral overlap of p orbitals of oxygen with d orbitals of sulphur. The bond angle of 119·5° is in close agreement with the angle of 120° predicted from sp^2 hybridization.

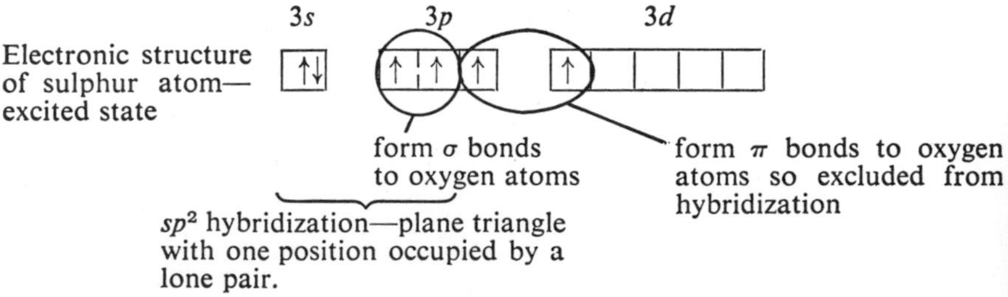

Fig. 5.32

Electronic structure of sulphur atom—excited state

3s   3p   3d

form σ bonds to oxygen atoms

form π bonds to oxygen atoms so excluded from hybridization

sp^2 hybridization—plane triangle with one position occupied by a lone pair.

SeO$_2$ is solid at room temperature. The gas has the same structure as SO$_2$, but the solid forms infinite chains which are not planar (Fig. 5.33). TeO$_2$ and PoO$_2$ both crystallize in two ionic forms.

The reaction of the dioxides with water also differs. SO$_2$ dissolves, but the resultant sulphurous acid H$_2$SO$_3$ cannot be isolated. SeO$_2$ forms selenious acid, H$_2$SeO$_3$, which may be obtained in a crystalline state. TeO$_2$ is almost insoluble in water, but dissolves in alkali to form tellurites and in acids to form basic salts; these reactions illustrate its amphoteric character. The increase in basic character is usual on descending a group.

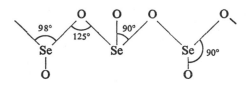

Fig. 5.33

SO$_2$ is important in the manufacture of sulphuric acid. It also acts as a mild reducing agent in acidic solution and as a strong reducing agent in alkaline solution. SO$_2$ has also been used as a non-aqueous solvent, but there is some doubt about its postulated self ionization.

$$2SO_2 \rightleftharpoons SO^{2+} + SO_3^{2-}$$

SeO$_2$ is used to oxidize aldehydes and ketones.

$$R—CH_2—CO—R + SeO_2 \rightarrow R—CO—CO—R + Se + H_2O$$

Sulphur trioxide is the only important trioxide. It is manufactured by the direct reaction of O$_2$ on SO$_2$ and is an important step in the manufacture of sulphuric acid. The reaction is slow, and in the contact process a catalyst of Pt or V$_2$O$_5$ is used. SO$_3$ reacts with water and forms H$_2$SO$_4$; but commercially, SO$_3$ is dissolved in 98% H$_2$SO$_4$ to give oleum or fuming sulphuric acid. This is mainly pyrosulphuric acid H$_2$S$_2$O$_7$, which is eventually diluted. SO$_3$ gas has a plane triangular structure and may be formulated:

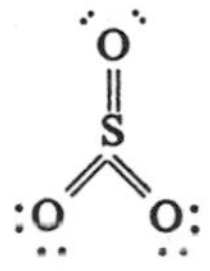

Fig. 5.34

(Fig. 5.34). $p\pi$—$d\pi$ bonding occurs as in SO_2. The bond angles of 120° accord with sp^2 hybridization.

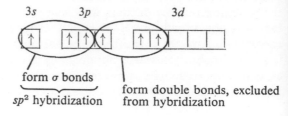

Electronic structure of sulphur atom—excited state

3s   3p   3d

form σ bonds   form double bonds, excluded
sp^2 hybridization   from hybridization

At room temperature SO_3 is solid and exists in three distinct forms. One form is ice-like and is a cyclic trimer $(SO_3)_3$. The other two forms are asbestos-like, one having infinite helical chains the other having chains cross-linked into sheets (Fig. 5.35). SO_3 is a powerful oxidizing agent, especially when hot; it oxidizes HBr to Br_2 and P to P_4O_{10}.

SO_3 *chain* (made up of linked SO_4 tetrahedra, each tetrahedron sharing two oxygens)

SO_3 *Trimer*

Fig. 5.35

SeO_3 is formed by a silent electric discharge on Se and O_2 gases, and TeO_3 is formed from telluric acid H_6TeO_6 by strong heating. Both trioxides are acid anhydrides.

$$SeO_3 + H_2O \rightarrow H_2SeO_4 \quad \text{selenic acid}$$
$$TeO_3 + 3H_2O \rightarrow H_6TeO_6 \quad \text{telluric acid}$$

Sulphur forms a tetroxide SO_4, but the other elements do not. SO_4 is made by passing SO_2 and O_2 through a silent electric discharge. It is a white solid, monomeric, and a stronger oxidizing agent than SO_3. Because it does not form H_2O_2 with water, it does not contain a peroxide link: O—O.

General Properties of Oxides

Oxides may be classified according to their geometric structure into:

(1) *Normal oxides.* In these, the oxidation number of M can be deduced from the empirical formula M_xO_y, if we assume that oxygen is divalent and

has an oxidation number of -2. These oxides, for example H_2O, MgO and Al_2O_3, contain only $M—O$ bonds.

(2) *Peroxides*. These contain more oxygen than would be expected from the oxidation number of M. They involve $O—O$ bonds as well as $M—O$ bonds, for example H_2O_2 ($H—O—O—H$) and BaO_2. Superoxides also contain more oxygen than would be expected, and these are discussed on p. 66.

(3) *Suboxides*. Here the formula contains less oxygen than would be expected from the oxidation number of M. They involve $M—M$ bonds in addition to $M—O$ bonds, for example $O=C=C=C=O$.

Regardless of the structure, oxides may be classified in an entirely different way, depending on their acid/base properties. Oxides are generally listed as acidic, basic, amphoteric or neutral, depending on the products formed when they react with water. Thus metallic oxides are generally basic, and non-metallic oxides usually acidic.

$$Na_2O + H_2O \rightarrow 2NaOH$$
$$SO_3 + H_2O \rightarrow H_2SO_4$$

More important than the reaction of an oxide with water is its relation to, and its reaction with other oxides. If oxides are arranged in a series from the most basic to the most acidic, then the further apart two oxides are in the series, the more stable the compound formed when they react together. This can be put on a quantitative basis by considering the changes in standard free energy.

$$Na_2O_{(s*)} + H_2O_{(l*)} \rightarrow 2NaOH_{(s)}$$

Standard free energies $\quad -90 \qquad -56 \qquad 2(-90) \quad \Delta G = -34 \text{ kcal/mole}$

$$CaO_{(s)} + H_2O_{(l)} \rightarrow Ca(OH)_{2(s)}$$

Standard free energies $\quad -144 \qquad -56 \qquad -214 \quad \Delta G = -14 \text{ kcal/mole}$

$$Al_2O_{3(s)} + 3H_2O_{(l)} \rightarrow 2Al(OH)_{3(s)}$$

Standard free energies $\quad -376 \qquad 3(-56) \quad 2(-272) \; \Delta G = 0$

* (s = solid, l = liquid).

From the ΔG values, Na_2O is the most basic and Al_2O_3 the least basic. In fact Na_2O is strongly basic and Al_2O_3 amphoteric. From the free energy values for the hydroxides, NaOH is chemically the most reactive and $Al(OH)_3$ the most stable. This is also true in the following reactions:

$$CaO_{(s*)} + CO_{2(g*)} \rightarrow CaCO_{3(s)}$$

Standard free energies $\quad -144 \qquad -94 \qquad -270 \quad \Delta G = -32 \text{ kcal/mole}$

* (s = solid, g = gas).

$$CaO_{(s)} + N_2O_{5(g)} \rightarrow Ca(NO_3)_{2(s)}$$

| Standard free energies | -144 | $+32$ | -177 | $\Delta G = -65$ kcal/mole |

$$CaO_{(s)} + SO_{3(g)} \rightarrow CaSO_{4(s)}$$

| Standard free energies | -144 | -88 | -315 | $\Delta G = -83$ kcal/mole |

From the ΔG values, SO_3 is the most strongly acidic oxide, N_2O_5 is the next strongest, and CO_2 is the weakest. From the free energy values of the salts formed, $Ca(NO_3)_2$ is the least stable and the most reactive, whilst $CaSO_4$ is the most stable and the least reactive.

The order of acidic strength of oxides can be obtained as follows:

$$K_2O, \; CaO, \; MgO, \; CuO, \; H_2O, \; SiO_2, \; CO_2, \; N_2O_5, \; SO_3$$
$\leftarrow$ most basic   most acidic $\rightarrow$

It is possible to predict the products of a reaction. If CaO is added to a mixture of H_2O and SO_3 (H_2SO_4), the more stable $CaO.SO_3$ ($CaSO_4$) will form, that is:

$$H_2SO_4 + CaO \rightarrow CaSO_4 + H_2O$$
but $CuSO_4 + CO_2 \rightarrow$ no reaction.

Whilst thermodynamic data and acidic power are clearly related and it is possible to predict the products of a reaction, it is not possible to predict the rate of a reaction. Thus the reaction:

$$CaO + SiO_2 \rightarrow CaSiO_3$$

is extremely slow at normal temperatures, though it is more rapid in a blast furnace.

Much inorganic chemistry consists of remembering which compounds react, and comparing the different stabilities of hydroxides, silicates, carbonates, nitrates, sulphates etc. The use of a series such as the one above minimizes this memory work.

Comprehensive lists of standard free energy data are given by LATIMER, W. M., *The Oxidation States of the Elements and their Potentials in Aqueous Solution*, Prentice Hall, 2nd Edn., 1959.

Oxy-Acids of Sulphur

The oxy-acids of sulphur are more numerous and more important than those of Se and Te. Many of them do not exist as free acids, but are known as anions and salts. Acids ending in —ous have salts ending in —ite, whilst acids ending in —ic have salts ending in —ate. To emphasize structural similarities the acids are listed in five groups: (1) sulphoxylic acid; (2) sulphurous acid series; (3) sulphuric acid series; (4) thionic acid series; and (5) peroxo acid series.

(1) *Sulphoxylic acid*

H_2SO_2 sulphoxylic acid

(2) *Sulphurous acid series*

H_2SO_3 sulphurous acid

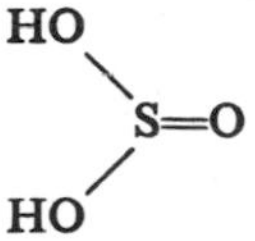

$$\begin{array}{c} HO \\ \diagdown \\ \;S{=}O \\ \diagup \\ HO \end{array}$$

$H_2S_2O_2$ thiosulphurous acid

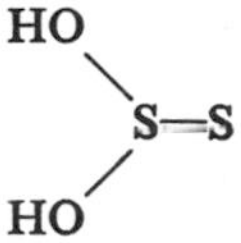

$$\begin{array}{c} HO \\ \diagdown \\ \;S{=}S \\ \diagup \\ HO \end{array}$$

$H_2S_2O_5$ di or pyro sulphurous acid

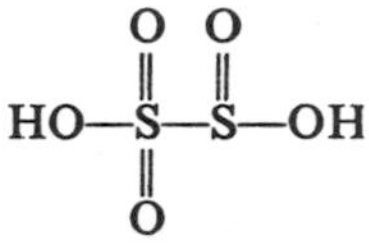

$$\begin{array}{c} O \quad O \\ \| \quad \| \\ HO{-}S{-}S{-}OH \\ \| \\ O \end{array}$$

$H_2S_2O_4$ dithionous acid

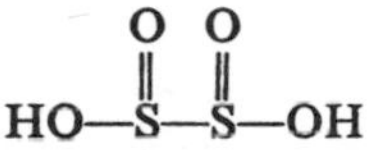

$$\begin{array}{c} O \quad O \\ \| \quad \| \\ HO{-}S{-}S{-}OH \end{array}$$

(3) *Sulphuric acid series*

H_2SO_4 sulphuric acid

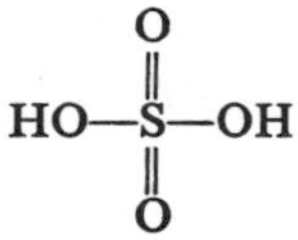

$$\begin{array}{c} O \\ \| \\ HO{-}S{-}OH \\ \| \\ O \end{array}$$

$H_2S_2O_3$ thiosulphuric acid

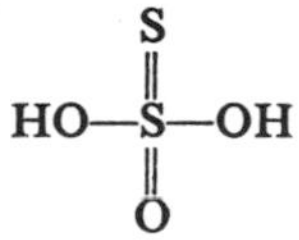

$$\begin{array}{c} S \\ \| \\ HO{-}S{-}OH \\ \| \\ O \end{array}$$

$H_2S_2O_7$ di or pyro sulphuric acid

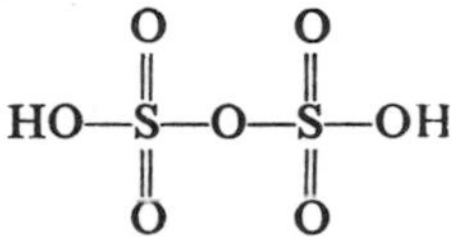

$$\begin{array}{c} O \qquad O \\ \| \qquad \| \\ HO{-}S{-}O{-}S{-}OH \\ \| \qquad \| \\ O \qquad O \end{array}$$

(4) *Thionic acid series*

$H_2S_2O_6$ dithionic acid

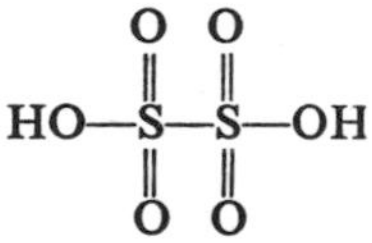

$$\begin{array}{c} O \quad O \\ \| \quad \| \\ HO{-}S{-}S{-}OH \\ \| \quad \| \\ O \quad O \end{array}$$

$H_2S_nO_6$ polythionic acid

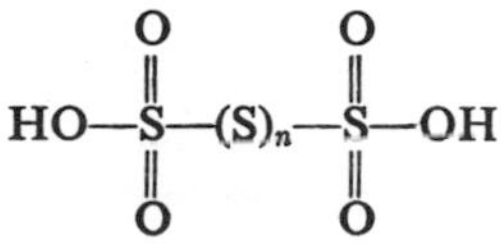

$$\begin{array}{c} O \qquad\qquad O \\ \| \qquad\qquad \| \\ HO{-}S{-}(S)_n{-}S{-}OH \\ \| \qquad\qquad \| \\ O \qquad\qquad O \end{array}$$

(5) *Peroxo acid series*

H_2SO_5 peroxosulphuric acid

$$HOO{-}\overset{\overset{\displaystyle O}{\|}}{\underset{\underset{\displaystyle O}{\|}}{S}}{-}OH$$

$H_2S_2O_8$ peroxodisulphuric acid

$$HO{-}\overset{\overset{\displaystyle O}{\|}}{\underset{\underset{\displaystyle O}{\|}}{S}}{-}O{-}O{-}\overset{\overset{\displaystyle O}{\|}}{\underset{\underset{\displaystyle O}{\|}}{S}}{-}OH$$

Sulphoxylic acid is only known as its zinc and cobalt salts, which can be made thus:

$$Na_2S_2O_4 + Co(OAc)_2 \rightarrow CoS_2O_4$$

sodium
dithionite

$$\begin{array}{c} + 2NH_3 \\ + H_2O \\ \downarrow \\ CoSO_2 + (NH_4)_2SO_3 \end{array}$$

cobalt
sulphoxylate

It is doubtful if sulphurous acid is formed when SO_2 is passed into water, though the solution is acidic. However two series of salts, the sulphites SO_3^{2-} and hydrogen sulphites (bisulphites) HSO_3^- are well known and the latter is predominant in dilute solution. Sulphurous acid and bisulphites are reducing agents possibly because of tautomerism.

$$\begin{array}{cc} HO \\ \searrow \\ S{=}O \\ \nearrow \\ HO \end{array} \qquad \begin{array}{cc} HO O \\ \searrow \nearrow \\ S \\ \nearrow \searrow \\ O H \end{array}$$

By analogy with the phosphorous acids, the S—H bonds should be reducing and this would also account for the formation of the HSO_3^- ion. Tautomeric esters of these forms have been characterized. The sulphite ion exists in crystals and has a pyramidal structure which may be expected from the orbitals used.

Electronic structure of sulphur atom—excited state

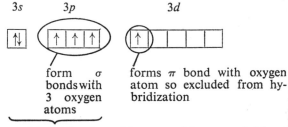

$3s$ $3p$ $3d$

form σ bonds with 3 oxygen atoms

forms π bond with oxygen atom so excluded from hybridization

sp^3 hybridization with one position occupied by a lone pair.

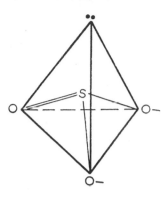

Fig. 5.36

Sulphites and bisulphites evolve SO_2 on treatment with acids.

$$Na_2SO_3 + 2HCl \rightarrow 2NaCl + H_2O + SO_2$$

On heating solid bisulphites or treating a solution with SO_2, pyrosulphites are formed, which contain an S—S linkage.

$$2NaHSO_3 \xrightarrow{\text{heat}} Na_2S_2O_5 + H_2O$$
$$\text{sodium bisulphite} \qquad \text{sodium pyrosulphite}$$
$$\text{(sodium metabisulphite)}$$

On oxidation sulphites form sulphates and with sulphur, thiosulphates are formed.

$$SO_3{}^{2-} \xrightarrow{\text{oxidize}} SO_4{}^{2-} \quad \text{sulphate}$$

$$SO_3{}^{2-} + S \rightarrow S_2O_3{}^{2-} \quad \text{thiosulphate.}$$

Reduction of sulphites with Zn yields dithionites.

$$SO_3{}^{2-} + SO_2 \xrightarrow{\text{Zn}} S_2O_4{}^{2-} \quad \text{dithionite.}$$

Sodium dithionite is a powerful reducing agent, and in NaOH solution it is used to absorb oxygen in gas analysis.

Sulphuric acid is commercially the most important acid, and is made by oxidation of SO_2 to SO_3 followed by reaction with water. In the contact process the oxidation takes place at a catalytic surface, such as Pt or V_2O_5. In the lead chamber process NO acts as a homogeneous catalyst. Pure sulphuric acid has been used as a non-aqueous solvent and as a sulphonating agent. It has slight oxidizing properties and can remove the elements of water, thus charring organic compounds. In aqueous solution it acts as a strong dibasic acid and forms sulphates SO_4^{2-} and hydrogen sulphates HSO_4^-. The SO_4^{2-} ion is tetrahedral as expected from the orbitals used.

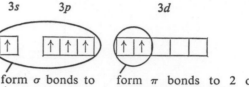

Electronic structure of
sulphur atom—excited
state

form σ bonds to
4 · oxygen atoms

sp^3 hybridization.

form π bonds to 2 oxygen
atoms, so excluded from hybridization

The bond lengths are all rather short because of resonance of the double bonds. Thiosulphates are made by boiling alkaline or neutral sulphite solutions with sulphur. The free acid is not known, but stable salts are numerous. The thiosulphate ion is structurally similar to the sulphate ion (Fig. 5.37).

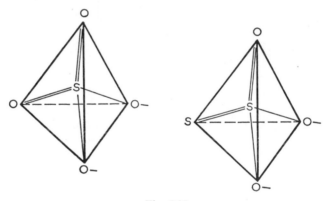

Fig. 5.37

Sodium thiosulphate is used in volumetric analysis and in photography since it forms a soluble complex with silver salts.

$$2S_2O_3^{2-} + I_2 \rightarrow \underset{\substack{\text{tetrathionate} \\ \text{ion}}}{S_4O_6^{2-}} + 2I^-$$

$$Na_2S_2O_3 + AgNO_3 \rightarrow Ag_2S_2O_3 \xrightarrow{+3Na_2S_2O_3} 2Na_3[Ag(S_2O_3)_2]$$

Pyrosulphates can be made by heating hydrogen sulphates strongly.

$$2NaHSO_4 \rightarrow H_2O + Na_2S_2O_7$$

Pyrosulphuric acid is made by dissolving SO_3 in H_2SO_4. No polysulphuric acids higher than pyrosulphuric acid are known.

Dithionic acid is dibasic, and although normal salts are known, no acid salts exist and the acid itself is known only in solution. Dithionates are made by oxidizing sulphurous acid with MnO_2.

$$MnO_2 + 2SO_3{}^{2-} + 4H^+ \rightarrow Mn^{2+} + S_2O_6{}^{2-} + 2H_2O$$

Dithionates are stable to oxidizing agents and mild reducing agents, but on heating in acid solution they give sulphuric and sulphurous acids.

sulphuric acid   sulphurous acid

The bond angles in the dithionate ion are approximately tetrahedral and the S—O bonds are again rather short.

Polythionates exist only as salts and are called trithionate $S_3O_6{}^{2-}$, tetra-thionate $S_4O_6{}^{2-}$, pentathionate $S_5O_6{}^{2-}$ and hexathionate $S_6O_6{}^{2-}$ depending on the total number of sulphur atoms present.

Two peroxo-acids of sulphur are known: peroxosulphuric acid H_2SO_5 and peroxodisulphuric acid $H_2S_2O_8$. No peroxo-acids of Se and Te are known. $H_2S_2O_8$ is obtained by electrolysis of sulphates at high current density. It is a powerful and useful oxidizing agent and will convert Mn^{2+} to per-manganate and Cr^{3+} to chromate. Hydrolysis of the acid gives peroxo-sulphuric acid, often called Caro's acid.

Oxyacids of Selenium and Tellurium

Selenium forms two oxyacids, selenious acid H_2SeO_3 and selenic acid H_2SeO_4. Selenious acid is formed when SeO_2 dissolves in water. The solid acid can be isolated and two series of salts (the normal and acid selenites) are known. The acid is converted to selenic acid by refluxing with H_2O_2. H_2SeO_4 like H_2SO_4 is a strong acid, and selenates are isomorphous with sulphates. Both H_2SeO_4 and H_2SeO_3 are moderately strong oxidizing agents.

TeO_2 is almost insoluble in water so that tellurous acid has not been characterized. The dioxide does react with strong bases and forms tellurites, acid tellurites and various polytellurites. Telluric acid H_6TeO_6 is quite different from sulphuric and selenic acids and exists as octahedral $Te(OH)_6$

molecules in the solid. It is a fairly strong oxidizing agent, but a weak dibasic acid and forms two series of salts. The acid is prepared by the action of powerful oxidizing agents on Te or TeO_2.

Oxyhalides

Only S and Se form oxyhalides. These are called thionyl and selenyl halides, and the following are known:

$$SOF_2 \quad SOCl_2 \quad SOBr_2$$
$$SeOF_2 \quad SeOCl_2 \quad SeOBr_2$$

Thionyl chloride is usually prepared:

$$PCl_5 + SO_2 \rightarrow SOCl_2 + POCl_3$$

$SOCl_2$ is used by organic chemists to convert carboxylic acids to acid chlorides

$$SOCl_2 + R—COOH \rightarrow R—COCl + SO_2$$

Thionyl bromide is prepared from the chloride and HBr, and thionyl fluoride is obtained from the chloride by reacting with SbF_3. These react with water readily, though SOF_2 only reacts slowly.

$$SOCl_2 + H_2O \rightarrow SO_2 + 2HCl$$

The structure of these oxyhalides is tetrahedral with one position occupied by a lone pair—an arrangement which corresponds to sp^3 hybridization.

In addition sulphuryl halides are known.

$$SO_2F_2 \quad SO_2Cl_2 \quad SO_2FCl \quad SO_2FBr$$
$$SeO_2F_2$$

Sulphuryl chloride is made by direct reaction of SO_2 and Cl_2 in the presence of a catalyst. Sulphuryl fluoride is a gas and is not hydrolysed by water, but the chloride fumes in moist air and is hydrolysed by water. The sulphuryl halides have a distorted tetrahedral structure. The sulphuryl halides may be regarded as derivatives of H_2SO_4, where both OH groups have been replaced by halogens. If only one group is replaced, halosulphonic acids are obtained.

$$FSO_3H \quad ClSO_3H \quad BrSO_3H$$

Fluorosulphuric acid forms many salts, but chlorosulphonic acid forms none and is used as a chlorinating agent in organic chemistry.

A review of the stereochemistry of Group VI elements is given by ABRAHAMS, S. C., *Quarterly Reviews of the Chemical Society*, **10**, 407, 1956.

Group VII—The Halogens (Table 5.15)

TABLE 5.15

Element	Symbol	Electronic configuration	Oxidation states*
Fluorine	F	[He] $2s^2\,2p^5$	-1
Chlorine	Cl	[Ne] $3s^2\,3p^5$	$-1,\ +1,\ +3,\ +4,\ +5+6+7$
Bromine	Br	[Ar] $3d^{10}\,4s^2\,4p^5$	$-1,\ +1,\ +3,\ +4,\ +5+6$
Iodine	I	[Kr] $4d^{10}\,5s^2\,5p^5$	$-1,\ +1,\ +3,\qquad +5\quad +7$
Astatine	At	[Xe] $4f^{14}\,5d^{10}\,6s^2\,6p^5$	

* See page 77.

Electronic Structure and Oxidation States

The halogens show very close group similarities. The elements all have seven electrons in their outer shell, and they either gain an electron by forming an ionic bond (giving X^-) or form a covalent bond, in order to complete their octet. Fluorine is always univalent. Since it is the most electronegative element it always has the oxidation number -1. Among the other elements, oxidation numbers of $+1$, $+3$, $+5$ and $+7$ are possible. The higher valency states arise by the use of d orbitals and are found in the interhalogens and halogen oxides. The oxidation states $+4$ and $+6$ occur in the oxides and the oxyacids.

General Properties

The melting points and boiling points of the elements increase with increased atomic number. Fluorine and chlorine are gases, bromine is liquid, and iodine is a solid.

The elements all form diatomic molecules. The bond energy in a fluorine molecule is very low, about 38 kcal/mole. This is due to the repulsion between non-bonding electrons. In Cl_2, Br_2 and I_2 there is the possibility of multiple bonding involving d orbitals. This accounts for the increased bond energy of Cl_2, Br_2 and I_2.

The ionization potentials of the halogens are all very high, which indicates that there is little tendency to lose electrons. The value for F is highest, since the electrons are firmly held in a small atom and the ionization potential of I is lower because I is a larger atom (see Table 5.16). The halogen molecules are all coloured. This is due to the absorption of visible light, which results in the excitation of outer electrons to higher energy levels. The excitation energies follow the same trend as the ionization potentials, that is excitation of the small F atom requires a large amount of energy, and excitation of the larger I atom requires less energy. F absorbs violet light (high energy) and therefore appears yellow, whilst I absorbs yellow light (lower energy) and appears violet.

TABLE 5.16

	M.p.	B.p.	Heat of dissociation or bond energy	First ionization potential	Electron affinity	Hydration energy X^-
	°C	°C	kcal/mole	eV	eV	kcal/g. ion
F_2	−220	−188	38	17·4	3·62	122
Cl_2	−101	−35	58	13·0	3·79	89
Br_2	−7	58	46	11·8	3·56	81
I_2	114	183	36	10·4	3·28	72

Oxidizing Power

The electron affinity, or tendency of the atoms to gain electrons, reaches a maximum at chlorine. Oxidation may be regarded as the removal of electrons, so that an oxidizing agent gains electrons. Thus the halogens act as oxidizing agents. The strength of an oxidizing agent (that is, its oxidation potential) depends on several energy terms and is best represented by a Born-Haber type of cycle.

$$\tfrac{1}{2}X_{2(\text{solid})} \xrightarrow{\tfrac{1}{2}\text{ht. fusion}} \tfrac{1}{2}X_{2(\text{liquid})} \xrightarrow{\tfrac{1}{2}\text{ht. evaporation}} \tfrac{1}{2}X_{2(\text{gas})} \xrightarrow{\tfrac{1}{2}\text{ht. dissociation}} X_{(\text{gas})}$$

$$X_{(\text{hydrated})}^{-} \xleftarrow{\text{ht. hydration}} X_{(\text{gas})}^{-}$$

with downward arrows labelled: oxidation potential (on left), electron affinity (on right).

For fluorine and chlorine which are gaseous at room temperature, the heats of fusion and evaporation are omitted and their oxidation potential depends only on the sum of the heat of dissociation, electron affinity, and heat of hydration. (The heats of fusion, evaporation and dissociation are positive because energy must be supplied, and the factor 23·06 converts eV to kcal.) Thus despite the electron affinity of chlorine being highest (see Table 5.17),

TABLE 5.17

	$\tfrac{1}{2}$ heat fusion	$\tfrac{1}{2}$ heat sublimation	$\tfrac{1}{2}$ heat dissociation	Electron affinity	Heat of hydration	Sum kcal.
F_2	—	—	+38/2	−3·62 × 23·06	−122	= −186·5
Cl_2	—	—	+58/2	−3·79 × 23·06	−89	= −147·4
Br_2	—	+7·4/2	+46/2	−3·56 × 23·06	−81	= −136·4
I_2	+3·6/2	+10·4/2	+36/2	−3·28 × 23·06	−72	= −122·6

F is the strongest oxidizing agent because of its low heat of dissociation and high heat of hydration. F is an extremely strong oxidizing agent, and it will replace Cl^- both in solution and even when dry. Similarly, chlorine gas will displace Br^- from solution and this fact is used in the preparation of bromine. In general any halogen of low atomic number will oxidize halide ions of higher atomic number.

The decrease in oxidizing power on descending Group VII is illustrated by the reaction of the halogens with water. Fluorine is so strong an oxidizing agent that it oxidizes water to oxygen. The large negative free energy change indicates a strongly exothermic and spontaneous reaction.

$$F_2 + H_2O \rightarrow 2H^+ + 2F^- + \tfrac{1}{2}O_2 \qquad \Delta G = -190 \text{ kcal/mole}$$

The oxidation of water by chlorine is thermodynamically possible, but since the energy of activation is high, this reaction does not occur. In fact, another reaction occurs:

$$Cl_2 + H_2O \rightarrow HCl + HOCl$$

Iodine is an even weaker oxidizing agent, and the free energy change indicates that energy would have to be supplied to make it oxidize water.

$$I_2 + H_2O \rightleftharpoons 2H^+ + 2I^- + \tfrac{1}{2}O_2 \qquad \Delta G = +25 \text{ kcal/mole}$$

In fact the reverse process occurs and oxygen can oxidize iodide ions to iodine.

Reactivity of the Elements

The halogens all react with metals, and also with many non-metals. Fluorine is the most reactive, and reactivity decreases with increased atomic number. Fluorine and chlorine frequently oxidize elements further than bromine and iodine, thus they bring out higher valencies, for example PBr_3, PCl_5, SbF_5, and S_2Br_2, SCl_2 and SF_6.

The great reactivity of fluorine is due to the low energy of the F—F bond, the extremely high oxidizing power, the small size of the atoms or ions and the high electroncgativity. The small size of the ions results in a high co-ordination number, and hence a high lattice energy in the crystal. The high electronegativity results in the formation of very strong bonds with most other elements.

Separation of the Elements

The main source of fluorine is from the mineral fluor-spar, CaF_2. This is treated with concentrated sulphuric acid and distilled, yielding both an aqueous solution and anhydrous HF. Fluorine is then obtained by electrolyzing a mixture of KHF_2 and HF at 100°C. Water must be rigorously excluded or the fluorine will oxidize it to oxygen. The hydrogen liberated at the cathode is prevented by a diaphragm from mixing with the fluorine liberated at the anode, because these two elements react explosively. Because fluorine is so reactive, the apparatus was originally made of platinum. This has been found to be unnecessary because copper or Monel metal (Cu/Ni alloy) are protected from further attack by a fluoride film after a short time. The cathodes are steel, the anodes are carbon, and teflon is used for electrical insulation. Graphite anodes were originally used, but they were attacked by fluorine forming the lamellar compound CF. This forced the graphite sheets apart, increased the electrical resistance and resulted in more current being needed, more heat produced and eventually an explosion. To prevent this from happening, coke impregnated with copper is used as the anode. Production of fluorine became important when it was discovered that the isotopes of uranium could be separated by gaseous diffusion of UF_6. Because the F—F bond is so weak, and atomic fluorine is a highly exothermic oxidizing agent, fluorine can be used as a rocket fuel.

Chlorine is produced by the electrolysis of aqueous chloride solutions or fused chlorides. It is a by-product in the production of NaOH and metallic sodium.

$$2NaCl + 2H_2O \xrightarrow{\text{electrolyse}} 2NaOH + Cl_2 + 2H_2$$

$$2NaCl \xrightarrow{\text{electrolyse}} 2Na + Cl_2$$

Chlorine is used in large amounts as a bleach, and because it kills bacteria it is used to purify water. Its many other industrial uses include the manufacture of polyvinyl chloride.

At one time bromine was obtained by electrolysis of its salts, but it is now obtained from sea-water. If chlorine is passed into sea-water, it oxidizes the bromide ions present to bromine.

$$Cl_2 + 2Br^- \rightarrow 2Cl^- + Br_2$$

The bromine is absorbed in Na_2CO_3 solution, giving a mixture of NaBr and $NaBrO_3$, which when acidified and distilled gives bromine.

$$HBrO_3 + 5HBr \rightarrow 3Br_2 + 3H_2O$$

Iodine is obtained from Chile saltpetre, which is mainly KNO_3, but contains traces of potassium iodate and potassium periodate. The iodate concentrate is reduced to iodine by $NaHSO_3$.

$$2IO_3^- + 5HSO_3^- \rightarrow 3HSO_4^- + 2SO_4^{2-} + H_2O + I_2$$

Naturally occurring astatine has not been found, but it has been made synthetically by bombarding bismuth with high energy α-particles

$$^{209}_{83}Bi \xrightarrow{\alpha,\, 2n} {}^{211}_{85}At$$

The chemistry of ^{211}At has only been studied by tracer methods because it decays by orbital electron capture and by α-emission and has a half-life period of $7\frac{1}{2}$ hours. It appears to resemble iodine quite closely.

Hydrogen Halides

The halogens all react with hydrogen and form hydrides HX. Whilst the reaction of hydrogen with fluorine is quite violent, the reaction with iodine is slow at room temperature, and illustrates the decreasing reactivity with increased atomic number.

HF and HCl are usually prepared by treatment of salts with strong sulphuric acid. CaF_2 is the most readily available fluoride. NH_4Cl is generally used to make HCl in the laboratory, because the resultant NH_4HSO_4 is soluble, and the reaction proceeds smoothly; however, NaCl is used in industry because it is cheaper.

$$CaF_2 + H_2SO_4 \rightarrow CaSO_4 + 2HF$$
$$NH_4Cl + H_2SO_4 \rightarrow NH_4HSO_4 + HCl$$
$$NaCl + H_2SO_4 \rightarrow NaHSO_4 + HCl$$

HBr and HI are not made by this method since the sulphuric acid oxidizes them to Br_2 and I_2. HBr can be produced by the action of H_3PO_4 on a bromide, but in the laboratory the usual method is to add bromine to a mixture of red phosphorus and water.

$$2P + 3Br_2 \rightarrow 2PBr_3$$
$$PBr_3 + 3H_2O \rightarrow H_3PO_3 + 3HBr$$

In a similar way, HI can be made by adding water to phosphorus and iodine.

HCl, HBr and HI are gases, but HF is a liquid with a boiling point of 19°C. The unexpectedly high boiling point of HF is due to hydrogen bonding between molecules.

In the gaseous state the hydrides are essentially covalent, but in aqueous solutions they ionize, and HCl, HBr and HI function as strong acids.

$$HCl + H_2O \rightarrow H_3O^+ + Cl^-$$

The aqueous solutions form azeotropic mixtures with maximum boiling points due to a negative deviation from Raoult's Law. Such solutions can be used as standards for volumetric analysis. In dilute aqueous solutions HF is only slightly ionized, but HCl, HBr and HI are completely ionized. In poorer ionizing solvents such as methanol, ionization is much less complete and HCl is less ionized than HI. Thus HI is the strongest acid followed by HBr and HCl, and HF is the weakest. It is at first surprising that though HF has a greater electronegativity difference and more ionic character than the other hydrides, it is the weakest acid in water. Acidic strength is the tendency of $HX_{(gas)} \rightarrow H^+_{(hydrated)} + X^-_{(hydrated)}$. This may be represented in stages: dissociation, ionization and hydration.

11—C.I.C.

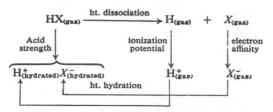

The H—F bond is much stronger than the H—Cl, H—Br or H—I bonds, and twice as much energy is needed to dissociate HF as is required to dissociate HI.   The acid strength depends on the sum of all these stages, but since the dissociation energies differ so greatly the trend in acid strengths follows the trend in H—*X* bond energies.   The strength of the H—F bond is related to the short bond length of 1·0 Å compared with 1·7 Å for HI.

Liquid HF has been used as a non-aqueous solvent.   It undergoes self ionization:

$$2HF \rightleftharpoons H_2F^+ + F^-$$

Acid-base reactions occur in this solvent system, but few substances act as acids because of the strong proton-donating properties of HF.   Mineral acids dissolved in HF do not behave as acids, except for perchloric acid. Many compounds react with HF, and this therefore limits its use as a solvent, though it is a useful medium for preparing fluoro complexes and fluorides.

Halogen Oxides

Numerous compounds have been reported, although many of them are unstable and are shown in brackets.   The bonds are largely covalent because of the similarities in electronegativity (F = 4·0, Cl = 3·0, Br = 2·8, I = 2·5, O = 3·5).   Fluorine is more electronegative than oxygen; hence compounds of F and O are fluorides of oxygen rather than oxides of fluorine (see Table 5.18).   In addition, iodine forms I_2O_4 and I_4O_9 which are ionic and salt-like. Of these compounds, ClO_2, I_2O_5 and OF_2 are the most important.

TABLE 5.18

Fluorides		Oxides		
oxidation -1 OF_2	$+1$ Cl_2O	$+1$ Br_2O	
number -1 O_2F_2	$+2$ (ClO)		
-2 (OF)	$+4$ ClO_2	$+4$ BrO_2	$+5$ I_2O_5
(O_2F_3)	$+6$ Cl_2O_6	$+6$ BrO_3	
	$+7$ Cl_2O_7	$+7$ (Br_2O_7)	
	$+8$ (ClO$_4$)		

OF_2 is a colourless gas and has been used as a rocket fuel.   It reacts vigorously with metals, S, P and halogens, and gives fluorides and oxides. It is formed by passing F_2 into dilute NaOH.

$$2F_2 + 2NaOH \rightarrow 2NaF + H_2O + OF_2$$

OF_2 dissolves in water and gives a neutral solution, and with NaOH it gives fluoride ions and oxygen. It is not an acid anhydride. Cl_2O is a gas and Br_2O is a liquid, and they are both prepared by heating freshly precipitated mercuric oxide with the halogen gas.

$$2Cl_2 + 2HgO \xrightarrow{300°C} HgCl_2.HgO + Cl_2O$$

They are both coloured and explode in the presence of reducing agents, or on heating. Cl_2O dissolves in water and forms hypochlorous acid HOCl. With NaOH, Cl_2O and Br_2O form hypochlorites and hypobromites. These oxides are thus acidic. The oxides may further oxidize these products.

$$\underset{\text{hypobromite}}{NaOBr} \rightarrow \underset{\text{bromate}}{NaBrO_3}$$

All three oxides have structures related to a tetrahedron with two positions occupied by lone pairs of electrons.

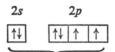

Electronic structure of
oxygen atom—ground state

two unpaired electrons form bonds to two halogen atoms—sp^3 hybridization—tetrahedral with two lone pairs.

Fig. 5.38

The bond angles are distorted because of the lone pairs (Fig. 5.38). In OF_2, the bonding electrons are nearer the F atom because of its greater electronegativity. Thus repulsion between lone pairs exceeds that between bond pairs; hence the bond angle is less than 109° 28'. In Cl_2O the bonding electrons are nearer the oxygen since this is more electronegative. Repulsion between bond pairs now exceeds that between lone pairs, hence the bond angle is greater than the tetrahedral angle. Because the difference in electronegativity between Br and O is greater than between Cl and O, the bonding electrons are probably even closer to the O in Br_2O; thus repulsion between bond pairs should be even greater, and a bond angle greater than 111° is predicted.

Dioxygen difluoride O_2F_2 is produced by passing an electric discharge through a mixture of F_2 and O_2 at very low pressure and at liquid air temperature. It decomposes at −95°C and its structure (Fig. 5.39) is possibly

F
 \
  O→O
 /
F

Fig. 5.39

Chlorine dioxide ClO_2 is a coloured liquid b.p. 11°C. It is a powerful oxidizing and chlorinating agent and is used in large quantities for water purification. It is a good bleach and is used to bleach cellulose. It is thirty times as effective as chlorine in bleaching flour. ClO_2 reacts with water and alkali to form chlorites and chlorates, and is thus a mixed anhydride.

$$ClO_2 + 2NaOH \rightarrow \underset{\text{chlorite}}{NaClO_2} + \underset{\text{chlorate}}{NaClO_3} + H_2O$$

ClO_2 explodes in the presence of reducing agents. The pure gas also explodes, but it is safe if diluted with air or CO_2. It is manufactured from potassium chlorate. Oxalic acid is added to provide some CO_2.

$$2KClO_3 + 2(COOH)_2 \rightarrow 2ClO_2 + 2CO_2 + (COOK)_2 + 2H_2O$$

ClO_2 is made in the laboratory from silver chlorate and chlorine, the ClO_2 being separated by condensation:

$$2AgClO_3 + Cl_2 \xrightarrow{90°C} 2AgCl + 2ClO_2 + O_2$$

ClO_2 gas is paramagnetic and contains an odd number of electrons. Odd electron molecules are generally highly reactive and ClO_2 is typical. The bond lengths are appreciably shorter than in a single bond, and resonance is thought to occur between the two structures (Fig. 5.40). This structure

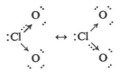

Fig. 5.40

involves two co-ordinate bonds and a three-electron bond which may occupy either position as shown. The three-electron bond accounts for the shorter bond lengths and is about half as strong as a normal covalent or co-ordinate bond. Three-electron bonds may also be described in terms of the molecular orbital theory (see O_2, NO and NO_2). Bromine dioxide BrO_2 has a similar structure, but is only stable below $-40°C$ when it exists as a yellow solid. It is less explosive than ClO_2 and on hydrolysis gives bromide and bromate.

$$BrO_2 + 6NaOH \rightarrow NaBr + 5NaBrO_3 + 3H_2O$$

It is prepared by the action of an electric discharge on Br_2 and O_2 gases at low temperature and pressure, and is much less important than ClO_2.

Dichlorine hexoxide Cl_2O_6 is a red liquid which can be prepared from

ClO_2 and ozone. It is a strong oxidizing agent and explodes on contact with grease. With alkali it forms chlorate and perchlorate.

$$Cl_2O_6 + 2NaOH \rightarrow \underset{\text{chlorate}}{NaClO_3} + \underset{\text{perchlorate}}{NaClO_4} + H_2O$$

Cl_2O_6 has no unpaired electrons and is diamagnetic. It is probably in equilibrium with ClO_3, which is an odd electron molecule and is paramagnetic.

$$Cl_2O_6 \underset{}{\overset{\text{heat}}{\rightleftharpoons}} 2ClO_3$$

BrO_3 is a white solid and is produced from ozone and bromine, or from oxygen and bromine under the influence of a silent electric discharge. It is an oxidizing agent and gives acidic solutions with water. Until 1955 it was incorrectly formulated Br_3O_8. It is unstable above $-70°C$.

Dichlorine heptoxide Cl_2O_7 is a moderately stable liquid and is the only exothermic oxide of chlorine. It is made by dehydrating perchloric acid with phosphorus pentoxide, and with water forms perchloric acid.

$$2HClO_4 \underset{H_2O}{\overset{P_4O_{10}}{\rightleftharpoons}} Cl_2O_7$$

Iodine pentoxide I_2O_5 is a white solid and is the only true oxide of iodine. It is formed by dehydrating iodic acid by heating to 170°C.

$$2HIO_3 \rightarrow I_2O_5 + H_2O$$

Heating to 300°C decomposes I_2O_5 to the elements. It is the anhydride of iodic acid and is also an oxidizing agent. An important analytical use of I_2O_5 is in the detection and estimation of carbon monoxide. It oxidizes CO to CO_2 quantitatively, liberating iodine, which can be titrated with sodium thiosulphate.

$$I_2O_5 + 5CO \rightarrow 5CO_2 + I_2$$

The structure of I_2O_5 is probably (Fig. 5.41):

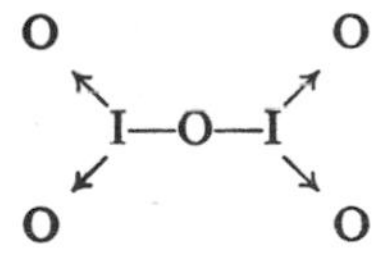

Fig. 5.41

The compounds I_2O_4 and I_4O_9 are ionic and are probably iodates $IO^+ . IO_3^-$ and $I^{3+} . (IO_3^-)_3$ respectively.

Oxy-Acids

Fluorine forms no oxy-acids. Chlorine, bromine and iodine form four series with formulae: HOX, HXO_2, HXO_3 and HXO_4, although many of these are known only in solution or as salts.

The hypohalous acids HOCl, HOBr and HOI are all weak acids and only exist in aqueous solutions. They are prepared by shaking freshly precipitated HgO in water with the appropriate halogen.

$$2HgO + H_2O + 2Cl_2 \rightarrow HgO.HgCl_2 + 2HOCl$$

Hypochlorous acid is the most stable and sodium hypochlorite is used for bleaching cotton fabric. NaOCl is prepared by electrolysing brine. Hydrogen is liberated at the cathode thus increasing the concentration of OH^- in the solution. By agitating the electrolyte, the chlorine formed at the anode reacts with the hydroxyl ions before it can escape.

$$anode\begin{cases} 2Cl^- \rightarrow Cl_2 \\ Cl_2 + 2OH^- \rightarrow OCl^- + Cl^- + H_2O \end{cases}$$
$$cathode \quad 2H^+ \rightarrow H_2$$

Hypobromites such as $NaOBr.5H_2O$ and $KOBr.3H_2O$ can be made by the addition of bromine to NaOH or KOH below 0°C, but they are less stable than hypochlorites and disproportionate to bromate and bromide.

$$3NaOBr \rightarrow Na(BrO_3) + 2NaBr$$

Hypoiodous acid is much less stable. It is amphoteric and may be regarded as iodine hydroxide IOH in many reactions. Hypoiodites cannot be isolated and they disproportionate, like the acid, into iodate and iodide.

$$3HOI \rightarrow H(IO_3) + 2HI$$

The only halous acid known is chlorous acid $HClO_2$. This only exists in solution, but is a stronger acid than HOCl. Chlorites are made from ClO_2, but disproportionate on heating to chlorate and chloride.

$$2ClO_2 + Na_2O_2 \rightarrow 2NaClO_2 + O_2$$
$$3NaClO_2 \rightarrow 2NaClO_3 + NaCl$$

The halic acids $HClO_3$ and $HBrO_3$ are known in solution, but iodic acid HIO_3 exists as a white solid. Thus the stability increases with increased atomic number. The acids are all strong oxidizing agents and strong acids. HIO_3 can be made by oxidizing iodine with fuming nitric acid. Chlorates are used in fireworks and matches, whilst sodium chlorate is a powerful weed-killer. Chlorates may be made by the action of chlorine on hydroxides or by electrolysing hot chloride solutions. It is thought that the hypochlorite first formed in this reaction, combines further:

$$6NaOH + 3Cl_2 \rightarrow NaClO_3 + 5NaCl + 3H_2O$$
$$2HOCl + OCl^- \rightarrow ClO_3^- + 2H^+ + 2Cl^-$$

The thermal decomposition of chlorates and bromates is complex and is not fully understood. $KClO_3$ may decompose in two different ways, depending on the temperature.

$$2KClO_3 \rightarrow 2KCl + 3O_2$$

This well-known experiment to produce oxygen frequently gives a trace of chlorine as well. $Zn(ClO_3)_2$ decomposes to zinc oxide, oxygen and chlorine.

$$2Zn(ClO_3)_2 \rightarrow 2ZnO + 2Cl_2 + 5O_2$$

$KClO_3$ decomposes at a lower temperature in the presence of a catalyst such as MnO_2. Secondly $KClO_3$ may disproportionate to perchlorate and chloride.

$$4KClO_3 \rightarrow 3KClO_4 + KCl$$

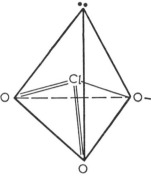

Fig. 5.42

Chlorates can explode on heating or when in contact with easily oxidized substances such as organic matter or sulphur. They are much more soluble than bromates and iodates. The ClO_3^- ion is pyramidal in structure; i.e. it has a tetrahedral arrangement with one position occupied by a lone pair of electrons (Fig. 5.42).

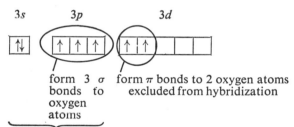

Electronic structure of chlorine atom—excited state

$$3s \qquad 3p \qquad 3d$$

form 3 σ bonds to oxygen atoms

form π bonds to 2 oxygen atoms excluded from hybridization

sp^3 hybridization—tetrahedral with one lone pair.

The Cl—O bonds are shortened by $p\pi$—$d\pi$ bonding and they are all of equal length due to resonance.

Whilst perchloric and periodic acids and their salts are well known, perbromates are not known. Perchloric acid $HClO_4$ is one of the strongest acids, and is a powerful oxidizing agent which explodes when in contact with organic matter and sometimes on its own. The commercial 70% $HClO_4$ has almost the composition of the dihydrate. It can be made from NH_4ClO_4 and dilute nitric acid, or from $NaClO_4$ and concentrated hydrochloric acid. $NaClO_4$ is made by electrolysing aqueous $NaClO_3$, using smooth platinum electrodes to give a high oxygen over-potential to prevent the electrolysis of water.

$$NaClO_3 + H_2O \xrightarrow{\text{electrolysis}} NaClO_4 + H_2$$

Except for the potassium, rubidium, caesium and ammonium salts most perchlorates are very soluble, but the insolubility of $KClO_4$ is used to detect potassium in qualitative analysis. Magnesium perchlorate is very hygroscopic and is used as a drying agent called 'anhydrone'. The perchlorate ion is tetrahedral. The common form of periodic acid is $HIO_4 . 2H_2O$ or H_5IO_6. This is obtained by passing chlorine into a solution of iodine in NaOH. The salt $Na_2H_3IO_6$ so formed is treated with $AgNO_3$ giving Ag_3IO_5, which on treatment with chlorine and water and evaporating with concentrated H_2SO_4 gives H_5IO_6. When heated, the acid first loses water, polymerizes, and forms an isopolyacid. More water is lost on further heating, and eventually oxygen is lost giving iodic acid.

$$2H_5IO_6 \xrightarrow[-3H_2O]{80°C} H_4I_2O_9 \xrightarrow[-H_2O]{100°C} 2HIO_4 \xrightarrow{140°C} 2HIO_3 + O_2$$

paraperiodic   metaperiodic   iodic
acid   acid   acid

Solutions of periodic acid are used to determine the structure of organic compounds by degradative methods, since HIO_4 splits $1:2$ glycols

$$R.CH.CH.R \rightarrow R.CHO + R.CHO$$
$$\quad\; | \quad\; |$$
$$\quad OH \;\; OH$$

Interhalogen Compounds

These are divided into four types (Table 5.19).

TABLE 5.19

AX	AX_3	AX_5	AX_7
ClF			
BrF	ClF_3	BrF_5	
BrCl	BrF_3	IF_5	IF_7
ICl	ICl_3		
IBr			

They can all be prepared by direct combination, or by the action of a halogen on a lower interhalogen. The product formed depends on the conditions.

$$Cl_2 + F_2 \text{ (equal volumes)} \xrightarrow{200°C} 2ClF$$

$$Cl_2 + 3F_2 \text{ (excess } F_2\text{)} \xrightarrow{300°C} 2ClF_3$$

$$I_2 + Cl_2 \text{ liquid (equimolecular)} \longrightarrow ICl$$
$$I_2 + Cl_2 \text{ liquid (excess } Cl_2\text{)} \longrightarrow ICl_3$$

$$Br_2 + F_2 \text{ (diluted with nitrogen)} \longrightarrow BrF_3$$
$$Br_2 + F_2 \text{ (excess } F_2\text{)} \longrightarrow BrF_5$$

There are never more than two different halogens in a molecule. The bonds are essentially covalent because of the small electronegativity difference, and the melting and boiling points increase as the difference in electronegativity increases.

The compounds formed in the AX and AX_3 groups are those where the electronegativity difference is not too great. The higher valencies AX_5 and AX_7 are shown by large atoms such as Br and I associated with small atoms such as F, because it is possible to pack more small atoms round a large one.

The interhalogens are generally more reactive than the halogens (except F) because the $A—X$ bond is weaker than the $X—X$ bond in the halogens. The reactions are similar to those of the halogens. Hydrolysis gives halide and oxyhalide ions, the oxyhalide ion being formed from the larger halogen present.

$$BrF_5 \xrightarrow{H_2O} 5F^- + \underset{\text{bromate}}{BrO_3^-}$$

$$ICl \xrightarrow{H_2O} Cl^- + \underset{\text{hypoiodite}}{OI^-}$$
$$\searrow$$
$$\underset{\text{iodate}}{Cl^- + IO_3^-}$$

Many metal oxides, metal halides and metals are fluorinated.

$$MO + BrF_3 \rightarrow MF_2 + Br_2 + O_2$$

Iodine monochloride ICl is the best known of the AX group. It is used as Wij's reagent in the estimation of the iodine number as a measure of the unsaturation of fats and oils.

$$—CH{=}CH— + ICl \rightarrow \underset{\substack{| \quad | \\ I \quad Cl}}{—CH{-}CH—}$$

It also forms addition compounds called polyhalides with alkali halides.

$$NaBr + ICl \rightarrow NaBrICl$$

ICl is used to iodinate organic compounds, though chlorination may occur depending on the conditions.

salicylic acid
- ICl vapour → chlorination
- ICl in nitrobenzene → iodination

Since the iodine atoms substitute in positions where there is an excess of electrons, it is thought that the attacking species is I^+. Conductivity measurements and electrolysis show that ICl ionizes about 1%.

$$2ICl \rightleftharpoons I^+ + ICl_2^-$$

The interhalogens are all potential non-aqueous, ionizing solvents. Bromine trifluoride BrF_3 has been used more than the others, largely because it is a liquid at room temperature and because it is a good, but not too violent fluorinating agent. It self-ionizes considerably.

$$2BrF_3 \rightleftharpoons BrF_2{}^+ + BrF_4{}^-$$

Thus substances producing $BrF_2{}^+$ ions are acids and $BrF_4{}^-$ ions are bases in this solvent. The structure of the AX_3 type of interhalogen molecule is of interest. In ClF_3, Cl is the central atom (Fig. 5.43).

Electronic structure of chlorine atom— excited state

three unpaired electrons form bonds with three fluorine atoms—sp^3d hybridization—trigonal bipyramid with two positions occupied by lone pairs.

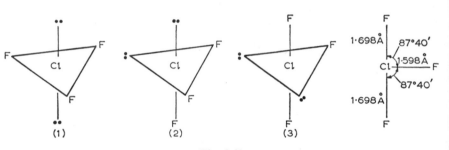

Fig. 5.43

It is not possible to predict which of the three possible arrangements will be formed. Structural studies show that ClF_3 is T-shaped with bond angles almost 90°. This indicates structure (3). The distortion is due to the lone pairs. It is of interest to note that two bond lengths are the same and different from the third, which is to be expected because a trigonal bipyramid is not a regular shape.

Of the AX_5 compounds, BrF_5 is too reactive to be suitable for preparing fluorides. In IF_5 vapour, I is the central atom in the molecule (Fig. 5.44).

Electronic structure of iodine atom— excited state

five unpaired electrons form bonds with five fluorine atoms— sp^3d^2 hybridization—octahedral with one position occupied by lone pair. (Alternatively described as square-based pyramid.)

Liquid IF_5 conducts electricity and self ionizes.

$$2IF_5 \rightleftharpoons IF_4^+ + IF_6^-$$

Complex salts are formed, by heating IF_5 with alkali halides.

$$KI + IF_5 \rightarrow K[IF_6]$$

IF_7 is formed by heating IF_5 with F_2. It is a violent fluorinating agent and has an unusual structure. This is a pentagonal bipyramid (Figure 5.45)

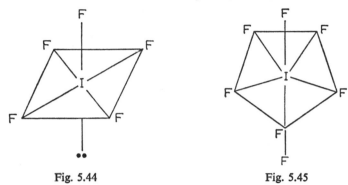

Fig. 5.44   Fig. 5.45

and is probably the only known example of a non-transition element using three d orbitals for bonding.

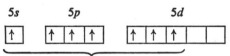

Electronic structure of iodine atom—excited state

seven unpaired electrons form bonds with seven fluorine atoms—sp^3d^3 hybridization.

Polyhalides

Halide ions often associate with molecules of halogens or interhalogens and form polyhalide ions. For example, the solubility of iodine in water is greatly increased by the addition of iodide ions, due to the formation of the triiodide ion I_3^-.

$$I_2 + I^- \rightarrow I_3^-$$

More complex ions such as pentaiodide I_5^-, heptaiodide I_7^- and enneaiodide I_9^- have also been prepared. The larger polyiodide ions are generally found combined with large metal ions or large complex cations, since this results in a more stable lattice. The direct addition of iodine to the iodide either with or without a solvent, results in polyhalides such as $KI_3.H_2O$, RbI_3, NH_4I_5, $[(C_2H_5)_4N]I_7$ and $RbI_9.2C_6H_6$.

The Br_3^- ion is much less stable than I_3^- and only a few unstable Cl_3^-

compounds are known. No F_3^- compounds are known, presumably because fluorine has no available *d* orbitals and therefore cannot expand its octet.

A number of polyhalides are known which contain two or three different halogens, for example $KICl_2$, $KICl_4$, CsIBrF and KIBrCl. These are formed from metal halides and interhalogens.

$$KCl + ICl \rightarrow KICl_2$$
$$KCl + ICl_3 \rightarrow KICl_4$$

Polyhalides are typically ionic compounds, though they tend to decompose on heating.

$$CsI_3 \xrightarrow{\text{heat}} CsI + I_2$$

$$RbICl_2 \xrightarrow{\text{heat}} RbCl + ICl$$

The structures of the polyhalides are known. The trihalides KI_3, $KICl_2$ and CsIBrF all contain a linear trihalide ion. This may be explained by considering the hybridization and orbitals used. For example in ICl_2^- (see Fig. 5.46):

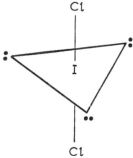

Fig. 5.46.   Structure of
ICl_2^- ion

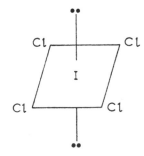

Fig. 5.47.   Structure of ICl_4^- ion
(the structure of the I_5^- ion is
different)

	5s	5p			5d					
Electronic structure of iodine atom— ground state	↑↓	↑↓	↑↓	↑						
Structure of I having formed one covalent and one co-ordinate bond in ICl_2^-	↑↓	↑↓	↑↓	↑↓	✕					

sp^3d hybridization—trigonal bipyramid with three positions occupied by lone pairs.

Similarly the structures of the pentahalide ions ICl_4^- and BrF_4^- are planar (see Fig. 5.47).

	$5s$	$5p$	$5d$

Electronic structure of iodine atom—excited state

Structure of iodine having formed three covalent and one co-ordinate bonds in ICl_4^-

sp^3d^2 hybridization—octahedral with two positions occupied by lone pairs.

Basic Properties of the Halogens

Metallic or basic properties increase on descending a group. Thus in Groups IV, V and VI the first elements C, N and O are non-metals, but the heavier members Sn, Pb, Bi and Po are metals. Since metallic properties decrease on crossing a period, and since little is known about astatine, the trend to metallic properties is less obvious in Group VII. The increasing stability of positive ions indicates an increasing tendency to basic or metallic character. It must be emphasized that iodine is not a metal.

Fluorine is the most electronegative element and has no basic properties (that is, it has no tendency to form positive ions). If ClF has any tendency to ionize it will form Cl^+ and F^- due to the greater electronegativity of F. Chlorine shows a slight tendency to form positive ions in this case, and it has an oxidation number of $+1$ in HOCl. Positive bromine exists in complexes such as $Br(pyridine)NO_3$ and BrF_3. These ionize and give [Br pyridine]$^+$ and NO_3^-, and BrF_2^+ and BrF_4^- respectively. Positive iodine compounds are more numerous and better established. The evidence for existence of positive iodine as I^+ and I^{3+} is given below.

(1) Evidence for I^+

ICl conducts electricity when molten. Both I_2 and Cl_2 are liberated at the anode, but only I_2 at the cathode. The ionization is probably:

$$2ICl \rightleftharpoons I^+ + ICl_2^-$$

Molten ICN behaves in a similar way, but in pyridine it gives I_2 only at the cathode. This suggests the more simple type of ionization:

$$ICN \rightleftharpoons I^+ + CN^-$$

ICl behaves as an electrophilic iodinating agent, converting acetanilide to 4-iodoacetanilide, and salicylic acid to 3,5 di-iodosalicylic acid. Because the attacked sites have an electron excess, the iodine must be positive. If iodine is dissolved in an inert solvent and passed down a cationic ion exchange column, some iodine is retained on the resin.

$$H^+ Resin^- + I_2 \rightarrow I^+ Resin^- + HI$$

The positive ion retained may be eluted with KI, to estimate the amount of I^+, or it may be allowed to react with various reagents.

$$I^+Resin^- + KI \rightarrow K^+Resin^- + I_2$$
$$I^+Resin^- + anhydrous\ H_2SO_4 \rightarrow I_2SO_4$$

$$\begin{array}{cc} or & or \\ alcoholic\ HNO_3 & INO_3 \end{array}$$

Since I^+ reacts with OH^- in aqueous solutions, it is rare in aqueous media.

$$I^+ + OH^- \rightarrow HOI$$
$$2HOI + OI^- \rightarrow IO_3^- + 2I^- + 2H^+$$

For this reason I^+ is rarely obtained unless it is stabilized by co-ordination. Many pyridine complexes are known, such as $I(pyridine)NO_3$, $I(pyridine)_2$ NO_3, $I(pyridine)_2ClO_4$, $I(pyridine)acetate$ and $I(pyridine)benzoate$. Electrolysis of $I(pyridine)_2NO_3$ in chloroform solution gives iodine at the cathode.

(2) *Evidence for I^{3+}*

Molten ICl_3 has a high conductivity ($8 \cdot 4 \times 10^{-3}$ ohms^{-1} cms^{-1}). Because I_2 and Cl_2 are liberated at both electrodes, ionization into ICl_2^+ and ICl_4^- is indicated. If I_2 is treated with fuming HNO_3 and acetic anhydride, $I(acetate)_3$ is formed. If this is electrolysed using silver electrodes, one equivalent of AgI is formed at the cathode for every three Faradays of electricity passed. This proves ionization:

$$I(acetate)_3 \rightleftharpoons I^{3+} + 3\ (acetate^-)$$

If I_2 is oxidized with concentrated HNO_3 in the presence of acetic anhydride and phosphoric acid, iodine phosphate is formed.

$$I + Ac_2O + H_3PO_4 \rightarrow IPO_4$$

If this ionizes, I^{3+} would be expected. Cationic iodine exists in sulphuric acid solutions. Iodine dissolves in dilute oleum and forms I^{3+}, but in more concentrated oleum I^+ is formed.

Group 0—The Noble Gases (Table 5.20)

TABLE 5.20

Element	Symbol	Electronic structure		
Helium	He			$1s^2$
Neon	Ne	[He]		$2s^2\ 2p^6$
Argon	Ar	[Ne]		$3s^2\ 3p^6$
Krypton	Kr	[Ar]	$3d^{10}$	$4s^2\ 4p^6$
Xenon	Xe	[Kr]	$4d^{10}$	$5s^2\ 5p^6$
Radon	Rn	[Xe]	$4f^{14}\ 5d^{10}$	$6s^2\ 6p^6$

Electronic Structure and General Properties

The two electrons of He form a complete shell and all the other inert gases have an octet of electrons in their outer shell. The electronic configuration is related to their chemical inactivity. These atoms have an electron affinity near to zero and have higher ionization potentials than any other elements. Consequently they do not gain or lose electrons under normal conditions and do not form many bonds. Thus they exist as single atoms. The only forces between these atoms are very weak Van der Waals forces, and so the melting points and boiling points are very low.

TABLE 5.21

Element	First ionization potential eV	M.p. °C	B.p. °C
He	24·6		−268·9
Ne	21·6	−248·6	−246·0
Ar	15·7	−189·4	−185·9
Kr	14·0	−157·2	−153·2
Xe	12·1	−111·9	−108·1
Rn	10·8	−71	−62

Helium is unique because it only forms a solid under pressure and exists in two liquid phases. Helium I is a normal liquid, but helium II is a super-fluid. This is a liquid with the properties of a gas. Its energy is so low that thermal motion of the atoms has ceased, but the interatomic forces are not strong enough to form a solid. When He I changes to He II many physical properties change abruptly. The thermal conductivity becomes 800 times greater than for copper, the viscosity becomes 1/100th of that of gaseous hydrogen, and the liquid flows up the sides of the vessel. The specific heat, surface tension and compressibility are also anomalous.

Radon is radioactive. It is a decay product of radium, but decays itself to polonium, and has a half-life of under four days.

The gases exist as trace amounts in the atmosphere, and He is formed as a product of radioactive decay. They are used to provide an inert atmosphere for welding, and as fillings for electric light bulbs, radio valves and neon discharge tubes.

'Compounds' of the Noble Gases

Considerable efforts have been made to find evidence for compound formation by the noble gases.

(1) *Under Excited Conditions*

$$\text{Helium—ground state} \quad \underset{1s}{[\uparrow\downarrow]} \xrightarrow{460 \text{ kcal}} \text{Helium—excited state} \quad \underset{1s}{[\uparrow]} \quad \underset{2s}{[\uparrow]}$$

These high-energy conditions are only realized spectroscopically under conditions of electrical discharge, or electron bombardment. In a discharge tube He_2^+, HeH^+ and HeH^{2+} have been observed, but only survive momentarily. Metal electrodes in discharge tubes absorb inert gases, to form Pt_3He, $FeHe$ and $FeAr$, perhaps as interstitial compounds.

(2) *By Co-ordination*

Noble gas atoms may donate an electron pair to a suitable acceptor. Thermal analysis of Ar with BF_3 was said to give peaks in the freezing point curves corresponding to 1 Ar: 1, 2, 3, 6, 8 and 16 BF_3.

$$:\overset{..}{\underset{..}{Ar}}: \rightarrow BF_3$$

This work was not repeatable by other workers and is viewed with scepticism.

(3) *By Dipole/Induced Dipole Attractions*

The noble gas atoms may be polarized by a strong dipole on other molecules and thus possess a weak induced dipole of their own. The solubility of the noble gases in water is high and increases with increased size. This is probably because the larger atoms are more easily polarized by the surrounding water molecules. Certain derivatives of phenol $Kr(phenol)_2$, $Xe(phenol)_2$ and $Rn(phenol)_2$ may have this sort of attraction.

(4) *Clathrate Compounds*

Until recently, the only well established 'compounds' of the noble gases were those in which the gases are trapped in cavities in the crystal lattice of other compounds. If quinol (1·4 dihydroxy benzene) is crystallized in the presence of the heavier noble gases under a pressure of 10–40 atmospheres, the gas becomes trapped in cavities of about 4 Å diameter in the β quinol structure. When the clathrate is dissolved, the hydrogen-bonded arrangement of β quinol breaks down and the inert gas escapes. Other small molecules such as O_2, SO_2, H_2S, MeCN and CH_3OH form clathrates as well as Ar, Kr and Xe. The absence of He and Ne compounds occurs because they are too small and can escape from the cavities. The composition of these compounds corresponds to 3 quinol:1 trapped molecule, though normally all the cavities are not filled.

The gases Ar, Kr and Xe may be trapped in cavities in a similar way when water solidifies. The so-called inert gas hydrates have formulae approximating to $6H_2O$:1 gas atom.

Further details on quinol clathrate compounds are given in articles by POWELL, H. M., *Nature*, **164**, 240 (1949) and *Journal of the Chemical Society*, 298, 300 and 468 (1950).

In June 1962 it was reported that xenon and platinum hexafluoride vapour react together to form a yellow powder, xenon hexafluoroplatinate (V) $Xe^+PtF_6^-$. Soon after, a series of stable solid compounds XeF_2, XeF_4 and XeF_6 were reported. These may be prepared from the elements: XeF_2 by a photochemical method under the influence of a mercury vapour lamp; XeF_4 by heating the gases together at 400°C, or by passing an electric discharge through them, and XeF_6 by heating them under high pressure. The crystal structures of XeF_2 and XeF_4 are linear and square planar respectively, and spectroscopic data suggests that XeF_6 is octahedral. If XeF_4 is irradiated with γ-radiation at low temperatures, XeF radicals may be trapped in the crystal lattice. These are paramagnetic with one unpaired electron, and colour the crystal blue. If crystals are grown in the vapours of XeF_4 and XeF_2, a diamagnetic solid of formula XeF_3 is formed, which is a mixed crystal of XeF_4 and XeF_2. There are unconfirmed reports of XeF_8. The fluorides react quantitatively with hydrogen:

$$XeF_2 + H_2 \rightarrow 2HF + Xe$$
$$XeF_4 + 2H_2 \rightarrow 4HF + Xe$$
$$XeF_6 + 3H_2 \rightarrow 6HF + Xe$$

Hydrolysis of XeF_4 by water or alkali yielded the expected amount of F^-, but the amounts of Xe and O_2 were low, and the reaction is probably more complicated than indicated by the equation:

$$XeF_4 + 2H_2O \rightarrow Xe + O_2 + 4HF?$$

XeF_6 reacts violently with water, but slow hydrolysis by atmospheric moisture gives the highly explosive XeO_3, which has a pyramidal structure like the IO_3^- iodate ion. Oxyfluorides $XeOF_3$ and $XeOF_4$ have been detected in mass spectrographic studies of XeF_4. Xenon oxytetrafluoride $XeOF_4$ is also formed by the hydrolysis of XeF_6 with a limited amount of water, and it has a square-based pyramid structure like the isoelectronic bromine pentafluoride (see page 159). Force constant data indicate double bond character in the $Xe\!=\!O$ bond. KrF_2 and KrF_4 are known, but are less stable than the corresponding xenon compounds. Hydrolysis of KrF_4 at room temperature yields Kr, O_2 and HF, but hydrolysis with ice below $-30°C$ gave 2–3% of an acid which may be $KrO_3.(H_2O)_x$, e.g. H_2KrO_4, H_4KrO_5 or H_6KrO_6. Hydrolysis of KrF_4 with aqueous $Ba(OH)_2$ gave a 7% yield of a compound thought to be barium kryptate $BaKrO_4$. Perxenates may be prepared by the alkaline hydrolysis of XeF_6, the $Xe(+6)$ disproportionating into $Xe(+8)$ and lower oxidation states of xenon. A similar reaction occurs with XeO_3:

$$2XeO_3 + 4NaOH + 6H_2O \rightarrow Xe + O_2 + Na_4XeO_6.8H_2O$$

The solubility of Na_4XeO_6 in water at room temperature is 7 g/l, and in 0·5N NaOH is 0·2 g/l, so perxenates could be used for the gravimetric

molecular orbitals, one bonding, one non-bonding and one antibonding. In a simplified way this can be represented:

F   Xe   F

⊖⊕   ⊖⊕   ⊖⊕   antibonding (orbitals have wrong symmetry for overlap indicated by + and − signs).

⊖⊕   ⊖⊕   ⊕⊖   non-bonding (The Xe $5p$ orbital has no contribution, since the bonding effect in one half is cancelled by the antibonding effect in the other half).

⊖⊕   ⊕⊖   ⊖⊕   bonding (orbitals have correct symmetry for overlap).

The original three atomic orbitals contained four electrons (2 in Xe $5pz$ and 1 in each of F $2pz$). These occupy the molecular orbitals of lowest energy, and since the order of energy is bonding MO < non-bonding MO < antibonding MO, two electrons occupy the bonding MO and two occupy the non-bonding MO. A linear arrangement of the atoms gives the best overlap of orbitals, in accordance with the observed structure.

In a similar way the MO theory predicts a square planar structure for XeF_4, and a regular octahedral structure for XeF_6. This sort of MO treatment is not limited to inert gas compounds, but covers interhalogen compounds, polyhalides and many others.

The high heat of sublimation of the solid fluorides indicates a high polarity for the Xe—F bond, and u.v. spectroscopic data for XeF_2 and XeF_4 has been interpreted by the use of only $5p$ xenon orbitals and $2p$ fluorine orbitals, analogous to structure (2). The structure of XeF_6 should be particularly interesting in the structure controversy because if only p orbitals are used, a regular octahedral structure should be formed.

Further details may be obtained from the following reviews and books:

BARTLETT, N., *Endeavour*, **88**, 3, 1964.
GREENWOOD, N. N., *Education in Chemistry*, **1** (4), 176, 1964.
HYMAN, H. H. (Editor), *Noble-Gas Compounds*, University of Chicago Press, Chicago, 1963.
MOODY, G. J. and THOMAS, J. D. R., *Noble Gases and Their Compounds*, Pergamon Press, 1964.

PROBLEMS

1. From the position of Al in the electrochemical series, would you expect it to be stable in water? Why is it stable in air and water?
2. Give reasons for trivalency and monovalency in Group III elements, and comment on the validity of divalent compounds such as $GaCl_2$.
3. (a) List features which make borax a useful primary standard, and give a balanced equation to show its use in titrations.
   (b) Work out the shape of the BO_3^{3-} ion and explain why it has this structure.

4. (a) Explain the difference in density and electrical conductivity between diamond and graphite.

   (b) Why is it possible for two or more allotropic forms of an element to exist, since one must have the lower energy and thus be thermodynamically favoured?

5. List the advantages and limitations of CO as a reducing agent in the extraction of metals from their oxides.

6. Give reasons why CO_2 and SiO_2 are so different in structure, and why CCl_4 and $SiCl_4$ are so different in chemical behaviour.

7. With special reference to the elements C, Si, Ge, Sn and Pb illustrate the trends which may be observed in physical properties and chemical behaviour on descending a group in the periodic table.

8. Describe the conditions under which the following react, and give the products in each case:

   (a) copper and nitric acid;

   (b) nitrous oxide and sodamide;

   (c) calcium carbide and nitrogen;

   (d) cyanide ions and cupric sulphate;

   (e) ammonia and an acidified solution of sodium hypochlorite;

   (f) nitrous acid and iodide ions.

9. Discuss the uses of phosphates in analysis and in industry.

10. Compare and contrast the structures and behaviour of phosphates, silicates and borates.

11. In what ways and on what basis may oxides be classified?

12. Explain (a) the anomalous properties of fluorine; (b) the order of strength of the halogen acids.

13. With reference to specific examples, outline the properties and the nature of the bonding in odd electron molecules.

14. In what ways may the noble gases form compounds, and what is the nature of the bonds?

CHAPTER 6

d-BLOCK ELEMENTS

(Table 6.1)

General Properties

The transition or *d*-block elements are so called because their position in the periodic table is between the *s*- and *p*-block elements and their penultimate shell of electrons is being expanded from eight to eighteen by the addition of *d* electrons. The elements make up three complete rows of ten elements and an incomplete fourth row. The position of the incomplete fourth series will be discussed with the *f*-block elements.

TABLE 6.1

Sc	Ti	V	Cr	Mn	Fe	Co	Ni	Cu	Zn
Scan-dium	Tita-nium	Vana-dium	Chro-mium	Man-ganese	Iron	Cobalt	Nickel	Copper	Zinc
Y	Zr	Nb	Mo	Tc	Ru	Rh	Pd	Ag	Cd
Yttrium	Zir-conium	Nio-bium	Molyb-denum	Tech-netium	Ruthe-nium	Rho-dium	Palla-dium	Silver	Cad-mium
La	Hf	Ta	W	Re	Os	Ir	Pt	Au	Hg
Lan-thanum	Haf-nium	Tan-talum	Tungsten	Rhenium	Osmium	Iridium	Platinum	Gold	Mer-cury
Ac	Th	Pa	U						
Acti-nium	Tho-rium	Protac-tinium	Ura-nium						

Because the penultimate shell of electrons of all these elements is expanding, it is to be expected that they may have many physical and chemical properties in common. Thus all the transition elements are metals and are good conductors of electricity and heat. They are ductile and form alloys with other metals.

Density

The atomic volumes of the transition elements are low compared with neighbouring Groups I and II, because inner orbitals become filled and the increased nuclear charge pulls the electrons in. Consequently the densities of the transition metals are high. In fact Sc 3·0 g/cm³ and Y and Ti 4·5 g/cm³ are the only elements with a density less than five.

Melting and Boiling Points

The melting and boiling points of the transition elements are generally very high. Zn, Cd and Hg are notable exceptions because the *d* block is complete. Apart from these and from La and Ag which melt at 920°C and 961°C respectively, all the others melt above 1000°C. This is in marked contrast to the *s*-block metals where Li melts at 181°C and Cs melts at 29°C.

Reactivity of Metals

The metals show an increasing tendency to remain unreactive or noble. This is favoured by high heats of sublimation, high ionization potentials and low heats of solvation. (See page 48.) The high melting points indicate high heats of sublimation, and the smaller the atoms, the greater the ionization potentials. This tendency is most pronounced in platinum and gold.

Ionization Potentials

The ease with which an electron may be removed from a transition metal atom (that is, its ionization potential), is intermediate between that for the *s* and *p* blocks. This would suggest that the transition elements are less electropositive than Groups I and II and may form ionic or covalent bonds depending on the conditions. Generally, the lower valent states are ionic and the higher valent states covalent. The tendency to be ionic decreases as the atoms get larger. The variation in ionization potential within the *d* block is small—in all cases, it lies between 5 and 10 electron volts.

Colour

Ionic and covalent compounds of transition elements are usually markedly coloured, in contrast to compounds of the *s*- and *p*-block elements which are often white and are generally not strongly coloured. Colour is associated with incomplete electron shells and the ability to promote an electron from one energy level to another. Exactly the right amount of energy to do this is obtained by absorbing the light of a particular wavelength. In the transition elements, *d* electrons are promoted to a higher energy level within the *d* shell. This corresponds to a fairly small energy difference, and so light is absorbed in the visible region. If red light is absorbed, then the transmitted light contains an excess of the other colours of the spectrum—particularly blue, so that the compound appears blue, for example Cu^{2+}. In the *s*- and *p*-block elements the energy difference is much greater because the electron must be promoted to an outer shell and may correspond to ultraviolet light, in which case the compound will not appear coloured to the eye.

Magnetic Properties

Most of the transition elements are paramagnetic; that is, they attract magnetic lines of force. This property is associated with unpaired electron spins in the atom. Other substances in which all the electron spins are paired do not attract lines of force and are termed diamagnetic. It should be noted that Fe, Co and Ni are ferromagnetic, that is, they can be magnetized.

Catalytic Properties

Many transition metals and their compounds have catalytic properties, perhaps the most common being Fe, Pt, V_2O_5 and Ni. In some cases the transition metals with their variable valency may form unstable intermediate compounds, and in other cases the transition metal provides a suitable reaction surface.

Variable Valency

One of the most striking features of the transition elements is that they exhibit variable valency. Many of the elements show a wide range of valencies and the valency changes in units of one, e.g. Fe^{3+} and Fe^{2+}, Cu^{2+} and Cu^+. This is in contrast to the *s*-block elements, where the valency always equals the group number, and the *p*-block elements, where the valency either equals the group number or eight minus the group number. Variable valency does occur to a limited extent in the *p* block, but the valency always changes by two, e.g. $TlCl_3$ and $TlCl$, $SnCl_4$ and $SnCl_2$, PCl_5 and PCl_3 and is due to a different cause. The term oxidation state is preferred to valency, and may be defined as the charge left on the central atom when all the other atoms of the compound have been removed as ions, e.g. N^{3-}, O^{2-}, Cl^- and H^+. Thus Tl shows oxidation states of $+3$ and $+1$, Sn $+4$ and $+2$ and P $+5$ and $+3$. The oxidation number can be found equally well for ionic or covalent compounds, and without knowing the types of bonds. Thus the oxidation number of Mn in $KMnO_4$ may be worked out as follows: remove K^+ ion (leaving one negative charge behind) and remove four O^{2-} ions (leaving eight positive charges behind) so that the charge left on Mn is $-1 + 8 = +7$. It must be emphasized that the oxidation number is not necessarily the charge on the ion, for whilst Tl^+ and Tl^{3+} exist, Mn^{7+} does not exist, as $KMnO_4$ ionizes into K^+ and MnO_4^-.

The oxidation states shown by the transition elements may be related to their electronic structures. Calcium, the element preceding the first row of transition elements, has the electronic structure:

$$Ca \quad 1s^2\ 2s^2\ 2p^6\ 3s^2\ 3p^6\ 4s^2$$

It might be expected that the next ten transition elements would have this electronic arrangement with from one to ten $3d$ electrons added. This is true except in the case of Cr and Cu, where one of the s electrons moves into the d shell, because of the additional stability when the d orbitals are exactly half filled or completely filled (Table 6.2).

TABLE 6.2

	Sc	Ti	V	Cr	Mn	Fe	Co	Ni	Cu	Zn
Electronic Structure	$d^1 s^2$	$d^2 s^2$	$d^3 s^2$	$\cancel{d^4 s^2}$ $d^5 s^1$	$d^5 s^2$	$d^6 s^2$	$d^7 s^2$	$d^8 s^2$	$\cancel{d^9 s^2}$ $d^{10} s^1$	$d^{10} s^2$
Oxidation States	2 3	2 3 4	2 3 4 5	1 2 3 4 5 6	2 3 4 5 6 7	2 3 4 5 6	2 3 4 5	2 3 4	1 2 3	2

Thus Sc could have an oxidation number of $+2$ if both s electrons are used for bonding and $+3$ when two s and one d electrons are involved. Ti has an oxidation state $+2$ when both s electrons are used for bonding, $+3$ when two s and one d electrons are used and $+4$ when two s and $2d$ electrons are used. Similarly, V shows oxidation numbers 2, 3, 4 and 5. In the case of Cr, by using the single s electron for bonding we get an oxidation number of $+1$; hence by using varying numbers of d electrons oxidation states of $+2$, 3, 4, 5 and 6 are possible. Mn has oxidation states 2, 3, 4, 5, 6 and 7. Among these first five elements the correlation between electronic structure and minimum and maximum oxidation states in simple compounds is complete. In the remaining five elements the minimum oxidation state is still equal to the number of s electrons present, but there is no correlation between electronic structure and maximum oxidation states. These facts may be conveniently memorized however, because the oxidation states form a regular 'pyramid' in Table 6.2. Only Sc $(+2)$ and Co $(+5)$ are in doubt. In addition, several of the elements have zero valent and other low valent states in complexes, particularly with carbon monoxide and dipyridyl.

This type of table of oxidation states is only partially valid in the case of the other rows of transition elements. In both the second and third rows, a maximum oxidation state of $+8$ is found in the iron group (e.g. RuO_4 and OsO_4) though iron shows a maximum oxidation number of 6. (Reports of osmium octafluoride have proved to be incorrect.) Also, the electronic structures of the atoms in the second and third rows do not exactly follow the pattern of the first row. The structures of the nickel group are:

$$\text{Ni} \quad 3d^8 \, 4s^2$$
$$\text{Pd} \quad 4d^{10} \, 5s^0$$
$$\text{Pt} \quad 5d^9 \, 6s^1$$

Ability to form Complexes

Transition elements form many co-ordination compounds, in contrast to the *s*- and *p*-block elements. This is because the transition elements have small, highly-charged ions and vacant orbitals of approximately the correct energy to accept lone pairs of electrons donated by other groups or ligands.

Non-Stoichiometry

A further feature of the transition elements is the existence of non-stoichiometric compounds; that is, compounds of indefinite structure and proportions. For example, ferrous oxide $\overline{\text{FeO}}$ should be written with a bar over the formula to indicate that this formula does not imply that iron and oxygen atoms are exactly in the ratio 1:1, because analysis shows that the formula varies between $Fe_{0.94}O$ and $Fe_{0.84}O$. Vanadium and selenium form a series of compounds ranging from $VSe_{0.98}$ to VSe_2. These are given the formulae:

$$\overline{\text{VSe}} \qquad (VSe_{0.98} \rightarrow VSe_{1.2})$$
$$\overline{\text{V}_2\text{Se}_3} \qquad (VSe_{1.2} \rightarrow VSe_{1.6})$$
$$\overline{\text{V}_2\text{Se}_4} \qquad (VSe_{1.6} \rightarrow VSe_2)$$

This non-stoichiometry is shown particularly among compounds of the Group VI elements (O, S, Se, Te) and is due to the variable valency of transition elements and also to defects in the solid structures.

The *d* levels are complete at copper, palladium and gold in their respective series,

$$\text{Cu} \qquad 3d^{10}\,4s^1$$
$$\text{Pd} \qquad 4d^{10}\,5s^0$$
$$\text{Au} \qquad 5d^{10}\,6s^1$$

but because the *d* electrons are still available for bonding, they are typical transition elements. However in zinc, cadmium and mercury the *d* levels are full and are not available for bonding, so that these elements do not show the properties characteristic of transition elements.

Abundance

Considering the first row of transition elements, those with even atomic numbers are in general more abundant than those with odd atomic numbers in the same part of the table. Manganese is exceptional. The second and third rows of elements are generally less abundant than the first row. Of the last six elements in the second and third rows (Tc, Ru, Rh, Pd, Ag, Cd; Re, Os, Ir, Pt, Au, Hg) none occurs more than 0·15 parts per million (p.p.m.) in the earth's crust.

Scandium Group

TABLE 6.3

Element	Symbol	Electronic structures	Oxidation states*
Scandium	Sc	[Ar] $3d^1 4s^2$	3
Yttrium	Y	[Kr] $4d^1 5s^2$	3
Lanthanum	La	[Xe] $5d^1 6s^2$	3
Actinium	Ac	[Rn] $6d^1 7s^2$	3

* See page 77.

These four elements are sometimes grouped with the fourteen lanthanons and called collectively the 'rare earths'. This is a misnomer because the scandium group are *d*-block elements and the lanthanons *f*-block elements; also the scandium group is by no means rare, except for actinium which is radioactive.

The elements are invariably trivalent in solution. Removal of two *s* and one *d* electrons results in trivalent ions with no incomplete electron shells, so that the compounds are colourless and diamagnetic. Scandium carbide ScC_2 was at one time thought to be divalent, $Sc(—C≡C—)$. Magnetic and conductivity measurements have shown this to contain Sc^{3+} ions, C_2^{2-} ions and free electrons. It is prepared by heating the oxide with carbon, and is an acetylide.

$$Sc_2O_3 + C \xrightarrow{1000°C} ScC_2 \xrightarrow{H_2O} C_2H_2 + Sc(OH)_3$$

The metals are reactive and high melting. They react with water, liberate hydrogen and form basic oxides and hydroxides. $Sc(OH)_3$ is less basic than $Ca(OH)_2$, but more basic than the amphoteric $Al(OH)_3$. Here, as in the main groups, the basic nature of elements increases with size, and in the series $Sc(OH)_3$, $Y(OH)_3$, $La(OH)_3$, lanthanum hydroxide is the strongest base. Because they are basic, the oxides and hydroxides form salts with acids and react increasingly easily with carbon dioxide.

$$Y(OH)_3 + CO_2 \rightarrow Y_2(CO_3)_3$$

Since the oxides are weak bases, they can be formed by heating the hydroxides, or salts such as carbonates, nitrates or sulphates, in a similar way to Group II oxides.

Because the metal ions in this group are fairly large, the tendency to form complexes is not very strong. Scandium, the smallest metal ion, has the greatest complexing power, and forms complex fluorides and complexes with strong complexing agents such as acetyl acetone. Yttrium and lanthanum form complexes even less readily than scandium.

TABLE 6.4

Element	Ionic radius M^{3+}
	Å
Sc	0·83
Y	1·06
La	1·22

$$ScF_3 + NH_4F \rightarrow NH_4[ScF_4]$$
$$+ 2NH_4F \rightarrow (NH_4)_2[ScF_5]$$
$$+ 3NH_4F \rightarrow (NH_4)_3[ScF_6]$$

It is difficult to extract the metals from their compounds because they are difficult to separate from the lanthanons (see Chapter 7) and because of their melting points. Since they are highly electropositive they liberate hydrogen from water. Their oxides are very stable, so that a thermite reaction cannot be used. (Al_2O_3 heat of formation 400 kcal/mole; La_2O_3 heat of formation 450 kcal/mole.) The metal may be obtained by electrolysis of the fused chloride if an impurity such as NaCl is added to lower the melting point, or by reduction of the chlorides or oxides with sodium, potassium or calcium.

These elements react with hydrogen and form compounds of formula $MH_{<3}$ which are not quite stoichiometric. The exact composition depends on the temperature and pressure of the hydrogen. The hydrides probably contain the hydride ion H^- and react with water, liberating hydrogen.

Actinium is always found associated with uranium and thorium. There are two naturally occurring isotopes, which are both radioactive, with half-life periods of 22 years and 6 hours respectively. It follows that any actinium present when the earth was formed will have long since decayed, and any found now must have been produced fairly recently by radioactive decay of some other element. This explains the scarcity of naturally occurring actinium.

Titanium Group (Table 6.5)

TABLE 6.5

Element	Symbol	Electronic structure	Oxidation states*
Titanium	Ti	[Ar] $3d^2\ 4s^2$	-1, 0, 2, 3, **4**
Zirconium	Zr	[Kr] $4d^2\ 5s^2$	0, 2, 3, **4**
Hafnium	Hf	[Xe] $4f^{14}\ 5d^2\ 6s^2$	3, **4**
Thorium	Th	[Rn] $6d^2\ 7s^2$	3, **4**

* See page 77.

These elements all show a stable oxidation state of $+4$. The valency states $+3$ and $+2$ are much less stable and are reducing agents. The $+3$ and $+2$ valent states of titanium are known, but the others are progressively less stable and are almost unknown; titanium $+3$ is the only one stable enough to exist in solution. The lower oxidation states show a marked tendency to disproportionate.

$$2Ti^{3+} \xrightarrow{\text{heat}} Ti^{2+} + Ti^{4+}$$
$$2Ti^{2+} \xrightarrow{\text{H}_2\text{O}} Ti + Ti^{4+}$$

The zero and -1 oxidation states are found in dipyridyl complexes, $[Ti(dipy)_3]$ and $Li[Ti(dipy)_3] \cdot 3.5C_4H_8O$.

The energy to remove four electrons from an atom is large; therefore anhydrous compounds such as $TiCl_4$ are covalent. This latter is hydrolysed to the oxychloride $TiOCl_2$ or the oxide TiO_2. It is doubtful if M^{4+} ions exist, even in acid solutions. In the tetravalent state, two s and two d electrons are therefore shared with other atoms and form covalent bonds. $TiCl_4$ is a colourless, diamagnetic, fuming liquid. Ti^{3+} is ionic and has one unpaired electron, which may be promoted within the d level, this accounting for the purple colour of titanous compounds.

The elements of this group all form stable non-volatile dioxides MO_2 which are insoluble and are rendered refractory by strong ignition. TiO_2 is used in large amounts as a white pigment in the paint industry. Titanium group elements form peroxides and peroxy compounds on reaction with hydrogen peroxide. The oxides are considered to be ionic. Basic properties increase with atomic number in the group; TiO_2 is amphoteric (but is more acidic than basic), ZrO_2 and HfO_2 are amphoteric (more basic than acidic) and ThO_2 is purely basic. The oxides dissolve in alkali and form titanates such as Na_2TiO_3 and $Na_2Ti_2O_5$, and anhydrous titanates can be made by fusion of TiO_2 with metal carbonates or hydroxides. Zirconates and hafnates are formed less readily. Calcium titanate $CaTiO_3$ occurs naturally as perovskite, and ilmenite $Fe^{II}TiO_3$ is well known.

The elements all form phosphates, which do not dissolve, even in dilute acid. This property is used in qualitative analysis where the addition of zirconium oxychloride or zirconium nitrate precipitates zirconium phosphate and so removes the phosphate ion. Thorium or hafnium compounds could be used equally well for this purpose.

The metals form a number of complexes with fluoride ions or with many oxygen- or nitrogen-containing ligands; all these have a lone pair of electrons which can be donated to form a co-ordinate bond. Hexafluoro complexes are formed:

$$ZrF_4 + 2KF \rightarrow K_2[ZrF_6]$$

and fractional crystallization of hexafluorozirconates and hafnates has **been** used to separate these two metals. Ethyl alcohol, diethyl ether, acetyl acetone, trimethylamine, pyridine and many other donors form complexes of the type $TiCl_4 . 2$ donors, although because of the increase in size, the number of complexes falls from titanium to thorium.

Hafnium follows immediately after the lanthanide series of inner transition elements. As a result of the lanthanide contraction (see Chapter 7), the size of hafnium and zirconium atoms and ions are almost identical, and so their properties, too, are almost identical.

TABLE 6.6

Element	Ionic radius M^{4+} Å	Covalent radius Å	M.p. °C	Abundance in earth's crust p.p.m.
Ti	0·68	1·32	1668	4400
Zr	0·80	1·45	1852	220
Hf	0·80	1·44	2222	4·5
Th	0·95	1·65	1750	11·5

Separation of these two elements is difficult, and ion exchange of an alcoholic solution of the tetrachlorides is one of the best methods; although fractional crystallization, solvent extraction, ease of chelation and thermal decomposition have been used.

Titanium and zirconium are relatively abundant elements; titanium is the ninth most abundant element in the earth's crust. The metals are passive at low temperatures and resist attack by both acids and alkali. The passivity is probably due to the formation of a protective oxide film. However, titanium dissolves slowly in hot, concentrated hydrochloric and nitric acids, and explodes with fuming HNO_3, whilst zirconium dissolves in hot, concentrated sulphuric acid and aqua regia. The best solvent is hydrofluoric acid, because of the tendency of titanium to form hexafluoro compounds.

$$Ti + 6F^- \rightarrow [TiF_6]^{2-} + 4 \text{ electrons}$$

At temperatures over 600°C the metals form oxides MO_2, halides MX_4, interstitial nitrides MN, and interstitial carbides, by direct combination. Like the scandium group, the powdered metals absorb hydrogen, the amount absorbed depending on the temperature and pressure; they give non-stoichiometric interstitial hydrides of limiting composition MH_2; these hydrides are stable in air and unaffected by water. Pure titanium resembles stainless steel, but is much lighter. Small amounts alloyed with steel improve its properties, and about 10,000 tons of titanium are produced annually.　The metal is not easy to extract because of its high melting point and reactivity at high temperatures.　The following methods are used:

(1) *Electrolysis in an inert atmosphere.*　Because the tetrahalides are covalent, $TiCl_3$ or $K_2[TiF_6]$ is used with NaCl and KCl added to lower the melting point.

(2) *Kroll process.*　The tetrachloride is reduced by magnesium in an atmosphere of argon.

$$Mg + TiCl_4 \xrightarrow{800°C} MgCl_2 + Ti$$

$MgCl_2$ is removed by leaching or by vacuum distillation and the sponge of titanium which is left is converted to the massive form by melting in an electric arc under a high vacuum or an atmosphere of helium or argon.

(3) *I.C.I. process.*　$TiCl_4$ is reduced by sodium under an atmosphere of argon.

(4) *Van Arkel method.*　Impure titanium is heated with iodine and the resultant tetraiodide is decomposed on a tungsten filament.

$$\text{impure Ti} + I_2 \xrightarrow{50-250°C} TiI_4 \xrightarrow[\substack{\text{tungsten}\\\text{filament}}]{1400°C} Ti + I_2$$

Currently methods (2) and (3) are used commercially.　Method (4) is used to produce high purity material for research purposes.　The metal may be further purified by zone refining when a heating coil passes slowly along a tube containing the impure material.　The molten zone moves slowly and gives the equivalent of several recrystallizations.　Pure solid separates and the impurities stay in the liquid and finish in the end zone.

Vanadium Group (Table 6.7)

TABLE 6.7

Element	Symbol	Electronic structure	Oxidation states*
Vanadium	V	[Ar]　$3d^3\,4s^2$	$-1, 0, 1, 2, 3, 4, 5$
Niobium	Nb	[Kr]　$4d^3\,5s^2$	$-1,\qquad 2, 3, 4, 5$
Tantalum	Ta	[Xe]　$4f^{14}\,5d^3\,6s^2$	$-1,\qquad 2, 3, 4, 5$
Protactinium	Pa	[Rn]　$6d^3\,7s^2$	$4, 5$

* See page 77.

This group of metals shows variable valency, and vanadium has a wide range of oxidation states, which exist both as solids and in aqueous solution. Ionic character and basic properties decrease with increasing valency; and V^{2+}, vanadous compounds are ionic, reducing and basic, rather like Fe^{2+}; V^{3+} vanadic ions resemble Fe^{3+}.　The oxidation state +4 may be covalent as in VCl_4, but the oxide VO_2 is amphoteric, and vanadyl VO^{2+} salts and unstable vanadites exist. The oxidation state $+5$ is the maximum shown by the group. Vanadium $(+5)$ compounds are oxidizing agents, although niobium and tantalum $(+5)$ compounds are stable. Lower oxidation states become less stable and more difficult to prepare from $V \to Nb \to Ta \to Pa$, and whilst zinc and acid reduces $V(+5)$ to V^{2+}, it only reduces $Nb(+5)$ to Nb^{3+} and does not reduce $Ta(+5)$. This illustrates the increase in stability of the higher oxidation states on descending a transition metal group. The basic properties increase from $V \to Pa$; so far as the oxides M_2O_5 are concerned, vanadium is amphoteric but more acidic than basic, whilst the acidic nature diminishes in Nb, Ta and Pa. Because of the acidic properties of the pentoxides, these metals are sometimes called the 'acid earths'.

The lower valent ionic compounds have incomplete electron shells and are coloured, but in the higher oxidation states the electron shells are filled, so that these compounds are generally colourless.

Because of the lanthanide contraction, the ionic and covalent radii of Nb and Ta are almost identical. Consequently, these elements have similar properties, occur together, and are difficult to separate.

The metals are unreactive at normal temperatures, but on heating are quite reactive. Nb and Ta react with the halogens and give pentahalides, but V forms VF_5, VCl_4, VBr_3 and VI_3. These are all volatile, covalent and hydrolysed by water. V and Nb are hydrolysed first to the oxyhalides and then to the hydrous oxides. Ta does not readily form oxyhalides and this fact is utilized to separate Nb and Ta.

At high temperatures the metals form interstitial nitrides MN and two series of carbides MC and MC_2. The former are interstitial, refractory and very hard, and the latter are ionic and react with water, liberating acetylene.

These elements form non-stoichiometric hydrides, and the amount of hydrogen absorbed depends on the temperature and pressure. Here, as in the titanium group, the metal lattice expands as hydrogen enters interstitial positions; hence the density of the hydride is less than that of the metal. It is difficult to decide if these are true compounds or solid solutions, since the maximum hydrogen contents are: $VH_{0.71}$, $NbH_{0.86}$, $TaH_{0.76}$ and PaH_3.

The metals all react with oxygen at elevated temperatures and give pentoxides M_2O_5, although vanadium can also give VO_2. The oxides formed by vanadium are VO oxidation state $(+2)$, V_2O_3 $(+3)$, VO_2 $(+4)$ and V_2O_5 $(+5)$. $\overline{VO}$ is non-stoichiometric, of composition $VO_{0.94-1.12}$. It is a basic oxide and forms simple ions and in the solid has a NaCl type of structure. The V^{2+} ion is highly reducing and it contains an incomplete electron shell. The oxide is black and is made by reducing V_2O_5 with hydrogen at 1700°C. $\overline{V_2O_3}$ is non-stoichiometric: $VO_{1.35-1.5}$. It is basic and contains simple ions arranged in the solid in a corundum Al_2O_3 type of structure. It is produced by high temperature reduction of V_2O_5 with carbon or hydrogen. It contains an incomplete electron shell and is black in colour. VO_2 is stoichiometric and amphoteric. It can therefore react with acids to form salts and with alkali to form vanadites.

$$VO_2 + H_2O \rightarrow [H_2VO_3] \xrightarrow{-H_2O} [H_2V_4O_9]$$
$$\text{vanadite} \qquad\qquad \text{metavanadite}$$

The free acids are not known, but their salts, the vanadites, form simple and chain structures. The metavanadites are ring compounds. V (+4) has a partly-filled electron shell and the oxide, which is dark blue or dark green, is produced either by direct combination or by mild reduction of V_2O_5. It might be expected that the pentoxides, which have all their electrons paired in covalent bonds, would be unlikely to promote electrons, and so should be colourless. Nb_2O_5 and Ta_2O_5 are colourless, but V_2O_5 is red orange. An incomplete electron shell is not the only cause of coloured compounds, another possibility is defects in the solid state. V_2O_5 is by far the most important oxide and is more acidic than basic. As a basic oxide it reacts with acids and forms salts such as $VOCl_3$, vanadyl chloride, or VCl_5, and as an acidic oxide it forms vanadates. The orthovanadates, e.g. $Na_3[VO_4]$, are analogous to the salts of orthophosphoric acid H_3PO_4, and though the mechanism of hydrolysis of V_2O_5 is different from that of P_2O_5, the products are similar. The simple vanadate ions $[VO_4]^{3-}$ exist only in strongly alkaline solutions, and with decreasing pH they have a tendency to come together with the elimination of water, and form more complicated ions.

$$VO_4{}^{3-} \xrightarrow{\text{pH 11}} V_2O_7{}^{4-} \xrightarrow{\text{pH 9}} H_2V_4O_{13}{}^{4-} \xrightarrow{\text{pH 7}} H_4V_5O_{16}{}^{3-} \rightarrow$$
$$\text{orthovanadate} \quad\; \text{pyrovanadate} \qquad \text{tetravanadate} \qquad\quad \text{pentavanadate}$$
$$\xrightarrow{\text{pH2}} V_2O_5(H_2O)_n \xrightarrow{\text{pH} < 1} VO^{3+}$$

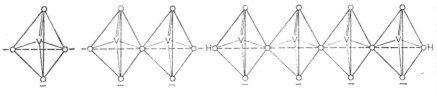

orthovanadate   pyrovanadate   tetravanadate

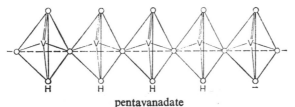

pentavanadate

Fig. 6.1

First the divanadate or pyrovanadate is formed, then the tetravanadate and finally the pentavanadate. In increasingly acid solutions this latter becomes unstable, and hydrated V_2O_5 is precipitated. Finally, in the presence of very strong acid, oxy salts containing oxovanadium ions VO^{3+} or VO_2^+ are formed, that is vanadic acid begins to dissociate as a base—a fact which indicates its amphoteric character.

If the two ends of the chain join together, a ring structure or metavanadate is formed such as the tetrametavanadate ion in Fig. 6.2. Acids of this kind,

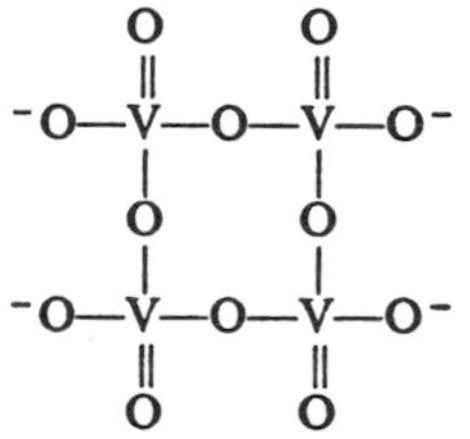

Fig. 6.2.   Tetrametavanadate ion

which are formed by the condensation of the same type of unit, are called isopoly acids. The vanadates, niobates and tantalates are all structurally similar. Some of the alkali metal salts of the isopoly acids are colourless, but others are coloured. The simpler salts are formed in alkaline solution and have a ratio of alkali metal to vanadium of at least unity, and are usually colourless. The coloured vanadates have an alkali metal to vanadium ratio less than unity and are formed in acid solution.

The number of complexes formed by these metals decreases with atomic number. Besides forming complexes with fluoride ions such as:

$$NbF_5 + 2KF \rightarrow K_2[NbF_7]$$
$$TaF_5 + 3KF \rightarrow K_3[TaF_8]$$

and other complexes with hydrogen peroxide and acetyl acetone, vanadate ions also form complexes with the ions of other acids. Because there is more than one acid unit which condenses, these are called heteropoly acids. They always contain vanadate, molybdate or tungstate ions together with one or more acidic ion (such as phosphate, arsenate or silicate) from about forty elements. The ratio between the numbers of the different types of units is usually 12:1 or 6:1. A study of heteropoly acids is very difficult because the molecular weight is frequently 3000 or more, and the water content is variable. (For further details, see EMELÉUS, H. J. and ANDERSON, J. S., *Modern Aspects of Inorganic Chemistry*, Routledge & Kegan Paul, 1960.)

V, Nb and Ta have odd atomic numbers and are relatively rare elements. They are difficult to extract because of their high melting points and reactivity at high temperatures. Normally an iron/vanadium alloy called ferrovanadium is prepared by a thermite reaction, but pure vanadium can be obtained by reducing VCl_3 with Na or H, VCl_4 with Mg (Kroll process) or by the Van Arkel method (pyrolysis of iodide). All three metals can be obtained by electrolysis of a suitable salt. The metals are passive unless finely divided. V resists attack by alkali and non-oxidizing acids, but dissolves in hydrogen fluoride, concentrated nitric acid and aqua regia. Nb and Ta are more inert, and only dissolve in hydrogen fluoride. Vanadium is used for alloying with steel and is an important catalyst in oxidation reactions such as naphthalene $\rightarrow$ phthalic acid, and toluene $\rightarrow$ benzaldehyde. V_2O_5 is an important catalyst in the manufacture of SO_3 by the contact process. Niobium is used in chromium nickel stainless steel, and because of its unreactivity tantalum is used for making surgical wire and surgical instruments.

Chromium Group (Table 6.8)

TABLE 6.8

Element	Symbol	Electronic structure	Oxidation states*
Chromium	Cr	[Ar] $3d^5\,4s^1$	$-2, -1, 0, 1, 2, 3, 4, 5, 6$
Molybdenum	Mo	[Kr] $4d^5\,5s^1$	$-2,\quad\ 0, 1, 2, 3, 4, 5, 6$
Tungsten	W	[Xe] $4f^{14}, 5d^4\,6s^2$	$-2,\quad\ 0, 1, 2, 3, 4, 5, 6$
Uranium	U	[Rn]$\begin{cases}6d^4\,7s^2\\5f^3\,6d^1\,7s^2\end{cases}$	$2, 3, 4, 5, 6$

* See page 77.

From the electronic structures, chromium and molybdenum might be expected to have oxidation states $+1$ to $+6$, and tungsten and uranium $+2$ to $+6$ inclusive. Whilst chromium ($+3$) is the most stable state, the $+6$ state is the most stable for Mo, W and U; this illustrates the increased stability of higher valencies with increased atomic number. The lower valency states decrease in stability and importance as the atomic size increases. Because of the lanthanide contraction, Mo and W are much the same size and have similar chemistry. It is not quite certain if uranium has any f electrons.

The zero oxidation state arises in metal carbonyls such as $Cr(CO)_6$, $Mo(CO)_6$ and $W(CO)_6$, where the bonding electrons are donated by the CO group. These may be sublimed under reduced pressure, and are soluble in organic solvents. The oxidation state $+1$ expected for the atoms with a d^5s^1 configuration is very uncommon, but tris dipyridyl chromium (I) perchlorate, $[Cr(dipyridyl)_3]^+ClO_4^-$, is known. It is doubtful if Cr^+ exists except when stabilized in a complex. Mo and W form sandwich type structures such as $(C_6H_6)_2Mo^+$ and $C_5H_5MoC_6H_6$ where the metal is in the $+1$ state. Chromous compounds Cr^{2+} are ionic and are well known. They are one of the strongest reducing agents known in aqueous solutions, and are oxidized by air to Cr^{3+}. The $+2$ valency state may be stabilized by forming co-ordination compounds. Chromic compounds Cr^{3+} are the most important and most stable compounds of chromium. They also occur prolifically in co-ordination complexes. Although this oxidation state is very stable in acidic solution, it is easily oxidized to $Cr(+6)$ in alkaline solution. $Cr(+6)$ compounds are very strong oxidizing agents and include chromates and dichromates.

The basic properties decrease with increased oxidation number. Cr^{2+} compounds are ionic and $Cr(OH)_2$ is basic. $Cr(+3)$ compounds ionize to some extent, and Cr_2O_3 is amphoteric, although it is more basic than acidic. $Cr(+6)$ compounds are covalent and CrO_3 is strongly acidic. The basic properties increase with atomic number, and although Cr_2O_3 and $Cr(OH)_3$ are amphoteric, Mo_2O_3 and $Mo(OH)_3$ are basic. $Mo(+3)$ is only formed by strong reducing agents. Molybdenum and tungsten form dioxides MoO_2 and WO_2 which are inert and refractory, but UO_2 dissolves with difficulty in acids which produce $U(+4)$ salts and shows the increase in basic nature.

The oxides in the $+6$ state show a decrease in acid strength from the very strongly acidic CrO_3 to the amphoteric WO_3. The acidic properties of the oxides are shown by their ability to dissolve in alkali to give chromates, molybdates, tungstates or uranates.

$$CrO_3 + 2NaOH \rightarrow 2Na^+ + CrO_4^{2-} + H_2O$$

The corresponding acid H_2CrO_4 is a very strong acid, but in $UO_3 \cdot H_2O$ the acid strength is slight and the oxide forms salts by reacting with acids. The formula is better written $UO_2 \cdot (OH)_2$ and the salts such as uranyl nitrate $UO_2^{2+}(NO_3)_2^-$.

The chromium group have six outer electrons, so they show some similarities with Group VI elements in their higher oxidation states. Thus CrO_4^{2-}, SO_4^{2-} and SeO_4^{2-} all have tetrahedral structures (Fig. 6.3). The similarities are somewhat superficial, however, because the chromate ion shows a strong tendency to condense as the pH falls, and form isopoly acids.

$$CrO_4^{2-} \rightarrow Cr_2O_7^{2-} \rightarrow Cr_3O_{10}^{2-} \rightarrow Cr_4O_{13}^{2-}$$

On acidification molybdate and tungstate solutions yield a considerable number of isopoly acids. These are subdivided into classes of normal, meta and para tungstates or molybdates, whilst UO_4^{2-} units condense up to hexauranates.

Alkali metal tungstates are reduced by heating with hydrogen or tungsten and give blue, purple, red or yellow tungsten bronzes. These are semi-metallic, have a lustre and conduct electricity, but are very inert. Their formula is M_xWO_3, where M is Na or K and x is always less than one. This produces a defective lattice and some of the sites which should be occupied by alkali metals are vacant. It might be thought that for each Na^+ removed from $NaWO_3$, one tungsten would change from $W(+5)$ to $W(+6)$. The properties of the tungsten bronzes are better explained by assuming that all the tungsten atoms are in the $(+6)$ state. The valency electrons from the alkali metals are free to move throughout the lattice as in a metal; hence the electrical conductivity. Lithium also forms bronzes, but these do not conduct electricity.

Heteropoly acids can also be formed by molybdenum and tungsten, where two different types of anion condense together; the most common are phosphate, silicate and borate. The ratio of MoO_3 or WO_3:P, Si or B is

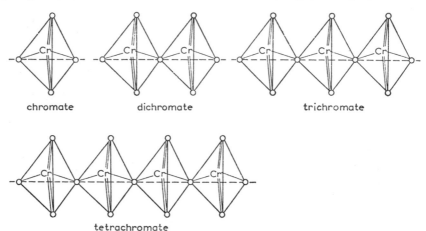

chromate   dichromate   trichromate

tetrachromate

Fig. 6.3

usually $12:1$ or $6:1$, although other ratios are known. The materials are hydrated and have extremely complicated structures.

No hexahalides of chromium are known. However, molybdenum forms MoF_6, tungsten forms WF_6, WCl_6 and WBr_6, and uranium forms UF_6 and UCl_6. The difference in behaviour between Mo and W is surprising in view of their similar sizes. These halides are all volatile, covalent and can be hydrolysed. The volatility of UF_6 was important in the production of the early atomic bombs, because the different rates of diffusion of the hexafluorides of the ^{235}U and ^{238}U isotopes was used to obtain fissile material. All the hexahalides can be prepared by direct union of the elements. The fluorides are colourless, but the chlorides and bromides are coloured.

Oxyhalides of the type MO_2Cl_2 may be formed by dissolving the trioxide in strong acid, or in some cases by the action of strong acids on salts such as dichromates, or by direct addition of the halogens to the dioxide.

$$CrO_3 + 2HCl \xrightarrow[\text{H}_2\text{SO}_4]{\text{Conc.}} CrO_2Cl_2 + H_2O$$

$$K_2Cr_2O_7 + 6HCl \xrightarrow[\text{H}_2\text{SO}_4]{\text{Conc.}} CrO_2Cl_2 + 2KCl + 3H_2O$$

Chromyl chloride CrO_2Cl_2 is a deep red liquid and its formation is used in qualitative analysis to confirm the presence of chloride ions. Chromyl and molybdenyl chlorides are covalent acid chlorides and are readily decomposed by water. Tungstenyl chloride hydrolyses less readily, but uranyl chloride is salt-like, $UO_2^{2+}Cl_2^-$. Uranyl nitrate and uranyl acetate are also ionic.

$$UO_3 + 2HNO_3 \rightarrow UO_2(NO_3)_2 + H_2O$$
$$UO_3 + 2HAc \rightarrow UO_2(Ac)_2 + 2H_2O$$

Uranyl acetate has a tendency to add on an extra acetate group and form a complex ion $[UO_2(Ac)_3]^-$; the formation of a crystalline complex salt $Na^+[UO_2(Ac)_3]^-$ is the usual test for sodium in qualitative analysis.

Chromium differs from Mo, W and U in that its most important oxidation state is $+3$, it is stable to oxidation in acid solution, and exists as simple ions. The sesquioxide Cr_2O_3 is green and is formed by the thermal decomposition of ammonium dichromate in the well-known volcano experiment.

$$(NH_4)_2Cr_2O_7 \rightarrow N_2 + 4H_2O + Cr_2O_3$$

Provided that the oxide has not been too strongly ignited, it dissolves both in strong acids to yield hydrated ions $[Cr(H_2O)_6]^{3+}$ and in alkalis to form chromites CrO_2^- or $Cr(OH)_4^-$.

The trihalides are known both as anhydrous and hydrated salts. Anhydrous $CrCl_3$ and $CrBr_3$ form layer lattices where the two dimensional $(CrX_3)_n$ layers are held together by van der Waals forces (see Chapter 2). Three different compounds of composition $CrCl_3.6H_2O$ have been obtained from aqueous solution and these are an example of hydrate isomerism (see Chapter 8).

$[Cr(H_2O)_6]Cl_3$	Violet
$[Cr(H_2O)_5Cl]Cl_2.H_2O$	Pale green
$[Cr(H_2O)_4Cl_2]Cl.2H_2O$	Dark green

A number of double salts are known, such as chrome alum K_2SO_4 $Cr_2(SO_4)_3.24H_2O$, which crystallizes from mixed solutions of $Cr_2(SO_4)_3$ and K_2SO_4. In solution, mixed salts dissociate completely into simple ions.

A large number of co-ordination complexes of Cr^{3+} are known, such as $[Cr(H_2O)_6]^{3+}$, $[Cr(NH_3)_6]^{3+}$, $[CrCl_6]^{3-}$ and $[Cr(CN)_6]^{3-}$. Complexing occurs with almost any ligand which has a lone pair of electrons to donate to the chromium ion, and forms a co-ordinate bond.

	3d	4s	4p
Electronic structure of chromium atom —ground state	↑ ↑ ↑ ↑ ↑	↑	
Cr^{3+} ion	↑ ↑ ↑		

Cr in $[Cr(NH_3)_6]^{3+}$
where chromium
has gained six lone
pairs from NH_3
molecules (shown
as X).

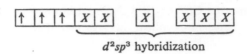

d^2sp^3 hybridization

Most of these complexes have an octahedral shape, the result of d^2sp^3 hybridization.

The metals are hard, have very high melting points and low volatility. Tungsten is the element with the next highest melting point to carbon. The drop in melting point from tungsten to uranium is so far unexplained.

TABLE 6.9

Symbol	Melting point °C	Abundance in earth's crust p.p.m.	Covalent radius Å
Cr	1875	200	1·17
Mo	2610	15	1·29
W	3410	70	1·30
U	1132	4	1·42

Like the vanadium group, these elements (Table 6.9) are unreactive at ordinary temperatures. Chromium dissolves in dilute hydrochloric and sulphuric acids giving Cr^{2+}, molybdenum and tungsten are resistant to acids and uranium reacts to give U(+4) salts. Strong alkali slowly converts chromium to chromites, but the other elements are unaffected, except by fused alkali melts.

At high temperatures reactions occur readily. Chromium forms Cr_2O_3 and CrF_3, and the other elements form complexes of the type MO_3 and MX_6. Sulphides and carbides of varying formulae are produced. Chromium forms a nitride CrN and absorbs hydrogen, whilst molybdenum and tungsten do not appear to do so, although uranium forms UH_3.

The elements have even atomic numbers and are fairly abundant. Chromium is prepared as an alloy by reducing chromite with carbon in an electric furnace, or by reduction of Cr_2O_3 with aluminium. Molybdenum is extracted from the disulphide by conversion to the oxide, followed by reduction with carbon or hydrogen. Tungsten is extracted from its ores by fusion with sodium carbonate. The sodium tungstate is leached out and converted first to the hydrated oxide by acidification and then to the anhydrous oxide by heating. Tungsten is obtained after reduction by carbon or hydrogen.

Chromium is used in electroplating and in making stainless steel. Molybdenum and tungsten alloyed with steel make very hard alloys, and determination of sodium. XeO_4 is a yellow solid, prepared from barium perxenate and anhydrous sulphuric acid:

$$Ba_2XeO_6 + 2H_2SO_4 \rightarrow XeO_4 + 2BaSO_4 + 2H_2O.$$

A fluoride of radon has been formed by heating the elements, but since the most stable isotope of radon has a half-life of 3·5 days, the composition and structure of radon fluoride have not been established.

The nature of the bonds and the orbitals used for bonding in these compounds are of great interest.   There are three possibilities for XeF_2:

(1) An ionic model $F^-Xe^{2+}F^-$, in which the outer shell of xenon contains only six electrons;
(2) A structure involving one-electron bonds, which can be represented by resonance between the forms

$$F—Xe^+F^- \leftrightarrow F^-Xe^+—F$$

In this, the outer shell of xenon would contain eight electrons, and on average there is one bonding electron in between Xe and each F atom.
(3) A covalent model F—Xe—F in which there are ten valency electrons. According to the valence bond theory, an electron in xenon must be unpaired and promoted to a higher energy level in order to form covalent bonds.   It seems improbable that the $6s$ level of xenon is used for bonding, because the observed bond lengths Xe—F are too short; so if these compounds are covalent, the $5d$ level must be used.

The covalent structure (3) accords with the tendency of the fluorides to sublime and hydrolyse, and with interaction force-constant data.   The linear structure of XeF_2 may be explained by sp^3d hybridization which gives a trigonal bipyramid with the three equatorial positions occupied by lone pairs. Similarly, in XeF_4, sp^3d^2 hybridization would give an octahedral structure with two positions occupied by lone pairs; but XeF_6 should have sp^3d^3 hybridization, and this produces a pentagonal bipyramid with one lone pair, i.e. a distorted octahedron.

Perhaps the most satisfactory bonding theory for these compounds is the molecular orbital theory.   Consider XeF_2; the outer electronic configurations of the atoms are

Assume that bonding involves the $5pz$ orbital of xenon and the $2pz$ orbitals of the two fluorine atoms.   These three atomic orbitals combine to give three molybdenum disulphide, MoS_2, is an excellent lubricant.   Uranium is used in nuclear reactors and weapons.   It is radioactive, and has the highest atomic number and highest atomic weight of all the naturally occurring elements.

Manganese Group (Table 6.10)

TABLE 6.10

Element	Symbol	Electronic structure	Oxidation states*
Manganese	Mn	[Ar] $3d^5 4s^2$	$-3, -1, 0, 1, 2, 3, 4, 5, 6, 7$
Technetium	Tc	[Kr] $4d^5 5s^2$	$0, 2, (3), 4, (5), (6), 7$
Rhenium	Re	[Xe] $4f^{14} 5d^5 6s^2$	$-1, 0, 1, 2, 3, 4, 5, 6, 7$

* See page 77.

The electronic structure of manganese suggests that it should have a maximum oxidation state of $+7$, but it exists in numerous lower states as well.   The oxidation states $+2$ and $+3$ are the most common.   Examples are the manganous salts Mn^{2+} and complexes Mn(acetyl acetone)$_3$ and Mn(oxalate)$_3{}^{3-}$.   Manganese dioxide MnO_2 is an example of Mn($+4$), and permanganates such as $KMnO_4$ have an oxidation number of Mn($+7$). Technetium, which does not occur in nature, was the first man-made element. It is radioactive and its chemistry has not been fully studied.   Rhenium shows a similar range of oxidation states to manganese, but the $+7$ state is by far the most common and stable and the lower states, except $+4$, and $+3$ have not been fully investigated.

The increased stability of the higher oxidation states on descending the group is shown since permanganates Mn($+7$) are strong oxidizing agents, whilst perrhenates Re($+7$) are stable.   The decrease in importance of the lower oxidation states is also shown.   The very low oxidation states exist as carbonyl compounds, or substituted carbonyl complexes.

The basic character of any element diminishes with increased oxidation state.   MnO and Mn_2O_3 are basic oxides and are ionic. MnO_2 is amphoteric and does not exist as Mn^{4+} ions.   Mn($+5$) is rather uncommon, but Mn($+6$) is represented by manganates such as $Na_2[MnO_4]$.   This may be regarded as a salt of the unstable acidic oxide MnO_3, which does not exist in the free state.   Mn($+7$) occurs as Mn_2O_7 which is strongly acidic, the corresponding acid, permanganic acid $HMnO_4$ being one of the strongest acids known.

Almost all manganese compounds are coloured, Mn^{2+} is pale pink and the permanganates are intensely coloured.   It is interesting to note that perrhenates, which contain Re($+7$), are colourless.

From the position of technetium in the periodic table, it would be expected that its chemical properties would be intermediate between those of manganese and rhenium. Technetium should resemble rhenium more closely than manganese, because the atomic sizes of technetium and rhenium should be similar on account of the lanthanide contraction, although little is known experimentally. The absence of technetium on the earth might be expected because Mattauch's rule states that if two elements with consecutive atomic numbers have an isotope of the same mass number, the isotopes are never both stable. Technetium is element 43 and the stable isotopes of element 42 (molybdenum) and 44 (ruthenium) are:

42 Mo stable isotopes 92,   94, 95, 96, 97, 98,   100
43 Tc
44 Ru   96,   98, 99, 100, 101, 102,   104.

Technetium could only have a mass number of 93 or 103 and these are too high or too low to be stable.

Manganese is a hard metal, similar to iron. It is an important additive to steel because it removes both oxygen and sulphur and so improves the strength of the final product. Manganese is much more reactive than rhenium, in the same way as, in adjacent groups, chromium is more reactive than tungsten, and iron more reactive than osmium. This decrease in electropositive character is opposite to the trend shown in the main groups of the periodic table. A comparison of some of the reactions of manganese and rhenium is given in Table 6.11.

TABLE 6.11

Reagent	Mn	Re
N_2	Mn_5N_3 formed at 1200°C	No reaction
C	Mn_3C	No reaction
H_2O	$Mn^{2+} + H_2$	No reaction
Dilute acid	$Mn^{2+} + H_2$	No reaction
Strong acid	$Mn^{2+} + H_2$	Dissolves slowly
Halogens	MnX_2 and MnF_3	ReF_6, $ReCl_5$, $ReBr_3$
S	MnS	ReS_2
O_2	Mn_3O_4	Re_2O_7

The oxide Mn_3O_4 is a mixed oxide, $MnOMn_2O_3$, rather like Fe_3O_4.

The manganese group have seven outer electrons, but the relationship to Group VII elements, the halogens, is very slight except in the highest oxidation state. Mn_2O_7 and Cl_2O_7 may be compared; MnO_4^- and ClO_4^- are isomorphous and have similar solubilities, and IO_4^- and ReO_4^- are quite similar. There are much closer similarities between manganese and its horizontal neighbours chromium and iron. The chromates CrO_4^{2-}, manganates MnO_4^{2-} and ferrates FeO_4^{2-} are similar, and the solubilities of the lower oxides are similar; hence the occurrence of iron and manganese together.

When a stable perrhenate $Re(+7)$ is reduced by potassium in a solution of water and ethylene diamine, potassium rhenide is formed. This was formulated $K[Re(H_2O)_4]$ and would therefore contain rhenide ions $Re(-1)$. Recent work suggests that the rhenide ion is a hydride species such as $[ReH_8]^{2-}$ or $[Re_2H_{16}]^{4-}$.

The zero valent state exists as the carbonyls $[Mn_2(CO)_{10}]$ and $[Re_2(CO)_{10}]$ and as a co-ordination complex $K_6[Mn(CN)_6].2NH_3$ which is unstable and highly reducing.

$Mn(+1)$ and $Re(+1)$ are only obtained with difficulty and are strongly reducing.

$$K_3[Mn^{III}(CN)_6] \xrightarrow{\text{K in liquid NH}_3} K_5[Mn^I(CN)_6]$$

$$[Re_2(CO)_{10}] \xrightarrow{\text{Cl}_2 \text{ under pressure}} 2[Re^I(CO)_5Cl]$$

Mn^{2+} ions are pink and are formed by dissolving the metal in acid, or by reducing higher oxidation states. Mn^{2+} has an electronic configuration $3d^5$ which corresponds to a half-filled d shell. Thus Mn^{2+} is more stable than other divalent ions and is more difficult to oxidize than Cr^{2+} or Fe^{2+}. Mn^{2+} can form co-ordination complexes which may be oxidized or reduced to the $+3$ and $+1$ states which are normally unstable in solution, but are stable when present as complexes.

$$[Mn(CN)_6]^{5-} \xleftarrow{\text{Zn reduction}} [Mn(CN)_6]^{4-} \xrightarrow{\text{air oxidation}} [Mn(CN)_6]^{3-}$$
$$Mn(+1) \qquad\qquad Mn(+2) \qquad\qquad Mn(+3)$$

$Re(+2)$ is not ionic, and $Re(pyridine)_2Cl_2$ has been resolved into *cis* and *trans* isomers which indicate that it is square planar rather than tetrahedral.

Mn^{3+} is a weak oxidizing agent and is much less stable than Mn^{2+} (which has enhanced stability due to the d^5 configuration). A number of Mn^{3+} salts are known, e.g. MnF_3 and $Mn_2(SO_4)_3$. These disproportionate in acid and hydrolyse in water.

$$Mn_3O_4 \xleftarrow{\text{water}} Mn^{3+} \xrightarrow{\text{acid}} Mn^{2+} + MnO_2$$

Thus $Mn(+3)$ can only exist in aqueous solution as part of a complex, such as $[MnCl_4]^-$ and $[Mn(CN)_6]^{3-}$. $[Mn(oxalate)_3]^{3-}$ is thermally unstable and decomposes at about 60°C, which explains why permanganate/oxalate titrations are performed hot. $Re(+3)$ is neither ionic nor simple, the trichloride is $(ReCl_3)_2$ and resembles $(FeCl_3)_2$ and $(AlCl_3)_2$

Mn($+4$) exists only in complex ions such as $[MnF_6]^{2-}$ and MnO_2. The catalytic activity of MnO_2 in the preparation of oxygen from $KClO_3$ is due to the formation of intermediate compounds. Re($+4$) forms ReF_4, ReO_2 and complexes such as the chlororhenates $[ReCl_6]^{2-}$ which are well known.

The oxidation state $+5$ is not common. If MnO_2 is fused with alkali and oxidized, the green coloured manganate ion $[MnO_4]^{2-}$, which contains Mn($+6$) is formed. This is unstable except in strongly alkaline solution, and on dilution or acidification it disproportionates into Mn($+4$) and Mn($+7$) permanganate.

$$3MnO_4{}^{2-} + 4H^+ \rightarrow MnO_2 + 2MnO_4{}^-$$

The rhenates ($+6$) are even less stable than the manganates, though ReF_6 and ReO_3 do occur.

Mn($+7$) is not common, but potassium permanganate, $KMnO_4$ is widely used as an oxidizing agent in both preparative and analytical chemistry. In titrations $MnO_4{}^-$ is reduced to Mn^{2+} in acid solution, whilst in alkaline solution MnO_2 is formed. Thus the equivalent weight depends on the pH. The purple colour of $MnO_4{}^-$ acts as indicator. Because $KMnO_4$ is not a primary standard, does not store well, and its use in the presence of hydrochloric acid involves complications, it has been partly replaced by other agents. Whilst permanganates can be made by acidifying manganates, better yields are obtained by electrolytic oxidation or oxidation with hypochlorite. Re($+7$) occurs as Re_2O_7, which on neutralizing with KOH gives normal colourless perrhenates $KReO_4$, but heating the metal or lower oxides with alkali and an oxidizing agent gives red or yellow coloured mesoperrhenates such as K_3ReO_5. The meso compound is hydrolysed to the normal perrhenate in neutral solution. Unlike the permanganates which lose oxygen on heating, perrhenates are thermally stable. In alkaline solution $ReO_4{}^-$ is stable, but in acid solution it is a weak oxidizing agent, and is converted to ReO_2.

Manganese is quite abundant (1000 p.p.m. of the earth's crust) much more so than is usually found among elements with odd atomic numbers. Technetium does not occur in nature and there are no ores of rhenium. Pure manganese may be obtained by reducing MnO_2 or Mn_3O_4 with aluminium, reducing the chloride with sodium or electrolysing $MnCl_2$. There is little use for the pure metal, but in the steel industry, alloys are produced from mixtures of iron and manganese oxides in a blast furnace. Rhenium has little commercial use.

Iron, Cobalt and Nickel Groups

Iron	Fe	Cobalt	Co	Nickel	Ni
Ruthenium	Ru	Rhodium	Rh	Palladium	Pd
Osmium	Os	Iridium	Ir	Platinum	Pt

The elements will be considered first in vertical groups: Fe, Ru, Os; Co, Rh, Ir and Ni, Pd, Pt.   However, the horizontal similarities between these elements are greater than anywhere else in the periodic table except among the lanthanides.   As a consequence of the lanthanide contraction, the second and third rows of transition elements are much alike, so that the horizontal similarities of the ferrous metals Fe, Co and Ni and the platinum metals Ru, Rh, Pd, Os, Ir and Pt can also be summarized.

Iron Group (Table 6.12)

TABLE 6.12

Element	Electronic structure	Oxidation states*
Fe	[Ar] $3d^6\,4s^2$	$-2,\ 0,\ (1),\ 2,\ 3,\ 4,\ 5,\ 6$
Ru	[Kr] $4d^7\,5s^1$	$(-2),\ 0,\ (1),\ 2,\ 3,\ 4,\ 5,\ 6,\ 7,\ 8$
Os	[Xe] $4f^{14}\,5d^6\,6s^2$	$0,\ \ \ \ \ 2,\ 3,\ 4,\ 5,\ 6,\ (7),\ 8$

* See page 77.

Iron has a maximum oxidation number of $+6$, whilst ruthenium and osmium have $+8$ states; this illustrates the trend to higher valent states on descending the group.

The basic properties decrease with increased oxidation number.   Thus ferrous oxide FeO is basic, Fe_3O_4 which is really a mixed oxide $Fe^{II}Fe_2^{III}O_4$ is also basic, but ferric oxide Fe_2O_3, though mainly basic, will react with alkali to give ferrites.   It is therefore amphoteric.

$$Fe_2O_3 + Na_2CO_3 \xrightarrow{\text{Fused}} 2NaFeO_2 + CO_2$$

Ferrites hydrolyse with water to form sodium hydroxide, and this property was used in the now obsolete Lowig process for caustic soda.   Higher oxides such as FeO_2, FeO_3 and Fe_2O_5 have been reported, but their existence is doubtful. FeO_3 has not been isolated, but its salts, the ferrates (e.g. $BaFeO_4$) are known, and this fact indicates that the oxide would be acidic.   The ferrates contain Fe($+6$) and the FeO_4^{2-} ion is an even stronger oxidizing agent than permanganate, and will oxidize ammonia to nitrogen and Cr^{3+} to chromate.

$$Fe_2O_3 + Na_2O_2 \rightarrow Na_2FeO_4$$
$$Fe(OH)_3 + NaOCl + Ba(OH)_2 \rightarrow BaFeO_4$$

The oxides are all in fact non-stoichiometric.

The elements show their greatest similarity in the $+6$ state, and on fusion with KOH and KNO_3 they give ferrates FeO_4^{2-} ruthenates RuO_4^{2-} and osmates OsO_4^{2-}. The stability of the +6 state decreases in the periodic table:

$$CrO_4^{2-} > MnO_4^{2-} > FeO_4^{2-} \gg CoO_4^{2-}.$$

The reactivity of the metals decreases with increasing atomic number, as illustrated by their lack of reaction with water and dilute acid (see Table 6.13).

TABLE 6.13

Reagent	Fe	Ru	Os
O_2	Fe_3O_4 at 500°C Fe_2O_3 at higher temp.	RuO_2 at 500°C	OsO_4 at 200°C
S	FeS FeS_2 with excess	RuS_2	OsS_2
F	FeF_3	RuF_5	OsF_6
Cl	$FeCl_3$	$RuCl_3$	$OsCl_4$
H_2O	Rusts slowly Fe_3O_4 formed at red heat	No reaction	No reaction
Dilute HCl	$Fe^{2+} + H_2$	No reaction	No reaction
Dilute HNO_3	$Fe^{3+} + H_2$	No reaction	No reaction
Aqua regia	Passive	No reaction	OsO_4

The zero valent state occurs in the carbonyls, e.g. $Fe(CO)_5$, $Fe_2(CO)_9$ and $Fe_3(CO)_{12}$, where the bonding electrons all come from the carbon monoxide. Iron is predominantly di- and trivalent. Pale green ferrous salts containing Fe^{2+} are well known, particularly $FeSO_4.7H_2O$. Ferrous compounds are reducing agents, and so are difficult to obtain pure. However, the double salt $FeSO_4.(NH_4)_2.SO_4.6H_2O$ is used in volumetric analysis for titrations with dichromate, permanganate and ceric solutions. Ferrous ions form complexes, perhaps the most important being haemoglobin, the red pigment in blood. Ferrocyanides $[Fe(CN)_6]^{4-}$ can be made by the action of a soluble cyanide on a ferrous salt, and are used in analytical chemistry to precipitate certain metals, for example: copper as the red-brown $Cu_2[Fe(CN)_6]$. Potassium ferrocyanide is used to test for iron, when ferrous ions give a white precipitate of $K_2Fe^{II}[Fe(CN)_6]$. In the presence of air, this precipitate is often pale blue, because of a partial oxidation to prussian blue, which is formed with ferric ions $KFe^{III}[Fe(CN)_6]$. Ferrous ions form a brown complex which is sometimes formulated as $Fe(NO)^{2+}$ in the brown-ring test for nitrates and nitrites. A red coloration, which is due to the complex cation $[Fe(orthophenanthroline)_3]^{2+}$, is formed when ortho-phenanthroline

is mixed with ferrous ions, and is used colorimetrically to determine iron.

Ferric (+3) salts are obtained by oxidizing the corresponding Fe(+2) compounds, or by dissolving $Fe(OH)_3$ in acid. Ferric compounds are less ionized than ferrous, hence $Fe(OH)_3$ is a weaker base than $Fe(OH)_2$, and Fe(+3) is in fact amphoteric. Moreover FeF_3 in solution does not give a positive test for either Fe^{3+} or F^-. Ferric solutions are frequently yellow-brown, but the colour is due to the presence of colloidal iron oxide or basic salts. The anhydrous salts show a variety of colours. Anhydrous $FeCl_3$ is brown. It sublimes and exists as the dimer in the gas, but in solutions, such as ether and water, which are electron donors, the monomer exists. The ordinary yellow solid is the hexahydrate.

Ferric chloride is used as an oxidizing agent and as a mordant in dying. The most important double salts are the alums, ferric ammonium alum $Fe_2(SO_4)_3 . (NH_4)_2SO_4 . 24H_2O$ and potash alum $Fe_2(SO_4)_3 . K_2SO_4 . 24H_2O$, which are also used as mordants. Fe^{3+} complexes with cyanide ions to form the ferricyanide ion $[Fe(CN)_6]^{3-}$. If a solution of a ferrous salt is treated with potassium ferricyanide, a dark blue precipitate is formed.

$$Fe^{2+} + [Fe^{III}(CN)_6]^{3-} \rightarrow Fe^{3+} + [Fe^{II}(CN)_6]^{4-}$$
$$\downarrow$$
$$KFe^{III}[Fe^{II}(CN)_6]$$
$$\text{or}$$
$$Fe_4{}^{III}[Fe^{II}(CN)_6]_3$$

The deep red complex ion $Fe(SCN)^{2+}$ formed by Fe^{3+} and SCN^- is also important in analysis, and the oxalate complex $[Fe(oxalate)_3]^{3-}$ is important in the removal of rust stains by oxalic acid.

Fe(+4) exists in K_2FeO_3 and Fe(+5) in K_3FeO_4. Both are formed by heating ferric oxide with potassium oxide or superoxide in oxygen. Fe(+6) occurs as the ferrates which contain the red coloured $FeO_4{}^{2-}$ ion in which iron shows its maximum valency. Ferrates are produced by oxidizing $Fe(+3)$ either with NaOCl or electrolytically. They are stronger oxidizing agents than permanganates, decompose to $Fe(+3)$ and oxygen in neutral solution, but are stable in alkaline solution.

Ruthenium shows all oxidation states from 0 to $+8$. The most important valencies are $+2$, $+3$ and $+4$. Whereas $Fe(+3)$ exists as ions but is more stable when covalent, $Ru(+3)$ does not form simple ionic salts, nor does it form alums. $Ru(+6)$ exists as ruthenates $RuO_4{}^{2-}$, which are similar to the ferrates and manganates. Unlike iron, ruthenium forms a $(+7)$ state exemplified by the perruthenates $RuO_4{}^-$, which are oxidizing and like the permanganates. They are converted to ruthenates by alkali, but perruthenates are reformed on acidification. $Ru(+8)$ is known as the unstable and highly oxidizing RuO_4. Ruthenium shows a strong tendency to form complexes. $[Ru(CN)_6]^{4-}$ resembles the ferrocyanides; complex halide ions, such as $[RuCl_5]^{2-}$ and $[RuCl_6]^{2-}$, and many ammines such as $[Ru(NH_3)_6]^{3+}$ are known.

Osmium shows oxidation states from $+2$ to $+8$, but the main valencies are $+4$ and $+6$, though the $+8$ state is fairly well known. A characteristic of osmium is the ease with which OsO_4 is formed. This is strongly oxidizing and is reduced readily by dust or grease to OsO_2. The $(+6)$ state exists as the osmates $[OsO_4]^{2-}$, which are less stable than the ferrates or ruthenates. OsF_6 is the maximum valency shown in the halides. The lower valency states do not occur as simple ionic salts. Osmium forms many co-ordination compounds including cyanides, ammines and nitrosyl compounds. The metal is an extremely good catalyst, though it is easily poisoned.

The rusting of iron is of practical importance, and is a special case of corrosion. Oxygen and either a high humidity or the presence of water seem to be necessary for rusting to occur at room temperature. A simplified explanation of the very complex process is that ferrous ions are formed from iron atoms, and the electrons thus liberated move to a more noble metal which is present as impurity in the iron, or in contact with it. The electrons discharge hydrogen ions and the hydrogen so formed reacts with atmospheric oxygen.

$$Fe \rightarrow Fe^{2+} + 2 \text{ electrons}$$
$$2H^+ + 2 \text{ electrons} \rightarrow 2H + \tfrac{1}{2}O_2 \rightarrow H_2O$$

The iron is therefore positive; that is, it forms the anode and the noble metal, the cathode. Subsequently the ferrous ions are oxidized to Fe_2O_3 or Fe_3O_4. The resultant oxide does not form a protective film, and so the corrosion continues. Oxygen, water or the impurities must be excluded to prevent corrosion. In practice, corrosion is prevented by giving the iron a protective coating. This may be done by dipping it in molten zinc, coating it with zinc by electrolysis, or Sherardizing, painting it with red lead or converting the outer layer of iron into ferrous phosphate by the Parkerizing and Bonderizing processes.

Iron normally dissolves in dilute acids liberating hydrogen, and in accordance with its position in the electrochemical series it displaces copper from solution. Iron loses these properties after immersion in concentrated nitric acid and is said to be passive. This resistance to chemical attack is derived from the formation of a protective oxide layer on the surface, but if this layer is scratched, the exposed metal is once again vulnerable to chemical attack. Certain metals and alloys such as aluminium and stainless steel can automatically use atmospheric oxygen to repair such damage to the film.

Ruthenium and osmium metals are very resistant to attack by acids, osmium being oxidized to OsO_4 by aqua regia.

Iron is the fourth most abundant element in the earth's crust and occurs to the extent of 50,000 p.p.m. Ruthenium and osmium are present in trace amounts of about 10^{-3} p.p.m.

The effect of the lanthanide contraction is less pronounced in this part of the periodic table; hence extremely close similarities are not expected (see Table 6.14).

TABLE 6.14

Element	Ionic radius M^{2+} Å	Ionic radius M^{3+} Å	Covalent radius Å	Density gcm³
Fe	0·76	0·64	1·17	7·9
Ru	0·81	0·72	1·24	12·2
Os	0·88	0·78	1·26	22·6

The close horizontal similarities in the ferrous metals and platinum metals is largely due to their similar sizes, for example: Fe^{2+} 0·76 Å, Co^{2+} 0·74 Å, Ni^{2+} 0·73 Å. Because osmium is only a little larger than ruthenium, it would be expected to have a much higher density and indeed it is the most dense element known.

Iron is extracted from its oxides by reduction with carbon and carbon monoxide in a blast furnace, to give pig-iron which is very hard and brittle, and contains 4% carbon. Carbon is removed either by heating with air in a Bessemer converter, open hearth furnace or electric furnace or by heating with oxygen in the more modern Kaldo and L. D. processes. A good review on iron and steel making is given by Thomas, R. W. Education in Chemistry, 1965, **4**, 167. Wrought iron has had all the carbon removed and is malleable. Usually the correct amount of carbon is added to give steel of varying properties: 0·15–0·3%C mild steel, 0·3–0·6%C medium steel, 0·6–0·8%C high carbon steel and 0·8–1·4%C tool steel. The production of alloys containing small amounts of V, Cr, Mo, W or Mn gives steels with special properties for particular purposes.

Cobalt Group (Table 6.15)

TABLE 6.15

Element	Symbol	Electronic structure	Oxidation states*
Cobalt	Co	[Ar] $3d^7 4s^2$	-1, 0, (1), 2, 3, 4, (5)
Rhodium	Rh	[Kr] $4d^8 5s^1$	-1, 0, **1**, 2, 3, 4,
Iridium	Ir	[Xe] $4f^{14} 5d^9$	0, 1, 2, 3, 4, 5, 6

* See page 77.

The majority of cobalt compounds are in the $+2$ and $+3$ states. Rhodium shows a marked preference for the $+1$ and $+3$ states, and nearly all its compounds are in these states, whilst iridium is most stable in the $+3$ and $+4$ states. Cobalt is harder than iron. Rhodium and iridium are also hard metals. Cobalt is a reactive metal, slightly less so than iron. Rhodium and iridium are much less reactive and are resistant to acids, but react with oxygen and the halogens on heating. The increased stability of higher oxidation states is shown both by the existence of a $+6$ state for iridium, and by the change in the most common valency state. Cobalt forms simple ionic compounds in the lower valency states, but these are uncommon for rhodium and iridium. All three elements form a large number of co-ordination compounds. Some reactions are given in Table 6.16.

TABLE 6.16

Reagent	Co	Rh	Ir
O_2	Co_3O_4	Rh_2O_3 at 600°C	IrO_2 at 1000°C
F	CoF_2 and CoF_3	RhF_3 at 600°C	IrF_6
Cl	$CoCl_2$	$RhCl_3$ at 400°C	$IrCl_3$ at 600°C
H_2O	No reaction	No reaction	No reaction
Dilute HCl or HNO_3	$Co^{2+} + H_2$	No reaction	No reaction
Conc HNO_3	Passive	No reaction	No reaction

The -1 oxidation state is found in the complexes $Co(CO)_3NO$, $Co(CO)_4^-$ and $Rh(CO)_4^-$. The zero oxidation state occurs in the carbonyls $Co_2(CO)_8$ and $Co_4(CO)_{12}$ and in the corresponding rhodium and iridium compounds. $Co(+1)$ exists in a few co-ordination compounds. $Rh(+1)$ for example, RhCl and Rh_2O are very unstable, and all the $Ir(+1)$ halides are known. They are reasonably stable but disproportionate with water to give $Ir(+3)$.

Simple cobalt compounds contain Co^{2+}, which is pink when hydrated, but turns blue when warmed. Cobalt chloride $CoCl_2$ is blue when anhydrous and is used to test for water. The majority of cobaltous $Co(+2)$ compounds are soluble and $Co(OH)_2$ is basic. Co^{2+} forms co-ordination compounds such as $[CoCl_4]^{2-}$ and $[CoBr_4]^{2-}$ which are tetrahedral. The majority have a co-ordination number of six and are octahedral; examples are $[Co(H_2O)_6]^{2+}$ and $[Co(NH_3)_6]^{2+}$. Rhodium and iridium occur in the $+2$ state, as $RhCl_2$, iridium halides, and IrS, but these are covalent structures. Complexes such as $K_4[Ir^{II}(CN)_6]$ are known.

Simple Co^{3+} salts are difficult to make since Co^{3+} is a strong oxidizing agent, which liberates oxygen from water. CoF_3 is commonly used as a fluorinating agent. This rather unstable oxidation state becomes completely stable when a co-ordination complex is formed. The chemistry of $Co(+3)$ is largely that of its co-ordination compounds. In contrast to the difficulty in preparing simple Co^{3+} ions, Co^{3+} complexes may be produced easily, either by aerial oxidation of Co^{2+} in the presence of appropriate ligands, or by substituting ligands in an existing complex. There are almost always six ligands in an octahedral arrangement, the ligands including CN^-, NH_3, amines, water, $C_2O_4^{2-}$, CO_3^{2-}, OH^-, Cl^-, Br^-, I^- and many others. Some common complexes are listed below with their colours. It can be seen that the cobalt may form either a positive or a negative complex ion, or an electrically neutral non-electrolyte complex.

$[Co(NH_3)_6]^{3+}$	yellow
$[Co(NH_3)_5.H_2O]^{3+}$	pink
$[Co(NH_3)_5Cl]^{2+}$	purple
$[Co(NH_3)_4CO_3]^+$	purple
$[Co(NH_3)_3(NO_2)_3]$	yellow
$[Co(CN)_6]^{3-}$	violet
$[Co(NO_2)_6]^{3-}$	yellow

Cobalt $(+3)$ forms more complexes than any other element. Rhodium $(+3)$ is not ionic and RhF_3 is more stable than CoF_3. Iridium $(+3)$ is fairly easily oxidized to $Ir(+4)$.

$Co(+4)$ is known in the complex $K_2[Co^{IV}O_3]$ and CoO_2 may be known. RhF_4 and IrO_2 are known and complexes like $K_2[RhCl_6]$ and $K_2[IrCl_6]$ resemble the hexachloroplatinates $K_2[PtCl_6]$.

The $(+5)$ state is known for iridium in $K[Ir^VF_6]$. $Co(+6)$ does not exist, $Rh(+6)$ has not been established, but $Ir(+6)$ is well known as IrF_6, IrO_3, IrS_3, $IrSe_3$ and $IrTe_3$.

Cobalt has an odd atomic number and only occurs to the extent of 23 p.p.m. in the earth's crust, whilst rhodium and iridium are present only as traces. Cobalt is extracted by converting sulphide or arsenide ores to the oxide, and reducing with hydrogen or charcoal. The metal forms important alloys with steel, and is used in the manufacture of cutting tools and magnets. The oxide is used as a blue pigment in the ceramic industry. Cobalt is an essential constituent in fertile soil and is present in vitamin B_{12}.

Nickel Group (Table 6.17)

TABLE 6.17

Element	Symbol	Electronic structure	Oxidation states*
Nickel	Ni	[Ar] $3d^8 4s^2$	0, (1), 2, 3, 4
Palladium	Pd	[Kr] $4d^{10}$	0, 2, 3, 4
Platinum	Pt	[Xe] $4f^{14} 5d^9 6s^1$	0, 2, 3, 4, 5, 6

* See page 77.

Nickel is much more reactive than the other two metals, but it is less reactive than iron and cobalt towards acids and oxygen. This fact accounts for its use in electroplating iron. The main valency is +2 and it is ionic. Palladium is much less reactive, but is more readily attacked by acids, oxygen and the halogens than are ruthenium and rhodium. The main valency is +2 which is not ionic, but the +4 state is also important. Compared with osmium and iridium, platinum is reactive towards acids, and forms hexachloroplatinic acid $H_2[PtCl_6]$ readily with aqua regia, but is hardly affected by oxygen. The +2 and +4 states are the most important, the +4 state is more stable than that of palladium, and a few +5 and +6 compounds such as PtF_5 and PtF_6, are known.

Despite the importance of the +2 state in all three metals, the trend to greater stability of higher valency states is shown by the increase in the maximum oxidation state from +4 to +6, and by the increased importance of the +4 state. The usual decrease in simple ionic forms with increased atomic number is also observed.

All three metals are important catalysts, and all form a large number of co-ordination complexes. Some reactions are given in Table 6.18.

TABLE 6.18

Reagent	Ni	Pd	Pt
O_2	NiO	PdO at red heat	PtO at high temp. and pressure
F_2	NiF_2	PdF_3 at 500°C	PtF_4 at red heat
Cl_2	$NiCl_2$	$PdCl_2$	$PtCl_2$
H_2O	No action	No action	No action
Dilute HCl or HNO_3	$Ni^{2+} + H_2$	Dissolves very slowly	No action
Concentrated HNO_3	Passive	Dissolves	No action
Aqua regia	Passive	Dissolves	$H_2[PtCl_6]$

The zero valent state is found in nickel palladium and platinum. A complex $K_4[Ni(CN)_4]$ and the tetracarbonyl $Ni(CO)_4$ are known; the latter is important in the recovery of nickel.

$Ni(+1)$ is best known as $K_2[Ni(CN)_3]$, which is probably dimerized.

The $+2$ state is the most important and stable in all three elements. The green colour of divalent nickel is due to the ion $[Ni(H_2O)_6]^{2+}$. Many anhydrous nickel salts are yellow, but the colour deepens as the negative ion becomes less electronegative, and $NiBr_2$ is yellow whilst NiI_2 is black. Double salts with alkali metals and ammonium are known, for example, $NiSO_4.(NH_4)_2SO_4.6H_2O$. These are isomorphous with the corresponding double salts of iron, cobalt, magnesium and other bivalent metals. $Ni(+2)$ forms many complexes, and these can be reduced to $Ni(+1)$ complexes, but are difficult to oxidize to $Ni(+3)$ complexes. This behaviour is the opposite of the behaviour of $Co(+2)$ and $Fe(+2)$ complexes.

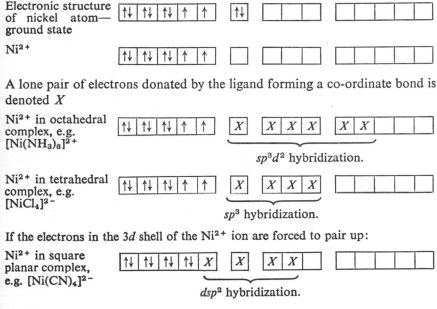

$Ni(+2)$ complexes may have an octahedral, tetrahedral or square planar structure, depending on the number of ligands and the orbitals used.

Which one of these is formed depends largely on the nature of the ligand,

and the ligand field theory is discussed later. An easy method of distinguishing between the tetrahedral and square planar complexes is their magnetic behaviour. The tetrahedral complexes have two unpaired electrons and are therefore paramagnetic, whilst the square planar ones are diamagnetic. The tetrahedral complexes are usually blue or green, and the square planar complexes red, brown or yellow. An important complex is formed with dimethylglyoxime. The red-coloured nickel bis-(dimethylglyoxime) molecule, which is electrically neutral, is precipitated from slightly ammoniacal solution and is used both to detect and estimate nickel. The complex molecule is a chelate (ring compound) and chelation stabilizes complexes. The hydrogen bonding, indicated by dotted lines, further stabilizes the complex.

$$2 \quad \begin{array}{c} CH_3-C=N \\ | \\ | \\ CH_3-C=N \end{array} \begin{array}{c} \diagup OH \\ \\ \\ \diagdown OH \end{array} \quad + Ni^{2+} \rightarrow \quad \begin{array}{c} CH_3-C=N \\ | \\ | \\ CH_3-C=N \end{array} \begin{array}{c} O\cdots HO \\ \diagup \quad \diagdown \\ Ni \\ \diagdown \quad \diagup \\ OH\cdots O \end{array} \begin{array}{c} N=C-CH_3 \\ | \\ | \\ N=C-CH_3 \end{array} \quad + 2H^+$$

When nickel cyanide is crystallized from a mixture containing ammonia and benzene, benzene ammino nickel cyanide is formed. The benzene molecules are not bonded, but are trapped in the cagework of the crystal. Such compounds are called clathrates and other molecules of a similar size may be trapped in a similar way. Palladium and platinum exist in the $+2$ state as halides, sulphates, nitrates and oxides, but the anhydrous solids are generally not ionic. PdF_2 is apparently ionic but $PdCl_2$ forms a linear polymer in the solid state.

$$\begin{array}{ccccccc} & Cl & & Cl & & Cl & & Cl \\ \diagup & & \diagdown \diagup & & \diagdown \diagup & & \diagdown \diagup \\ Pd & & Pd & & Pd & & Pd \\ & \diagdown \diagup & & \diagdown \diagup & & \diagdown \diagup & \\ & Cl & & Cl & & Cl & & Cl \end{array}$$

In aqueous solution $[Pd(H_2O)_4]^{2+}$ may be present, and in hydrochloric acid $[PdCl_4]^{2-}$ is formed. Ammines are also well known $[Pd(NH_3)_4]^{2+}$ and $[Pd(NH_3)_2X_2]$. A very large number of co-ordination compounds of platinum are known, including halide and ammine complexes, e.g. $[PtCl_4]^{2-}$, $[PtCl_3NH_3]^-$, $[Pt(NH_3)_4]^{2+}$, $[Pt(NH_3)_3Cl]^+$, $[Pt(NH_3)_2Cl_2]$. These complexes of $Pd(+2)$ and $Pt(+2)$ are all square planar.

Only a few $+3$ compounds are known, such as $Ni_2O_3.(H_2O)_n$, PdF_3 and $PtCl_3$. The stability of the $+4$ state increases from $Ni \rightarrow Pd \rightarrow Pt$. $NiO_2.(H_2O)_n$ is formed in an Edison nife battery, and although complexes such as $K_2[NiF_6]$ and $H_2[PdCl_6]$ are known, they are unstable. All the halides PtX_4 are known, and PtO_2 is amphoteric, and gives $[Pt(OH)_6]^{2-}$

with alkali.   Platinized platinum, or platinum black electrodes are often used for conductivity measurements, and are made by electrolysing hexachloro platinates $[PtCl_6]^{2-}$.   Platinum is unusual in that it forms alkyl derivatives by a Grignard reaction.

$$PtCl_4 + CH_3MgI \rightarrow (CH_3)_3PtI$$

Reaction of the trimethyl derivative with sodium methyl gives the tetra alkyl derivative.

$$(CH_3)_3PtI + NaCH_3 \rightarrow (CH_3)_4Pt$$

Both of these derivatives are stable and soluble in organic solvents, and they exist as tetramers in the solid state.   The $+5$ state is represented by PtF_5, and the compounds PtO_3 and PtF_6 are the only examples of the $+6$ state which are known to exist for certain.

The extraction of nickel is complicated by its occurrence in association with iron and copper.   Sulphide ores are converted to oxides, reduced to the metal by water gas, and then treated with carbon monoxide.   Nickel then forms the volatile carbonyl $Ni(CO)_4$, which is decomposed to give pure nickel.   The formation and pyrolysis of the carbonyl is the basis of the Mond process.

$$Ni + CO \underset{180°C}{\overset{60-80°C}{\rightleftharpoons}} Ni(CO)_4$$

Nickel forms important alloys with steel, copper and aluminium.   It improves both the strength of the steel and its resistance to chemical attack. Nickel is extensively used as a base metal in its own right.   Certain alloys such as the Nimonic series (75% Ni with Cr, Co, Al and Ti) are used in gas turbine and jet engines where they are subjected to high stresses and high temperatures, whilst others such as Hastelloy C are used for their corrosion resistance.

Horizontal Comparisons in the Iron, Cobalt and Nickel Groups

The ferrous metals Fe, Co and Ni show horizontal similarities and differ from the platinum metals in that they are much more reactive, the reactivity decreases Fe $\rightarrow$ Co $\rightarrow$ Ni.   Although the maximum oxidation states are Fe($+6$), Co($+4$) and Ni($+4$), they rarely exceed a valency of $+3$.   The tendency to trivalency decreases across the period. Fe^{3+} is the usual state but Co^{3+} is a strong oxidizing agent unless complexed, and nickel is divalent in all its simple compounds.   The lower valency states exist as simple ions. The elements are relatively abundant.

The platinum metals Ru, Rh, Pd and Os, Ir, Pt are much more noble than the ferrous metals, and are little affected by acids.   The reactivity of the metals increases from Ru → Pd and Os → Pt, which is the opposite of the trend in the ferrous metals.   The halogens react at high temperatures only and bring out the higher valencies, e.g. OsF_6, IrF_6, PtF_6.   The lower valency states are unstable except in complexes, and few simple ions exist.   Because of the lanthanide contraction, the second and third rows of transition elements are similar.   Since their atomic volumes are almost the same, the densities of Os, Ir and Pt are almost double the values for Ru, Rh and Pd.   All six elements are rare.

Both the ferrous metals and the platinum metals are typical transition elements, and are characterized by coloured compounds, variable valency, catalytic properties and an ability to form co-ordination compounds.   The differences between the two groups, namely increased stability of higher oxidation states, disappearance of simple ionic forms and increased nobility, are the normal changes expected in a vertical group.

Copper Group (Currency Metals)

TABLE 6.19

Element	Symbol	Electronic structure	Oxidation states*
Copper	Cu	$[Ar]\ \ 3d^{10}\,4s^1$	1, **2**, 3
Silver	Ag	$[Kr]\ \ 4d^{10}\,5s^1$	**1**, 2, 3
Gold	Au	$[Xe]\ \ 4f^{14}\,5d^{10}\,6s^1$	1, (2), **3**

* See page 77.

The atoms of these metals (Table 6.19) have one *s* electron in their outer orbital, but differ from Group I elements in that the penultimate shell has ten *d* electrons.   Apart from the high electrical conductivity of both groups, there are few similarities.   Group I metals, which are at the top of the electrochemical series, are the most reactive in the periodic table, whilst the currency metals are unreactive and conclude the electrochemical series. The nobility increases from Cu → Ag → Au.   For metals to react, first an atom must be removed, then ionized.   A high heat of sublimation and a high ionization potential will reduce reactivity, though this may be partly offset by the energy gained when the ion is hydrated.   Comparing copper and potassium, copper has a much higher melting point (hence a higher heat of sublimation), and because of the increased nuclear charge in copper, the orbital electrons are more tightly held (hence a higher ionization potential). The heat of hydration cannot offset these large amounts of energy, and so potassium is much more reactive than copper.   Group I oxides and hydroxides are strongly basic, and are soluble in water, although the copper group form insoluble weakly basic oxides. Compounds of the sodium group all contain simple colourless univalent ions and only form complexes with very strong complexing agents. The copper group elements show variable valency, the most common oxidation states being $Cu(+2)$, $Ag(+1)$ and $Au(+3)$. Their compounds are mainly coloured and they show a strong tendency to form co-ordination complexes.

In the $+1$ state most of the simple compounds and complexes are colourless, as a consequence of the d^{10} configuration with a complete electronic shell. Cu_2O is a notable exception and is red. It might be expected that the $+1$ state would be the most common and most stable because of the extra stability resulting from a full d shell. Although Ag^+ is stable in both the solid state and solution, Cu^+ and Au^+ disproportionate in water.

$$2Cu^+ \rightleftarrows Cu^{2+} + Cu \quad K = \frac{[Cu^{2+}]}{[Cu^+]^2} = 1.6 \times 10^6$$

$$3Au^+ \rightleftarrows Au^{3+} + 2Au \quad K = \frac{[Au^{3+}]}{[Au^+]^3} = 1 \times 10^{10}$$

From the equilibrium constants it is obvious that in solution Cu^+ is rare and Au^+ virtually non-existent. The only cuprous and aurous compounds that are stable to water are present as complexes, or are insoluble, so that the concentration in solution is very low. Cuprous thiocyanate is an example of an insoluble $Cu(+1)$ compound and is used to estimate copper gravimetrically

$$2Cu^{2+} + SO_3^{2-} + 2CNS^- + H_2O \rightarrow 2Cu^ICNS + SO_4^{2-} + 2H^+$$

Cu^{2+} is reduced to cuprous oxide Cu_2O by the action of sugars on Fehling's solution. It is a basic oxide and reacts with the halogen acids giving the insoluble CuCl, CuBr and CuI. In a similar way iodide ions reduce Cu^{2+} to cuprous iodide CuI and iodine. This reaction is used to estimate copper volumetrically, since iodine is easily titrated with sodium thiosulphate.

$$2Cu^{2+} + 4I^- \rightarrow 2CuI + I_2$$

Cyanide complexes are well known, and can be used to extract silver and gold, the metals being recovered from the complex by reduction with zinc.

$$4Au + 8CN^- + 2H_2O + O_2 \rightarrow 4[Au^I(CN)_2]^- + 4OH^-$$

Cyanide ions may react as both a reducing agent and a complexing agent,

$$2Cu^{2+} + 2CN^- \rightarrow (CN)_2 + 2Cu^+$$
$$\text{cyanogen}$$
$$Cu^+ + 4CN^- \rightarrow [Cu(CN)_4]^{3-}$$

Cuprous chloride CuCl in hydrochloric acid contains the ion $[CuCl_2]^-$ which is important because it forms complexes with carbon monoxide, but cuprous chloride in ammonia is also used to absorb carbon monoxide. Cuprous chloride is often formulated as a dimer Cu_2Cl_2, but in the vapour state is a mixture of a monomer, dimer and trimer CuCl, $(CuCl)_2$ and $(CuCl)_3$; it conducts electricity in the solid state, and then has the zinc blende structure.

Ag($+1$) forms many simple compounds which are ionic and stable to water. $AgNO_3$ is one of the most important salts. Ag_2O is mainly basic, dissolves in acids, and when moist absorbs carbon dioxide to form Ag_2CO_3. Since Ag_2O dissolves in NaOH it must have slight acidic properties too. Except for AgF, the silver halides are insoluble in water. AgCl is soluble in dilute ammonia and AgBr in 0·880 ammonia, and both form the ammine complex $[NH_3 \rightarrow Ag \leftarrow NH_3]^+$, which is linear. Sodium thiosulphate forms a soluble complex with silver halides $[Ag(S_2O_3)_2]^{3-}$ and this is important in the fixing of photographic plates.

The cupric ion Cu^{2+} has the electronic configuration d^9 and has an unpaired electron. Its compounds are therefore coloured and paramagnetic. $CuSO_4 . 5H_2O$ and many hydrated cupric salts are blue. The anhydrous salts of CuF_2 and $CuSO_4$ are colourless. Anhydrous $Cu(NO_3)_2$ is probably covalent since it sublimes, and anhydrous $CuCl_2$ and $CuBr_2$ form chain structures, but hydrolyse when dissolved in water.

$$
\begin{array}{ccccccc}
 & Cl & & Cl & & Cl & & Cl \\
 & \diagup \searrow & & \diagup \searrow & & \diagup \searrow & & \diagup \\
Cu & & Cu & & Cu & & Cu & \\
 & \diagdown \nearrow & & \diagdown \nearrow & & \diagdown \nearrow & & \diagdown \\
 & Cl & & Cl & & Cl & & Cl \\
\end{array}
$$

Cu forms three series of co-ordination compounds. Those with a co-ordination number of two, such as $[Cu^I(NH_3)_2](CNS)$, are linear. The well-known deep blue cuproammonium ion has a co-ordination number of four and is square planar.

$$CuSO_4 + 4NH_3 \rightarrow [Cu^{II}(NH_3)_4]^{2+}SO_4{}^{2-}$$

Some complexes have a co-ordination number of six and are octahedral like $[Cu(NH_3)_6]Br_2$. The electronic arrangement in the square planar complexes is controversial.

	3d	4s	4p	4d
Electronic structure of copper atom— ground state	↑↓ ↑↓ ↑↓ ↑↓ ↑↓	↓	□ □ □	□ □ □ □ □
Electronic structure of Cu^{2+}	↑↓ ↑↓ ↑↓ ↑↓ ↑	□	□ □ □	□ □ □ □ □
Pauling's suggestion for Cu^{2+} in square planar complex	↑↓ ↑↓ ↑↓ ↑↓ X	X	X X ↑	□ □ □ □ □
			dsp^2 hybridization.	
Huggins' suggestion for Cu^{2+} in square planar complex	↑↓ ↑↓ ↑↓ ↑↓ ↑	X	X X □	X □ □ □ □
			sp^2d hybridization.	

Ag($+2$) is unstable, though AgO and AgF$_2$ are known. The fluoride is a good fluorinating agent.

$$AgF_2 \xrightarrow{\text{heat}} AgF + F$$

Au($+2$) is even less stable, although AuO and AuS probably exist. CsAuCl$_3$ does not contain Au($+2$) as it has [AuCl$_2$]$^-$ and [AuCl$_4$]$^-$ ions corresponding to Au($+1$) and Au($+3$).

The $+3$ state is uncommon for copper and silver, though KCu^{III}O$_2$, KCu^{III}F$_6$ and KAg^{III}F$_4$ are known. The $+3$ state is the most common for gold, and all the halides AuX_3 are known. AuCl$_3$ is made from the elements, or by dissolving gold in aqua regia and evaporating.

$$Au + HNO_3 + HCl \rightarrow H[AuCl_4] \rightarrow AuCl_3$$

The bromide is made from the elements and the iodide is made from the bromide. AuF$_3$ can only be formed with a strong fluorinating agent

$$Au + BrF_3 \rightarrow AuF_3$$

The halides are covalent, and vapour density and cryoscopic measurements suggest that they are probably dimeric.

Hydrated gold oxide is amphoteric, and dissolves in alkalis to give salts such as sodium aurate NaAuO$_2$.H$_2$O, and in strong acids to give H[AuCl$_4$], H[Au(NO$_3$)$_4$] and H[Au(SO$_4$)$_2$]. Cationic Au($+3$) complexes are also known, e.g. [Au(NH$_3$)$_4$](NO$_3$)$_3$ in which the co-ordination number is again four, and which is probably square planar.

The metals in this group have the highest electrical and thermal conductivities known. They are attacked only by oxidizing acids. Copper reacts with nitric acid of all concentrations:

$$3Cu + 8HNO_3 \xrightarrow{\text{dilute}} 2NO + 3Cu(NO_3)_2 + 4H_2O$$
$$Cu + 4HNO_3 \xrightarrow{\text{concentrated}} 2NO_2 + Cu(NO_3)_2 + 2H_2O$$

and with concentrated sulphuric acid. To dissolve gold, aqua regia is needed, the nitric acid acting as an oxidizing agent and the chloride ions as a complexing agent.

Copper occurs to the extent of 70 p.p.m. in the earth's crust. Sulphide ores are concentrated, partly converted to the oxide, and then coverted to the metal by self-reduction.

$$Cu_2S + 2Cu_2O \rightarrow 6Cu + SO_2$$

Alternatively lean ores are weathered and leached, and the copper displaced from the resulting copper sulphate solution by scrap iron. Zinc is used to extract silver by solvent extraction from molten lead in Parke's process, and silver and gold are extracted by making soluble complex cyanides.

Zinc Group (Table 6.20)

TABLE 6.20

Element	Symbol	Electronic structures	Oxidation states*
Zinc	Zn	[Ar] $3d^{10} 4s^2$	2
Cadmium	Cd	[Kr] $4d^{10} 5s^2$	2
Mercury	Hg	[Xe] $4f^{14} 5d^{10} 6s^2$	(1), 2

* See page 77.

The elements in this group all have two *s* electrons beyond a completed *d* shell. Removal of the *s* electrons results in divalent compounds, and the +2 oxidation state is characteristic of the group. Hg(+1) is important, but mercurous compounds are dimerized and contain a pair of linked mercury atoms. Thus in mercurous chloride Cl—Hg—Hg—Cl, mercury forms two bonds, and Hg^+ does not exist. Valencies higher than two are not found, presumably because removal of more electrons would destroy the symmetry of a completed *d* shell.

Since the *d* shell is complete, and is not available for bonding, the elements in this group show few of the properties associated with typical transition elements. They do not show variable valency and many of their compounds are white. The melting points and boiling points are very low and this explains why the metals are more reactive than the copper group, even though the ionization potentials for the two groups suggest the reverse. (Nobility is favoured by a high heat of sublimation, a high ionization potential and a low heat of hydration.)

Similarities between Group II elements with an electronic structure ——s^2 and the zinc group ——$d^{10}s^2$ are slight. Both groups are divalent. The hydrated sulphates are isomorphous, and double salts such as K_2SO_4. $HgSO_4.6H_2O$ are analogous to $K_2SO_4.MgSO_4.6H_2O$. However, the zinc group is more noble, more covalent, has a greater ability to form complexes and is less basic.

The reactivity decreases Zn → Cd → Hg and mercury is in fact quite noble. Thus zinc and cadmium react with dilute acids, but mercury is only soluble in oxidizing acids. Zinc is fairly readily soluble in alkalis and forms zincates (e.g. Na_2ZnO_2) which are rather like aluminates.

Basic properties increase within the group, ZnO being amphoteric, but CdO and HgO are basic. All three oxides are formed by direct combination of the elements, and since ZnO and CdO sublime, they must be appreciably covalent. HgO does not sublime since it decomposes on heating. This property has been utilized in the preparation of oxygen. The thermal stability of the oxides thus decreases $Zn \rightarrow Cd \rightarrow Hg$.

Zinc oxide is yellow when hot, but white when cold. Cadmium oxide is a chocolate brown colour at room temperature but is white at liquid air temperature. These divalent compounds have a complete d shell, and it is thought that their colour may be due to defects in the solid structure. The number of defects increases with temperatures and is zero at absolute zero.

Zinc salts are usually hydrated and the halides are hygroscopic. When they dissolve in water $[Zn(H_2O)_4]^{2+}$ ions are formed. Cadmium salts are less hydrated and when the halides dissolve they do not ionize completely, and may undergo self-complexing. Thus CdI_2 may give a mixture of Cd^{2+}, CdI^+, CdI_2, CdI_3^- and CdI_4^{2-} in solution, the proportions depending on the concentration. Mercuric salts are usually anhydrous and do not ionize appreciably.

The halides, which may be formed from the elements, show the effect of polarization on the type of bond formed. The greater the polarizing power of the positive ion and the greater the polarizability of the negative ion, the greater is the tendency to covalency. Normally, small highly-charged positive ions are the most polarizing, but the polarizing power increases from $Zn \rightarrow Cd \rightarrow Hg$. The polarizability of the halide ion increases $F \rightarrow Cl \rightarrow Br \rightarrow I$. Thus CdF_2 is ionic and has a fluorite structure as predicted by the radius ratio. $CdCl_2$ forms a layer lattice and $HgCl_2$ forms a covalent molecular lattice.

The elements all form complexes readily with cyanide ions, ammonia and amines, halide ions and many other ligands. The stability of $Hg(+2)$ complexes is much greater than that of the other two elements. This is unusual because smaller ions usually complex best. $Zn(+2)$ and $Cd(+2)$ usually have a co-ordination number of four in their complexes, for example $K_2[Zn(CN)_4]$ and $[CdI_4]^{2-}$. The tetrahalide complexes form quite readily from the dihalide and excess halide ions. These complexes have been shown to be tetrahedral.

	$4d$	$5s$	$5p$
Electronic structure Cd^{2+} ion	↑↓ ↑↓ ↑↓ ↑↓ ↑↓	☐	☐ ☐ ☐
Electronic structure in $[CdI_4]^{2-}$	↑↓ ↑↓ ↑↓ ↑↓ ↑↓	X	X X X

sp^3 hybridization—
tetrahedral.

Zinc forms basic zinc acetate, $(CH_3COO)_6.Zn_4O$, a complex very like basic beryllium acetate both in structure and properties (see Fig. 6.4). The zinc complex hydrolyses more readily than the beryllium complex, since zinc can increase its co-ordination number to six. Both zinc and cadmium form a few complexes such as $[Zn(ethylenediamine)_3]^{2+}$ and $[Cd(orthophenanthroline)_3]^{2+}$ with a co-ordination number of six. Cadmium has a slight tendency to a co-ordination number of two, but this is much more strongly marked in mercury complexes. Mercury can show four co-ordination as well, but two ligands are more strongly held. Thus some ammine complexes lose ammonia in the solid.

$$[Hg(NH_3)_4]NO_3 \rightarrow [Hg(NH_3)_2]NO_3 + 2NH_3$$

and mercuric chloride in solution is mainly $HgCl_2$, although $[HgCl_4]^{2-}$ can be formed. The complex potassium mercuric iodide $K_2[HgI_4]$ is well known as Nessler's reagent, which gives a yellow colour or a brown precipitate with ammonia. Mercuric sulphate forms a red complex when treated with a protein and sodium nitrite; this is the basis of Millon's colour test for proteins.

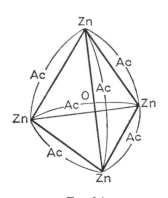

FIG. 6.4

Mercury is unique in the $Hg(+1)$ state in that it consists of two directly linked metal atoms. The mercurous ion thus has the structure $[-Hg-Hg-]^{2+}$. Evidence for this comes from a number of sources:

(1) *Equilibrium constant*

Mercurous compounds can often be made from the corresponding mercuric compound by treatment with mercury. If the reaction is:

$$Hg(NO_3)_2 + Hg \rightarrow 2HgNO_3$$
$$Hg^{2+} + \quad Hg \rightarrow 2Hg^+$$

Then by the law of mass action

$$\frac{[Hg^+]^2}{[Hg^{2+}]} = \text{constant}$$

Experiments have shown this to be untrue. If, however:

$$Hg^{2+} + Hg \rightarrow (Hg_2)^{2+} \quad \text{then} \frac{[(Hg_2)^{2+}]}{[Hg^{2+}]} = \text{constant}.$$

This has been verified experimentally, and so mercurous ions are $(Hg_2)^{2+}$

(2) *Concentration cell*

A concentration cell was set up.

Hg	N/20 HgNO$_3$ in N/10 HNO$_3$ (1)	N/2 HgNO$_3$ in N/10 HNO$_3$ (2)	Hg

$$E = \frac{2 \cdot 303\,RT}{nF} \log \frac{c_2}{c_1}$$

The potential E was measured and since R the gas constant, T the absolute temperature, F the faraday, c_1 and c_2 the concentrations of the solutions are known, n the number of charges on the ion can be found. The value of n was two, confirming $(Hg_2)^{2+}$.

(3) *Electrical conductivity*

The conductivity of mercurous nitrate solution was compared with other salts. If ionization was $HgNO_3 \rightarrow Hg^+ + NO_3^-$, it should behave like $Ag^+NO_3^-$. But it does not do so. The conductivity is similar to lead nitrate, and so by analogy:

$$Pb(NO_3)_2 \rightarrow Pb^{2+} + 2NO_3^-$$
$$Hg_2(NO_3)_2 \rightarrow (Hg_2)^{2+} + 2NO_3^-$$

(4) *Raman spectra*

All metal nitrates have the same Raman spectrum, due to the covalent bonding in NO_3^-. Mercurous nitrate has an extra line in the spectrum, because of the Hg—Hg bond.

(5) *X-ray diffraction*

The crystal structure of mercurous chloride has been found by X-ray diffraction. The unit cell does not contain discrete ions, but linear molecules Cl—Hg—Hg—Cl; this proves the Hg—Hg bond and suggests *sp* hybridization.

Most mercurous Hg(+1) compounds are insoluble and can be prepared by treating the corresponding Hg(+2) compound with mercury. No complexes of Hg(+1) are known, mainly because of the large size of the mercurous ion. Salts of Millon's base $(Hg_2N)OH$ may be formed in very dilute solutions.

$$2Hg_2Cl_2 + 4NH_3 \rightarrow 2Hg + [Hg_2N]Cl + 3NH_4Cl$$

Zinc occurs in the earth's crust to the extent of 132 p.p.m., but cadmium and mercury are scarce. The elements are familiar because their extraction and purification are simple. Zinc sulphide is roasted to the oxide and reduced by carbon at 1200°C, when the zinc distils off and condenses to give zinc dust. Lower temperature oxidation of ZnS yields ZnO and $ZnSO_4$ which may be dissolved and electrolysed to give pure zinc. Since zinc has an electrode potential of -0.76 volts, this phenomenon would appear to be impossible, but because of the hydrogen overvoltage, metal ions are discharged rather than hydrogen and hydroxyl ions. Cadmium occurs with zinc in sulphide ores, and because of its position in the electrochemical series, it is displaced from a solution of $ZnSO_4$ and $CdSO_4$ by the addition of zinc. Mercury is obtained from HgS by heating in air.

$$HgS \rightarrow HgO \rightarrow Hg$$

Zinc is used in large amounts (1,000,000 tons per year) in brass and in galvanizing, and ZnO is used as a paint pigment. Cadmium is used in alloys and for electroplating, and mercury is used in thermometers, in amalgams, as a detonator (mercury fulminate) and medicinally.

PROBLEMS

1. How do the following properties vary in the transition elements:
   (a) ionic character;
   (b) basic properties;
   (c) stability of the various oxidation states;
   (d) ability to form complexes?
2. Describe the methods by which extremely pure samples of metals may be prepared.
3. Why do metals such as iron corrode, and how may this be prevented?
4. Explain the following:
   (a) La_2O_3 is not reduced by Al;
   (b) Zn is sacrificed in the extraction of Cd;
   (c) carbonyl and cyanide complexes of the later transition elements Cr, Mn, Fe, Co, Ni are more stable, more common, and more likely to exist than similar compounds of the *s*-block or early transition elements;
   (d) certain ligands such as F^- tend to bring out the maximum oxidation state of an element, whilst others such as CO and dipyridyl bring out the lowest oxidation states.
5. Manganese has been described as 'the most versatile element'. Explain this, and show the similarities and differences between the chemistry of manganese and rhenium.
6. Write a critical account of the various ways in which the nine elements in the iron, cobalt and nickel groups have been grouped together.
7. Give an account of disproportionation. Why is the mercurous ion written Hg_2^{2+}, whilst the cuprous ion is written Cu^+?

f-BLOCK ELEMENTS

The Lanthanide Series (Table 7.1)

These 14 elements are alternatively called lanthanons, lanthanides or rare earths and are characterized by the filling up of the antepenultimate $4f$ energy levels.

TABLE 7.1

Element	Symbol	Electronic structure		Oxidation states
		Xenon core		
Cerium	Ce	$4f^1\ 5d^1\ 6s^2$	$4f^2\quad 6s^2$	$+3, +4$
Praseodymium	Pr	$4f^2\ 5d^1\ 6s^2$	$4f^3\quad 6s^2$	$+3, +4$
Neodymium	Nd	$4f^3\ 5d^1\ 6s^2$	$4f^4\quad 6s^2$	$+2, +3, (+4)$
Promethium	Pm	$4f^4\ 5d^1\ 6s^2$	$4f^5\quad 6s^2$	$+3$
Samarium	Sm	$4f^5\ 5d^1\ 6s^2$	$4f^6\quad 6s^2$	$+2, +3$
Europium	Eu	$4f^6\ 5d^1\ 6s^2$	$4f^7\quad 6s^2$	$+2, +3$
Gadolinium	Gd	$4f^7\ 5d^1\ 6s^2$	$4f^7\ 5d^1\ 6s^2$	$+3$
Terbium	Tb	$4f^8\ 5d^1\ 6s^2$	$4f^9\quad 6s^2$	$+3, +4$
Dysprosium	Dy	$4f^9\ 5d^1\ 6s^2$	$4f^{10}\quad 6s^2$	$+3, (+4)$
Holmium	Ho	$4f^{10}\ 5d^1\ 6s^2$	$4f^{11}\quad 6s^2$	$+3$
Erbium	Er	$4f^{11}\ 5d^1\ 6s^2$	$4f^{12}\quad 6s^2$	$+3$
Thulium	Tm	$4f^{12}\ 5d^1\ 6s^2$	$4f^{13}\quad 6s^2$	$+2, +3$
Ytterbium	Yb	$4f^{13}\ 5d^1\ 6s^2$	$4f^{14}\quad 6s^2$	$+2, +3$
Lutetium	Lu	$4f^{14}\ 5d^1\ 6s^2$	$4f^{14}\ 5d^1\ 6s^2$	$+3$

Electronic Structure

The electronic structures of the lanthanide metals are not known for certain. Since lanthanum, the element preceding this series has the electronic structure: xenon core $5d^1 6s^2$, it may be assumed that fourteen f electrons are filled in from cerium to lutetium. By utilizing the two s electrons and the one d electron, trivalent metal ions might be expected. The lanthanides are characterized by the uniform $+3$ oxidation state shown by all the metals.

An alternative suggestion for the electronic structures, involves moving the single $5d$ electron into the $4f$ shell, except where this destroys the symmetry of a half full f shell. Which of the two suggestions is true is of little importance because the lanthanides typically form compounds which are ionic and trivalent, and the electronic structures of the ions are $Ce^{3+}f^1$, $Pr^{3+}f^2$, $Nd^{3+}f^3$, $Pm^{3+}f^4$, $Sm^{3+}f^5$ ....

'Anomalous Valency States'

Cerium can not only be trivalent, but also tetravalent in many of its compounds. A few other lanthanides show valencies of two or four in addition to the typical oxidation state of $+3$. Many of these so-called 'anomalous valency states' are really to be expected when the extra stability of an empty, half full or completely full f level is allowed for. (Ce^{4+} f shell empty, Eu^{2+} f shell half full, Tb^{4+} f shell half full, Yb^{2+} f shell full.) The $+2$ and $+4$ valency states are not common and are unstable in aqueous solution except for the well-known Ce^{4+} salts such as ceric sulphate, which is used as an oxidizing agent in volumetric analysis.

Chemical Properties

The chemical properties of the group are essentially the properties of trivalent ionic compounds. They all form hydroxides $M(OH)_3$ which are ionic and basic. They are less basic than $Ca(OH)_2$ but more basic than the amphoteric $Al(OH)_3$. Salts such as carbonates and nitrates can therefore be more readily decomposed to the oxide by heating than calcium salts. Within the group, the size of the ions decreases from $Ce^{3+} \rightarrow Lu^{3+}$, thus $Ce(OH)_3$ is the most basic, and $Lu(OH)_3$ which is the least basic, is intermediate between scandium and yttrium in basic strength. In a similar way, the oxides M_2O_3 are ionic and basic oxides; the basic strength decreases as the ions get smaller.

Solubility

Salts of the lanthanides usually contain water of crystallization. The solubility of many of the salts follows the pattern of Group II elements, the chlorides and nitrates being soluble in water and the oxalates, carbonates and fluorides being almost insoluble. Unlike Group II, however, the sulphates are soluble. Many of the lanthanides form double salts with the corresponding Group I or ammonium salt, e.g. $Na_2SO_4L_2(SO_4)_3 . 8H_2O$ and since these double salts crystallize well, they are used to separate the rare earths from one another.

Colour

Many trivalent lanthanide ions are strikingly coloured both in the solid state and in aqueous solution. As may be seen from Table 7.2, the colour seems to depend on the number of unpaired f electrons, and elements with $x f$ electrons often have a similar colour to those with $(14 - x) f$ electrons.

TABLE 7.2

	Number of $4f$ electrons	Colour		Number of $4f$ electrons	Colour
La^{3+}	0	Colourless	Lu^{3+}	14	Colourless
Ce^{3+}	1	Colourless	Yb^{3+}	13	Colourless
Pr^{3+}	2	Green	Tm^{3+}	12	Very pale green
Nd^{3+}	3	Mauve	Er^{3+}	11	Pink
Pm^{3+}	4	(Not known perhaps purple)	Ho^{3+}	10	Pale yellow-brown
Sm^{3+}	5	Very pale yellow	Dy^{3+}	9	Colourless
Eu^{3+}	6	Colourless	Tb^{3+}	8	Colourless
Gd^{3+}	7	Colourless	Gd^{3+}	7	Colourless

This theory is complicated by the fact that the other valencies do not all have colours similar to their isoelectronic $3+$ counterparts. (Ce^{4+} orange-red; Sm^{2+} red-brown; Eu^{2+} straw; Yb^{2+} green.)

Colour arises because of the absorption of light of particular wavelengths corresponding to certain electronic transitions. The bands in these absorption spectra are unusually sharp, and arise from electronic transitions within the $4f$ level. This type of transition is normally a forbidden one, but it accounts for the sharp absorption bands of the lanthanons and the more diffuse bands of the transition metals. Since the f electrons responsible for the absorption spectra are 'inside' the atom in the ante-penultimate shell, environmental factors such as complexing, which affect the outer electrons, have little effect on the absorption spectra. The absorption spectra are useful in both qualitative detection and quantitative estimation of the lanthanons, and some of the colourless ions such as Ce^{3+} and Yb^{3+} show strong absorption in the ultraviolet region.

Lanthanide Contraction

Normally, on descending a group in the periodic table the covalent and ionic radii increase due to the filling of extra shells of electrons. On travelling across a period, the covalent and ionic radii decrease because the nuclear charge is increased, and hence the orbital electrons are pulled in closer. The radii decrease in the lanthanide series from Ce to Lu. The change in size of ions in the lanthanons is small and since their valency is the same, their

15—C.I.C.

chemical properties are similar. Note that the contraction is sufficient for the radii to drop below that for Y in the preceding transition series; thus the chemical properties of Y, Ho and Dy are very similar and their separation difficult.

TABLE 7.3.   IONIC RADII M^{3+} (Å)

Sc													
0·83													
Y													
1·06													
La	Ce	Pr	Nd	Pm	Sm	Eu	Gd	Tb	Dy	Ho	Er	Tm	Yb	Lu
1·22	1·18	1·16	1·15	—	1·13	1·13	1·11	1·09	1·07	1·05	1·04	1·04	1·00	0·99

The contraction effect is of sufficient magnitude to cause the elements which follow in the transition series to have sizes very similar to those of the previous row of transition elements.   (See Table 7.4.)

TABLE 7.4.   COVALENT RADII (Å)

Sc	Ti	V	Cr	Mn	Fe	Co	Ni
1·44	1·32	1·22	1·17	1·17	1·17	1·16	1·15
Y	Zr	Nb	Mo	Tc	Ru	Rh	Pd
1·62	1·45	1·34	1·29	—	1·24	1·25	1·28
La	↑ * Hf	Ta	W	Re	Os	Ir	Pt
1·69	1·44	1·34	1·30	1·28	1·26	1·26	1·29

* 14 Lanthanide elements

Ionic radii were not chosen in this table because the radius depends on how many electrons are removed.   If the sizes of ions of the same charge were compared, a similar variation would be observed.

The normal size increase Sc → Y → La disappears after the lanthanons, and pairs of elements such as Zr/Hf, Nb/Ta, Mo/W possess nearly identical sizes.   The similarity of properties within these pairs makes chemical separation very difficult.   In general, the second and third rows of transition elements resemble each other much more closely than do the first and second rows; this is a direct result of the lanthanide contraction.

Separation of the Lanthanide Elements

The properties of metal ions are determined by their size and charge and since the lanthanides are all typically trivalent and are almost identical in size, their chemical properties are almost identical. The separation of one metal from another is an exceedingly difficult task, almost as difficult as the separation of isotopes. The following methods utilize slight differences in basic properties, solubility and change of valency.

(1) *Precipitation.* With a limited amount of precipitating agent the substance with the lowest solubility product is precipitated most rapidly and most completely. If hydroxyl ions are added to a solution of lanthanide nitrates, the weakest base, $Lu(OH)_3$, is precipitated first, and the strongest base, $La(OH)_3$, last. Only a partial separation is effected, but the precipitate can be redissolved and the process repeated.

(2) *Thermal reaction.* If the nitrates are fused, a temperature will be reached when the least basic changes to the oxide. The mixture is leached with water; because the oxides are insoluble they remain, are reconverted to nitrates, and the process is repeated.

(3) *Fractional crystallization* of simple salts such as nitrates, sulphates, bromates, perchlorates and oxalates has been used and double salts such as $2L(NO_3)_3 3Mg(NO_3)_2 . 24H_2O$ crystallize well. The solubility decreases from La to Lu. The process needs repeating many times. Non-aqueous solvents such as ether have been used to separate $Nd(NO_3)_3$ and $Pr(NO_3)_3$.

(4) *Solvent extraction.* The ratios of the partition coefficients of $La(NO_3)_3$ and $Gd(NO_3)_3$ between water and normal butyl alcohol is $1:1.06$. This difference is small, but if a continuous counter-current method is used, solvent extraction is less tedious than crystallization.

(5) *Valency change.* A few lanthanons have oxidation states other than the characteristic $+3$, and the difference in properties of the $+2$ and $+4$ states makes separation fairly easy. Cerium can be removed from lanthanide mixtures by oxidizing the solution with permanganate or bromate under alkaline conditions. Ce^{4+} has a greater charge than Ce^{3+}, hence Ce^{4+} is smaller and less basic and is precipitated as $Ce(OH)_4$, CeO_2 or a basic salt, leaving the trivalent ions in solution. 99% pure Ce can be obtained in one stage from a mixture containing 40% Ce. Pr and Tb can both have oxidation states of $+4$, but these are unstable in aqueous solution. Separation is possible by fusion to the oxides, or by oxidizing in molten NaOH.

Europium can be obtained in the $+2$ state either by electrolytic reduction with a mercury cathode or by using zinc amalgam, followed by the precipitation of $EuSO_4$, which resembles the alkaline earth sulphates. Strong reducing agents such as sodium amalgam will produce divalent samarium and ytterbium.

Valency change is still a useful method despite the advent in recent years of ion exchange and complex formation.

(6) *Ion exchange.* This is the most rapid and most effective method for the separation and purification of the lanthanons. A solution of lanthanide ions is run down a column of synthetic ion exchange resin which has functional groups such as —COOH or —SO$_3$H. The lanthanide ions replace the functional hydrogen ions and become bound to the resin.

$$M^{3+} + 3H \text{ resin} \rightarrow M \text{ resin}_3 + 3H^+.$$

They are then eluted from the column using a citric acid/ammonium citrate solution. First the ammonium ions elute the metal ions from the resin.

$$3NH_4^+ + M \text{ resin}_3 \rightarrow 3NH_4 \text{ resin} + M^{3+}$$

The smaller lanthanide ions are the most heavily hydrated and the size of the hydrated ions increases La $\rightarrow$ Lu. Thus La is bound to the resin most firmly and Lu less firmly, so that Lu is eluted most readily. The metal ions then form a complex with citrate ions.

$$M^{3+} + \text{citrate ions} \rightarrow M \text{ citrate complex.}$$

Lower down the column, ammonium ions replace hydrogen ions on the resin.

$$NH_4^+ + H \text{ resin} \rightarrow NH_4 \text{ resin} + H^+.$$

These hydrogen ions compete with the lanthanide ions for citrate ions; hence the concentration of lanthanide ions increases, and they are reabsorbed on the resin slightly lower down the column. If the passage of ammonium citrate is continued, this sequence is repeated many times. Lu is eluted from the column first, and La last, and by careful control of conditions an extremely efficient separation is effected.

(7) *Complex formation.* The oxalates of the lanthanons are insoluble, but they can be held in solution by a complexing agent such as EDTA (ethylenediaminetetraacetic acid)

$$HOOC-CH_2 \diagdown \qquad \qquad CH_2-COOH$$
$$N-CH_2-CH_2-N$$
$$HOOC-CH_2 \diagup \qquad \qquad CH_2-COOH$$

The EDTA metal complexes are not all equally stable and addition of acid destroys the least stable complexes, which then precipitate as the oxalates.

Once the different lanthanide elements have been separated, the metal is obtained by electrolysis of the fused chloride, or by reduction of the chloride by sodium or potassium at a moderate temperature, or by calcium at a high temperature in an evacuated or argon-filled vessel. The metals are of little use, though Mischmetal (50% Ce, 40% La, 7% Fe, 3% other metals) is pyrophoric and is used for 'lighter flints'. La_2O_3 is used in Crooke's lenses, CeO_2 is used as an opacifier in paint and enamel and ceric salts are used as oxidizing agents in volumetric analysis.

Abundance and Number of Isotopes

The abundance of the elements and number of naturally occurring isotopes shows regular variations (Table 7.5).

TABLE 7.5

Atomic number	Element	Abundance p.p.m. earth's crust	Naturally occurring isotopes
58	Ce	46	4
59	Pr	5·5	1
60	Nd	24	7
61	Pm	0	0
62	Sm	6·5	7
63	Eu	1·1	2
64	Gd	6·4	7
65	Tb	0·9	1
66	Dy	4·5	7
67	Ho	1·2	1
68	Er	2·5	6
69	Tm	0·2	1
70	Yb	2·7	7
71	Lu	0·8	2

Elements with an even nuclear charge (atomic number) are more abundant, richer in isotopes and more stable than those of odd atomic number. Elements with odd atomic numbers never have more than two stable isotopes. Both the number of neutrons in the nucleus and the number of protons are related to the stability throughout the periodic table (Table 7.6).

TABLE 7.6

Atomic number	Number of neutrons	Stable nuclei
Even	Even	164
Even	Odd	55
Odd	Even	50
Odd	Odd	4

Element 61, promethium, does not occur naturally, but has been made artificially. Its absence may be explained by Mattauch's rule which states that if two elements with consecutive atomic numbers each have an isotope of the same weight, both isotopes are never stable. Since elements 60 and 62 have seven isotopes each, there are not many mass numbers available for promethium, element 61.

TABLE 7.7

| Element 60 | 142, 143, 144, 145, 146, | 148, | 150 | | |
| Element 62 | 144, | 147, 148, 149, 150, | 152, | 154 |

If promethium is to have a stable isotope, it must have a mass number outside the range 142–150. $^{151}_{61}$Pm is radioactive, so if promethium is present it is radioactive.

The Heavier Elements

TABLE 7.8

Atomic number	Element	Symbol	Oxidation states*
89	Actinium	Ac	3
90	Thorium	Th	(3), **4**
91	Protactinium	Pa	(3), (4), **5**
92	Uranium	U	3, 4, 5, **6**
93	Neptunium	Np	3, 4, **5**, 6
94	Plutonium	Pu	3, **4**, 5, 6
95	Americium	Am	**3**, (4), 5, 6
96	Curium	Cm	**3**, (4)
97	Berkelium	Bk	**3**, 4
98	Californium	Cf	3
99	Einsteinium	Es	3
100	Fermium	Fm	3
101	Mendeleevium	Md	3
102	Nobelium	No	
103	Lawrencium	Lw	

* See page 77.

The elements up to and including uranium have been known for a long time. The elements with higher atomic numbers than uranium are called the transuranic elements and have been obtained in the period since 1940 by bombardment of a suitable element with neutrons, α particles or stripped carbon atoms. The position occupied by the transuranic elements and those immediately before uranium in the periodic table is controversial.

Position in the Periodic Table

By comparison with the previous period in the periodic table, francium and radium have *s* electrons in their outer orbitals and belong to Groups I and II respectively. Actinium begins to fill the penultimate *d* shell (——$6d^1\ 7s^2$) and has properties typical of the Sc, Y, La group. After lanthanum, the antepenultimate *f* shell is filled to give the lanthanides, so that by analogy the actinide series (a second inner transition series) should begin with thorium and end with lawrencium (see Table 7.9).

TABLE 7.9

Transition elements	Lanthanides												
La	Ce	Pr	Nd	Pm	Sm	Eu	Gd	Tb	Dy	Ho	Er	Tm	Yb Lu
Ac	Th	Pa	U	Np	Pu	Am	Cm	Bk	Cf	Es	Fm	Md	No Lw
	Actinides												

There is a considerable amount of evidence to support this. Curium only shows one oxidation state +3, in the same way that gadolinium in the lanthanons is solely trivalent. This is thought to be due to the stable configuration of an exactly half-filled *f* shell which is left when two *s* and one *d* electrons are removed. By similar reasoning berkelium +4 was predicted and is, in fact, known, though americium +2 is not known.

The behaviour of Am, Cm, Bk and Cf on elution from an ion exchange column is exactly parallel to the behaviour of the appropriate lanthanons Eu, Gd, Tb and Dy.

The elements U, Np, Pu, Am and Cm have very sharp lines in their absorption spectra. In this they resemble the lanthanons and differ from the transition elements. These lines are associated with electronic transitions within the *f* shell. Since the crystal structures of such compounds as ThO_2 and AmO_2 are isostructural, this arrangement is regarded as evidence that Th is an inner transition element. However, since oxide structures are often determined by radius ratio or closest packing considerations, this argument is not necessarily valid.

Actinides or Uranides?

There is some doubt whether the elements before uranium contain any *f* electrons, and the chemical properties of Th, Pa and U fit better with the Ti, V and Cr groups of transition elements than with the transuranic elements. The increase in the number of oxidation states from Ac to U is characteristic of the transition series, and the increased stability of the higher oxidation states on descending a transition metal group is apparent. The lanthanons were noted for their uniform +3 oxidation state. In this series the lower oxidation states become increasingly stable with increased atomic number. This has led to the suggestion that Ac, Th, Pa and U are transition elements and that the second inner transition series begins with neptunium. Since this series begins after uranium, it should be called the uranide series. Alternative electronic structures have been suggested by Seaborg and Dawson (see Table 7.10).

TABLE 7.10. Electronic configurations

Element	Seaborg	Dawson
Ac	radon core $6d^1 7s^2$	$6d^1 7s^2$
Th	$5f^1 6d^1 7s^2$	$6d^2 7s^2$
Pa	$5f^2 6d^1 7s^2$	$6d^3 7s^2$
U	$5f^3 6d^1 7s^2$	$6d^4 7s^2$
Np	$5f^4 6d^1 7s^2$	$5f^4 6d^1 7s^2$
Pu	$5f^5 6d^1 7s^2$	$5f^5 6d^1 7s^2$
Am	$5f^7 \quad 7s^2$	$5f^6 6d^1 7s^2$
Cm	$5f^7 6d^1 7s^2$	$5f^7 6d^1 7s^2$
Bk	$5f^8 6d^1 7s^2$	$5f^8 6d^1 7s^2$
Cf	$5f^9 6d^1 7s^2$	$5f^9 6d^1 7s^2$

Direct evidence for the configuration of Np is lacking. Evidence for the existence of a second inner transition series is well established. The presence of *f* electrons in the posturanic elements is accepted, but whether the first 5*f* electron enters at thorium and gives an actinide series, or at neptunium and gives a uranide series is not known, although the energy levels of 5*f* and 6*d* are almost identical.

Further Extension of the Periodic Table?

All the transuranic elements are obtained synthetically by nuclear reactions and they are radioactive. Uranium and plutonium are fissile and are important for nuclear weapons and peaceful uses of atomic energy. It may well be asked how many new elements may be produced—or has the limit of the periodic table been reached? The last few elements have only been produced in trace amounts and since their half-life periods are only a few minutes they decay rapidly to other elements. Because nuclear stability decreases as the size of the nucleus increases, it seems improbable that the periodic table can be extended much further.

LISTER, M. W., *Quarterly Reviews of the Chemical Society*, **4**, 20, 1950.
J. Chem. Ed., **36**, 2, 1959, Symposium on the New Elements.

PROBLEMS

1. In what way are the observed oxidation states of the lanthanons related to their electronic structures?
2. What are the problems in the separation of the lanthanons, and in what ways are they overcome?
3. What is the lanthanide contraction, and what are its consequences?
4. In what ways does the filling of the $4f$ energy level affect the rest of the periodic table?
5. The electronic configurations and position of the heavier elements in the periodic table are controversial. What are the possibilities, and what is the evidence?

CHAPTER 8

CO-ORDINATION COMPOUNDS

Double Salts and Co-ordination Compounds

Molecular or addition compounds are formed when stoichiometric amounts of two or more stable compounds join together. For example:

$KCl + MgCl_2 + 6H_2O \rightarrow KCl.MgCl_2.6H_2O$ (carnallite)

$K_2SO_4 + Al_2(SO_4)_3 + 24H_2O \rightarrow K_2SO_4.Al_2(SO_4)_3.24H_2O$ (potassium alum)

$CuSO_4 + 4NH_3 + H_2O \rightarrow CuSO_4.4NH_3.H_2O$ (tetrammine copper (II) sulphate)

$Fe(CN)_2 + 4KCN \rightarrow Fe(CN)_2.4KCN$ (potassium ferrocyanide)

These fall into two categories:

(1) Those which lose their identity in solution.
(2) Those which retain their identity in solution.

An aqueous solution of carnallite shows the properties of K^+, Mg^{2+} and Cl^- ions. Potassium alum solutions similarly show the properties of K^+, Al^{3+} and SO_4^{2-} ions. They are called double salts and only exist in the crystalline state.

The other two examples of addition compounds behave in a very different way from the double salts. When dissolved they do not form Cu^{2+}, or Fe^{2+} and CN^- ions, but instead give more complicated structures—the cupro-ammonium ion $[Cu(NH_3)_4]^{2+}$ and the ferrocyanide ion $[Fe(CN)_6]^{4-}$. These are called complex ions and exist as a single entity. Complex ions are indicated by square brackets. Molecular compounds of this type are called co-ordination compounds.

Werner Theory

The structure of co-ordination compounds such as $CoCl_3.6NH_3$ and $CuSO_4.4NH_3$ was explained in 1893 by Werner's co-ordination theory. He distinguished between two sorts of valency:

(1) Primary valency, for example, between Co and Cl.

(2) Secondary valency, for example, between Co and NH_3.

Groups such as NH_3, held by secondary valencies, were regarded as being co-ordinated to the metal. Every metal has a fixed number of secondary valencies, which are directed in a particular way in space. This brilliant work took place before the electronic theory of valency was understood and won Werner the Nobel prize in chemistry. In modern terms the primary valencies are ionic bonds and the secondary valencies are co-ordinate bonds. The fixed number of secondary valencies is called the co-ordination number, and the co-ordinated groups are called ligands. Thus $CoCl_3.6NH_3$ is called hexammine cobalt (III) chloride because there are six ammonia ligands and the cobalt is in the $+3$ oxidation state (Fig. 8.1).

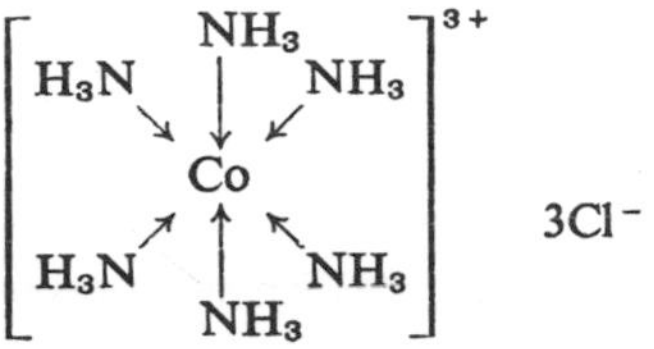

$$\begin{bmatrix} & & NH_3 & & \\ H_3N & \searrow & \downarrow & \swarrow & NH_3 \\ & & Co & & \\ H_3N & \nearrow & \uparrow & \nwarrow & NH_3 \\ & & NH_3 & & \end{bmatrix}^{3+} \quad 3Cl^-$$

Fig. 8.1

Similarly $CuSO_4.4NH_3$ is called tetrammine copper (II) sulphate and is written

$$[Cu(NH_3)_4]^{2+}SO_4^{2-}$$

Methods of Studying Complexes

Depression of freezing point measurements depend on the number of particles present and therefore indicate whether or not the molecules dissociate. Thus LiCl gives twice the expected depression. $MgCl_2$ gives three times, and $LaCl_3$ four times the depression for a single particle. Conductivity measurements indicate the number of charges present and the molar conductivities of some simple salts are: LiCl $= 112$, $MgCl_2 = 224$, $LaCl_3 = 411$. These data are consistent with the following structures:

$$LiCl = Li^+ + Cl^- \qquad \text{(2 particles)} \quad \text{(2 charges)}$$
$$MgCl_2 = Mg^{2+} + 2Cl^- \qquad \text{(3 particles)} \quad \text{(4 charges)}$$
$$LaCl_3 = La^{3+} + 3Cl^- \qquad \text{(4 particles)} \quad \text{(6 charges)}$$

The structures of many co-ordination compounds may be worked out in this way; see Table 8.1.

The replacement of a neutral ligand such as NH_3 by a negatively charged ligand such as Cl^- or NO_2^- decreases the positive charge on the complex ion. Other techniques for studying complexes include spectra, dipole moments, magnetic measurements and X-ray diffraction.

TABLE 8.1

Formula	Cryoscopic measurement	Molar conductivity	Structure
$CoCl_3 . 6NH_3$	4 particles	6 charges	$[Co(NH_3)_6]^{3+} 3Cl^-$
$CoCl_3 . 5NH_3$	3 particles	4 charges	$[Co(NH_3)_5 Cl]^{2+} 2Cl^-$
$CoCl_3 . 4NH_3$	2 particles	2 charges	$[Co(NH_3)_4 Cl_2]^+ Cl^-$
$CoCl_3 . 3NH_3$	1 particle	0 charges	$[Co(NH_3)_3 Cl_3]$
$Co(NO_2)_3 . KNO_2 . 2NH_3$	2 particles	2 charges	$K^+ [Co(NH_3)_2 (NO_2)_4]^-$
$Co(NO_2)_3 . 2KNO_2 . NH_3$	3 particles	4 charges	$2K^+ [Co(NH_3)(NO_2)_5]^{2-}$
$Co(NO_2)_3 . 3KNO_2$	4 particles	6 charges	$3K^+ [Co(NO_2)_6]^{3-}$

Effective Atomic Numbers

Co-ordinate bonds are formed between the ligands and the central metal ion in a complex; that is, a ligand donates an electron pair to the metal ion. Co-ordination compounds are formed very readily by the transition metals since they have vacant d orbitals which can accommodate donated electron pairs. The number of co-ordinate bonds which can be formed depends largely on the number of vacant orbitals of suitable energy. In many cases ligands are added until the central metal in the complex possesses or shares the same number of electrons as the next inert gas. The total number of electrons on the central metal in the complex including those gained by bonding, is called the effective atomic number (EAN).

Thus by forming complexes many metals attain an EAN of the next inert gas. However, a significant number of exceptions are known where the EAN is one or two units more or less than the corresponding inert gas (see Table 8.2).

TABLE 8.2   Effective atomic numbers of some metals in complexes

Atom	Atomic number	Complex	Electrons lost in ion formation	Electrons gained by co-ordination	EAN
Fe	26	$[Fe(CN)_6]^{4-}$	2	12	36
Co	27	$[Co(NH_3)_6]^{3+}$	3	12	36
Ni	28	$[Ni(CO)_4]$	0	8	36 (Kr)
Cu	29	$[Cu(CN)_4]^{3-}$	1	8	36
Pd	46	$[Pd(NH_3)_6]^{4+}$	4	12	54 (Xe)
Pt	78	$[PtCl_6]^{2-}$	4	12	86 (Rn)
Cr	24	$[Cr(NH_3)_6]^{3+}$	3	12	33
Fe	26	$[Fe(CN)_6]^{3-}$	3	12	35
Ni	28	$[Ni(NH_3)_6]^{2+}$	2	12	38
Pd	46	$[PdCl_4]^{2-}$	2	8	52
Pt	78	$[Pt(NH_3)_4]^{2+}$	2	8	84

The tendency to attain an inert gas configuration is a significant factor but not a necessary condition for complex formation, because it is also necessary to produce a symmetrical structure (tetrahedral, square planar, octahedral) irrespective of the number of electrons involved.

Shapes of d orbitals

Since d orbitals are frequently used in co-ordination complexes it is important to study their shapes and distribution in space. All the five d orbitals are not identical and there are in fact two sets. The $d\epsilon$ orbitals point in between the axes x, y and z and the $d\gamma$ orbitals point along the axes (Fig. 8.2). Alternative names for $d\epsilon$ and $d\gamma$ are t_{2g} and e_g respectively.

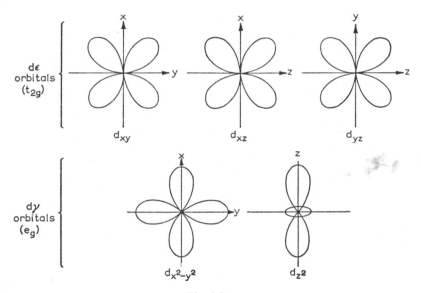

Fig. 8.2

When considering the structure and hybridization of compounds of the s and p blocks, all the outer electrons, that is all the outer orbitals, were included in the hybridization, regardless of whether they contained bonding electrons or non-bonding lone pairs of electrons. This is not usually the case with the transition elements, and normally one set of orbitals is used for bonding and is included in the hybridization, while the other set contains non-bonding electrons which are not included in hybridization. For example if the $d\gamma$ orbitals are used for bonding, they are included in hybridization and the $d\epsilon$ orbitals may contain non-bonding electrons which are not hybridized and have only a slight effect on the shape of the complex. Unpaired electrons are uncommon in compounds formed by s- and p-block elements, but are frequently found in the non-bonding set of d orbitals.

Theories of Metal to Ligand Bonding

The transition metal which forms the central atom in the complex is regarded as a positive ion, which is surrounded by negative ligands or molecules with lone pairs of electrons. If the ligand is a neutral molecule such as NH_3, the negative end of the dipole in the molecule is directed towards the metal ion. The electrons of the central metal ion are under repulsive forces from the electrons on the ligands, hence they will occupy the d orbitals furthest away from the direction of approach of ligands.

In the crystal field theory the attraction between central metal and ligands in a complex is regarded as purely electrostatic. The ligand field theory is a development of this electrostatic approach, but allows for some covalent interaction between the orbitals on the metal and the ligand. There are three types of interaction involving σ overlap of orbitals, π overlap of orbitals or $p\pi$—$d\pi$ bonding. The latter is due to π overlap of d orbitals on the metal with p orbitals on the ligand. In the molecular orbital theory, bonding between metal and ligand is due to the ligand providing electron pairs which occupy bonding σ molecular orbitals in the complex.

The approach to the bonding in complexes in this text is a combination of the crystal field splitting of energy levels, the formation of σ co-ordinate bonds and the hybridization of the bonding orbitals.

By studying the effect of the electrical field of the ligand on the central metal it is possible to predict which d orbitals are used for bonding, and hence the hybridization and shape of the complex. Further, the non-bonding electrons which do not directly affect the shape, may affect the stability and distort the regular shape. Most co-ordination compounds have a co-ordination number of six or four and the theory will be applied to octahedral, square planar and tetrahedral complexes in turn.

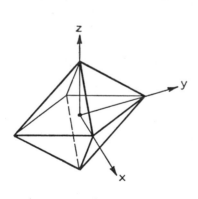

Fig. 8.3

Octahedral Complexes

The central metal is at the centre of an octahedral complex and the ligands are at the six corners. The directions x, y and z point to the corners of the octahedron (Fig. 8.3).

The $d\gamma$ orbitals are directed along the axes and the $d\epsilon$ orbitals are directed in between the axes x, y and z.   It follows that the approach of a ligand along x, y and z will increase the energy of the $d_{x^2-y^2}$ and d_{z^2} orbitals much more than the d_{xy}, d_{yz} and d_{zz} orbitals.   In an isolated atom all five d orbitals have the same energy and are termed 'degenerate', but under the influence of a ligand field they split into two groups of different energy.   In a weak ligand field the difference in energy between the two groups is small and in a strong ligand field it is large.   Figure 8.4 shows the splitting of energy levels in gaseous ions.

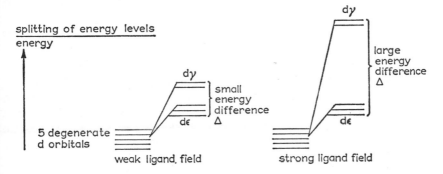

Fig. 8.4

Splitting of Energy Levels

The common ligands can be arranged in order of field strength; $CN^- >$ $NO_2^- > NH_3$ and amines $> H_2O > F^- > Cl^- > Br^- > I^-$.

Consider a complex like $[Ti(H_2O)_6]^{3+}$.   The Ti^{3+} ion has one d electron. In the complex, this will occupy the orbital with the lowest energy, that is, a $d\epsilon$ orbital.   The ligands utilize the $d\gamma$ orbitals and this set is included in the hybridization.

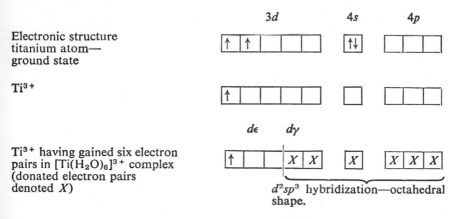

d^2sp^3 hybridization—octahedral shape.

If the central metal ion has more than three d electrons, complications arise. Consider the complexes $[CoF_6]^{3-}$ and $[Co(NH_3)_6]^{3+}$

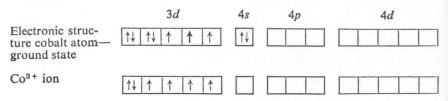

In a weak ligand field such as $[CoF_6]^{3-}$, the approach of ligands causes only a small energy difference between $d\gamma$ and $d\epsilon$. The $d\gamma$ electrons cannot move away from the approaching ligands since they have insufficient energy to pair up with the $d\epsilon$ electrons. Thus there are no vacant orbitals in the $3d$ shell and the ligands occupy the first six vacant orbitals (one $4s$, three $4p$ and two $4d$). Since outer d orbitals have been used, this is an outer orbital complex. The orbitals are hybridized and are written sp^3d^2 to denote this. Since none of the electrons has been forced to pair off, this is a spin-free complex and will be strongly paramagnetic because it contains four unpaired $3d$ electrons.

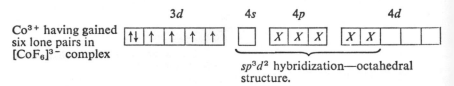

Under the influence of a strong ligand field as in the complex $[Co(NH_3)_6]^{3+}$, the energy difference between $d\gamma$ and $d\epsilon$ is much greater. This is sufficient to allow the $d\gamma$ electrons in the Co^{3+} to move into the half-filled $d\epsilon$ orbitals, even though this pairing requires energy. The six ligands each donate a lone pair to the first six vacant orbitals, which are: two $3d$, one $4s$ and three $4p$. Inner d electrons are used and so this is an inner orbital complex. The orbitals are hybridized and written d^2sp^3 to denote the use of inner orbitals. Thus the $d\gamma$ orbitals are used for bonding and are hybridized whilst the $d\epsilon$ orbitals contain non-bonding electrons and are not hybridized. Since the original unpaired electrons have been forced to pair off, this is a spin paired complex, and is in fact diamagnetic.

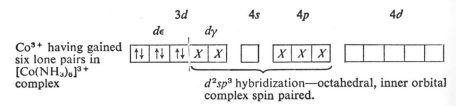

The inner and outer orbital complexes may be distinguished by magnetic measurements. Since the outer orbital complexes use high energy levels, they tend to be more reactive or labile, and ligands may be substituted fairly easily. The inner orbital complexes are sometimes called inert or non-labile since substitution is more difficult.

Both inner and outer orbital complexes give octahedral structures. A completely regular octahedron is only obtained when both the $d\epsilon$ and the $d\gamma$ orbitals are symmetrical. A set of orbitals is symmetrical when it is empty, half full or full, hence $d\epsilon^0$, $d\epsilon^3$, $d\epsilon^6$, $d\gamma^0$, $d\gamma^2$ and $d\gamma^4$ are stable configurations. In practice, dissymmetry of the non-bonding $d\epsilon$ orbitals results in only very slight distortion, which may be so slight that it is not always detected. Dissymmetry of the $d\gamma$ orbitals is important and results in severe distortion. For example, in the electronic configuration $d\epsilon^3 d\gamma^1$, the single $d\gamma$ electron occupies the d_{z^2} orbital. Thus the ligands approaching along the z and $-z$ directions are repelled and are unable to get as close to the central metal as ligands approaching along x and $-x$, y and $-y$. The octahedron is thus distorted, and four short bonds and two long bonds are formed. The arrangements of d electrons and the symmetrical or distorted nature of the octahedral complex formed can be worked out; see Table 8.3. The

TABLE 8.3

Number of d electrons	Arrangement in weak ligand field		Arrangement in strong ligand field	
d^1	$d\epsilon^1 d\gamma^0$	Almost symmetrical	$d\epsilon^1 d\gamma^0$	Almost symmetrical
d^2	$d\epsilon^2 d\gamma^0$	Almost symmetrical	$d\epsilon^2 d\gamma^0$	Almost symmetrical
d^3	$d\epsilon^3 d\gamma^0$	Symmetrical	$d\epsilon^3 d\gamma^0$	Symmetrical
d^4	$d\epsilon^3 d\gamma^1$	Distorted	$d\epsilon^4 d\gamma^0$	Almost symmetrical
d^5	$d\epsilon^3 d\gamma^2$	Symmetrical	$d\epsilon^5 d\gamma^0$	Almost symmetrical
d^6	$d\epsilon^4 d\gamma^2$	Almost symmetrical	$d\epsilon^6 d\gamma^0$	Symmetrical
d^7	$d\epsilon^5 d\gamma^2$	Almost symmetrical	$d\epsilon^6 d\gamma^1$	Distorted
d^8	$d\epsilon^6 d\gamma^2$	Symmetrical	$d\epsilon^6 d\gamma^2$	Distorted—see note on *Square Planar Arrangements*
d^9	$d\epsilon^6 d\gamma^3$	Distorted	$d\epsilon^6 d\gamma^3$	Distorted
d^{10}	$d\epsilon^6 d\gamma^4$	Symmetrical	$d\epsilon^6 d\gamma^4$	Symmetrical

unsymmetrical orbitals are underlined. Thus in the cobalt complexes previously mentioned, Co^{3+} has a d^6 configuration, thus $[CoF_6]^{3-}$ is almost symmetrical and $[Co(NH_3)_6]^{3+}$ is completely symmetrical. The electronic configuration d^8 gives a square planar arrangement as explained in the next section.

Square Planar Arrangements

If the central metal ion has eight d electrons, these will be arranged $d\epsilon^6 d\gamma^2$ regardless of whether the ion is in a strong or a weak octahedral ligand field. In a weak field the electrons are arranged:

$$d\epsilon \qquad d\gamma$$

A regular octahedral complex is thus formed by using outer d orbitals. However, under the influence of a strong ligand field, the $d\gamma$ electrons may pair up, leaving one vacant d orbital, which can accept a lone pair from a ligand. For example consider $[Ni(CN)_4]^{2-}$:

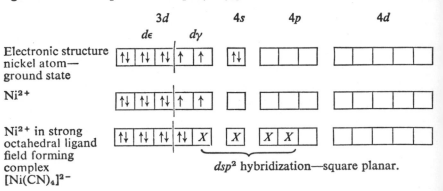

The square planar arrangement results from an unsuccessful attempt to form an octahedral complex. Consider a Ni^{2+} ion, with one electron in the $d_{x^2-y^2}$ orbital, and one in the d_{z^2} orbital (Fig. 8.5). The approach of ligands along x, y and z will result in the energy of these orbitals increasing. Because the $d_{x^2-y^2}$ orbital is 'attacked' by four ligands and the d_{z^2} by only two, the energy of the $d_{x^2-y^2}$ orbital will increase most. If the ligands have a strong enough field, the electron will be forced out of the $d_{x^2-y^2}$ orbital into the d_{z^2}. Thus four ligands can approach along x, $-x$, y and $-y$. A ligand approaching in the z or $-z$ direction attempting to donate a lone pair, meets the very strong repulsive forces from a completely full d_{z^2} orbital. Thus only four ligands succeed in bonding to the metal. A similar explanation accounts for the square planar structures from ions with a d^4 configuration in a weak ligand field, although in this case the d_{z^2} orbital only contains one electron.   Note that it is not possible to use both $3d$ and $4d$ orbitals, since a criterion for hybridizing orbitals is that they must be approximately the same energy.

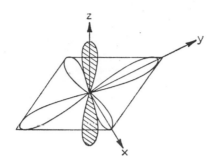

Fig. 8.5

Tetrahedral Complexes

A regular tetrahedron is related to a cube, with an atom at the centre and four of the eight corners occupied by ligands (Fig. 8.6).   The directions x, y

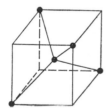 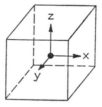

Fig. 8.6

and z point to the centres of the faces.   The $d\gamma$ orbitals point along x, y and z (that is, to the face centres) and the $d\epsilon$ orbitals point in between x, y and z (that is, towards the centres of the edges of the cube).

The directions of approach of the ligands does not coincide exactly with either the $d\gamma$ or the $d\epsilon$ orbitals (Fig. 8.7).   The angle between a $d\gamma$ orbital, the central metal and the ligand, is 54° 44', whilst the angle between a $d\epsilon$ orbital, central metal and ligand is 35° 16'.   The approach of ligands raises the energy of both sets of orbitals, but since the $d\epsilon$ orbitals correspond more closely to the positions of the ligands, their energy increases most and the $d\gamma$ orbitals are filled first.   This is opposite to what happens in octahedral complexes.

A strong ligand field causes a big energy difference between $d\epsilon$ and $d\gamma$ and electrons may move from $d\epsilon$ orbitals to vacant $d\gamma$ orbitals (Fig. 8.8). Tetrahedral complexes are less stable than octahedral complexes and generally only occur when both the $d\epsilon$ and $d\gamma$ orbitals are symmetrical (empty, half-filled or

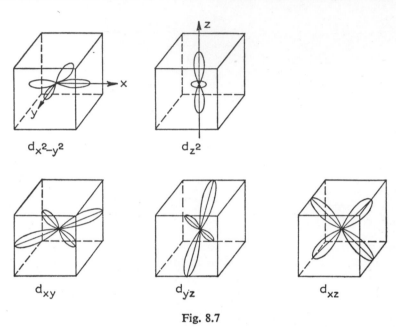

$$d_{x^2-y^2} \qquad d_{z^2}$$

$$d_{xy} \qquad d_{yz} \qquad d_{xz}$$

Fig. 8.7

completely filled). Asymmetry of $d\epsilon$ orbitals would be expected to distort the complex most, but tetrahedral complexes with asymmetry of either $d\epsilon$ or $d\gamma$ rarely occur. This is presumably because they are so distorted that they are unstable. One common exception occurs when the metal ion has a d^1

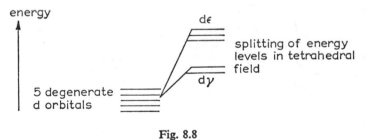

Fig. 8.8

electronic configuration. The arrangement of electrons and symmetry in strong and weak ligand fields can be worked out as in Table 8.4. The asymmetrical orbitals are underlined.

TABLE 8.4

Number of d electrons on central metal ion	Arrangement in weak ligand field	Arrangement in strong ligand field
d^0	$d\gamma^0\, d\epsilon^0$	$d\gamma^0\, d\epsilon^0$
d^1	$\underline{d\gamma^1}\, d\epsilon^0$	$\underline{d\gamma^1}\, d\epsilon^0$
d^2	$d\gamma^2\, d\epsilon^0$	$d\gamma^2\, d\epsilon^0$
d^3	$d\gamma^2\, \underline{d\epsilon^1}$	$\underline{d\gamma^3}\, d\epsilon^0$
d^4	$d\gamma^2\, \underline{d\epsilon^2}$	$d\gamma^4\, d\epsilon^0$
d^5	$d\gamma^2\, d\epsilon^3$	$d\gamma^4\, \underline{d\epsilon^1}$
d^6	$\underline{d\gamma^3}\, d\epsilon^3$	$d\gamma^4\, \underline{d\epsilon^2}$
d^7	$d\gamma^4\, d\epsilon^3$	$d\gamma^4\, d\epsilon^3$
d^8	$d\gamma^4\, \underline{d\epsilon^4}$	$d\gamma^4\, \underline{d\epsilon^4}$
d^9	$d\gamma^4\, \underline{d\epsilon^5}$	$d\gamma^4\, \underline{d\epsilon^5}$
d^{10}	$d\gamma^4\, d\epsilon^6$	$d\gamma^4\, d\epsilon^6$

Tetrahedral complexes in which the central metal ion has 0, 1, 2, 5, 7 and 10 d electrons are known; and all of these except d^1 would be expected to be regular and undistorted.

Thus in $TiCl_4$, the titanium atom has the electronic configuration $3d^2\, 4s^2$.

Since both $d\epsilon$ and $d\gamma$ are empty and symmetrical, the complex is both stable and undistorted.

Consider the complex ion $(FeCl_4)^-$

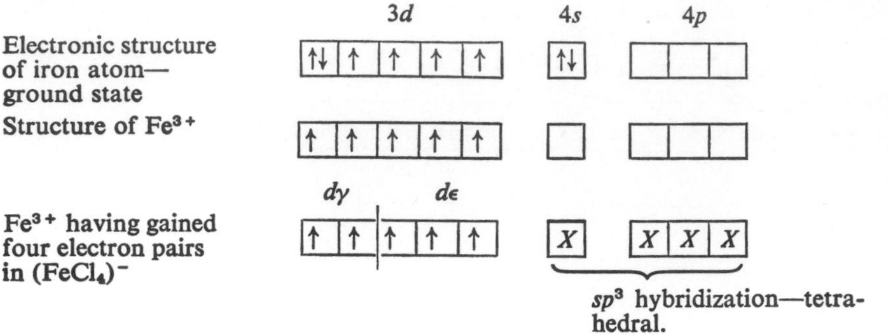

Since Cl^- is a weak ligand, the five d electrons are arranged $d\gamma^2\ d\epsilon^3$, which is symmetrical; hence the complex is regular and stable.

Chelates

Some of the factors which favour complex formation have already been mentioned. Small highly-charged ions with suitable vacant orbitals of the right energy, the satisfaction of the effective atomic number rule and the attainment of a symmetrical shape, all favour complex formation.

In some complexes a group occupies more than one co-ordination position, that is more than one atom in the group is bonded to the central metal. For example, ethylenediamine forms a complex with copper ions:

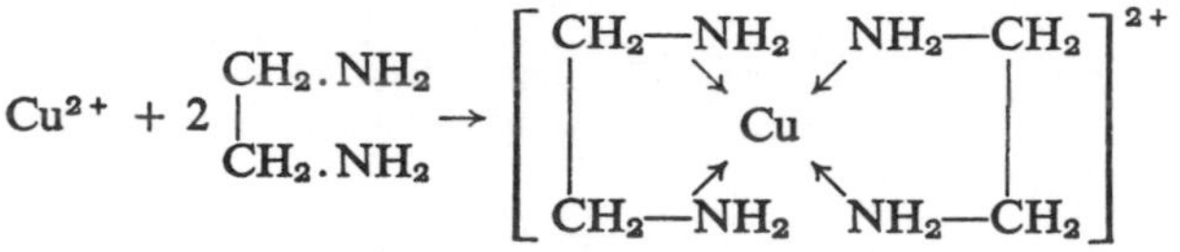

In this complex the copper is surrounded by four $-NH_2$ groups, each nitrogen atom donating a lone pair of electrons and forming a co-ordinate bond. Thus each ethylenediamine molecule is bonded to the copper in two places, hence it is called a bi-dentate group or ligand. A ring structure is thus formed (in this case a pair of five-membered rings) and such ring structures are called chelates. Normally chelated complexes are more stable than similar non-chelated complexes. Some common bi-dentate chelating agents are (Fig. 8.9):

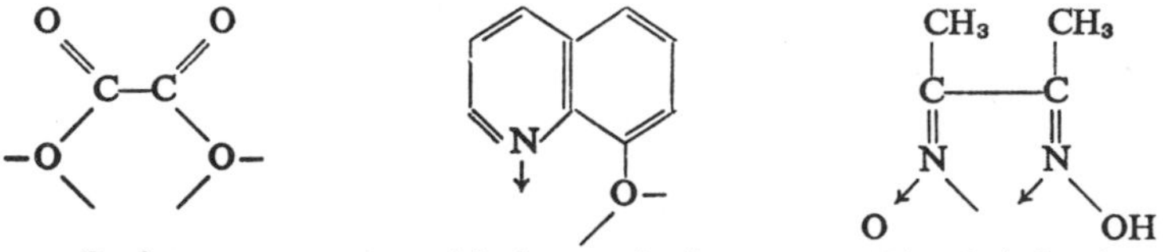

Oxalate   8 hydroxyquinoline   Dimethyl glyoxime

Fig. 8.9

The more rings that are formed, the more stable the complex. Chelating agents with three-, four- and six-donor atoms are known and are termed tri-, tetra- and hexa-dentate ligands. An important example of the latter is ethylenediaminetetra-acetic acid, which bonds through two nitrogen and four oxygen atoms to the metal, and so forms five rings. Due to this bonding, even complexes with large ions such as Ca^{2+} are stable.

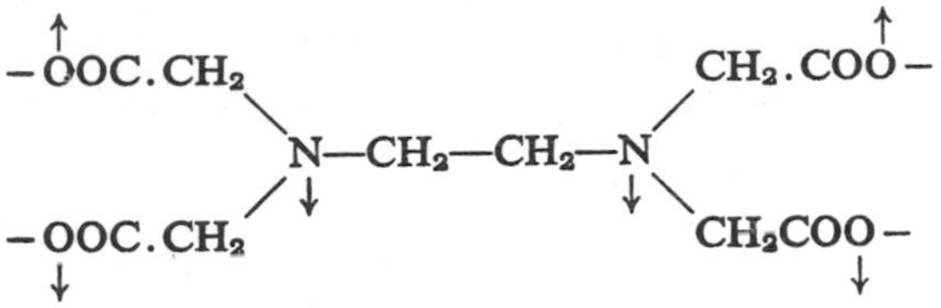

EDTA

Chelate compounds are even more stable when they contain a system of alternate double and single bonds. The π electron density is delocalized and spread over the ring, which is said to be stabilized by resonance. Examples of this include acetylacetone and porphyrin complexes with metals (Fig. 8.10).

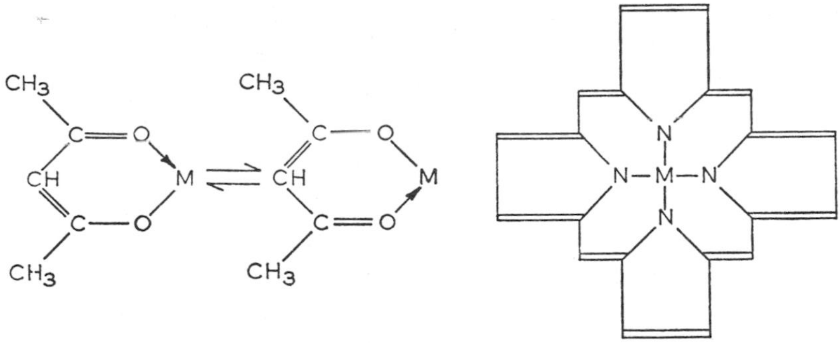

Resonance in acetylacetone chelate   Porphyrin complex

Fig. 8.10

Nomenclature of Co-ordination Compounds

The International Union of Pure and Applied Chemistry published rules for the systematic naming of co-ordination compounds in 1957. These are summarized in the Chemical Society's *Handbook for Authors* (special publication No. 11), and this system is widely accepted. Details of the recommended system are as follows:

(1) The positive ion is named first followed by the negative ion.

(2) Co-ordinated groups are listed in the following order: negative ligands, neutral ligands then positive ligands. Negative ligands end in -o for

example CN^- cyano, Cl^- chloro, NO_2^- nitro and OH^- hydroxo. Neutral groups have no special endings, e.g. NH_3 ammine and H_2O aquo. Positive groups end in -ium, e.g. NH_2—NH_3^+ hydrazinium. If there are several ligands within a group, they are listed alphabetically, and the prefixes di, tri, tetra, penta and hexa indicate the number of ligands of that type. When the name of the ligand includes a number, e.g. dipyridyl or ethylenediamine then bis, tris and tetrakis are used instead of di, tri and tetra and the group is placed in brackets.

(3) The oxidation state of the central metal is shown by a Roman numeral in brackets immediately following its name.

(4) Complex positive ions and neutral molecules have no special ending but complex negative ions end in -ate.

(5) If the complex contains two or more metal atoms, it is termed poly-nuclear. The ligands which link the two metal atoms are called bridge groups and are separated from the rest of the complex by hyphens and denoted by the prefix μ.

These rules are illustrated by the following examples:

$[Co(NH_3)_6]Cl_3$	Hexamminecobalt(III) chloride
$[Co(NH_3)_5Cl]^{2+}$	Chloropentamminecobalt(III) ion
$[Co(NH_3)_4SO_4]NO_3$	Sulphatotetramminecobalt(III) nitrate
$[Co(NH_3)_3(NO_2)_3]$	Trinitrotriamminecobalt(III)
$[Co(NH_3)_3NO_2.Cl.CN]$	Chlorocyanonitrotriamminecobalt(III)
$[Cr(en)_3]Cl_3$	*tris(ethylenediamine)chromium(III) chloride
$K_4[Fe(CN)_6]$	Potassium hexacyanoferrate(II)
$[(NH_3)_5Co.NH_2.Co(NH_3)_5](NO_3)_5$	Decammine-μ-amidodicobalt(III) nitrate

$$\left[(en)_2Co \underset{OH}{\overset{NH_2}{\diamondsuit}} Co(en)_2 \right] (SO_4)_2$$ tetrakis(ethylenediamine)-μ-amido-μ-hydroxo-dicobalt(III) sulphate

* Because two optical isomers exist for this complex, the name should have a prefix d, or l.

Isomerism

Compounds which have the same chemical formula but a different structural arrangement are called isomers. Because of the complicated formulae of many co-ordination compounds, the variety of bond types and the number of shapes possible, many different types of isomerism occur. Werner's classification into polymerization, ionization, hydrate, linkage, co-ordination, co-ordination position, geometric and optical isomerism is still generally accepted.

(1) *Polymerization isomerism.* This is not really true isomerism since it occurs between compounds having the same empirical formula, but different

molecular weights. Thus $[Pt(NH_3)_2Cl_2]$, $[Pt(NH_3)_4][PtCl_4]$, $[Pt(NH_3)_4]$ $[Pt(NH_3)Cl_3]_2$ and $[Pt(NH_3)_3Cl]_2[PtCl_4]$ all have the same empirical formula. Polymerization isomerism may be due to a different number of nuclei in the complex, e.g.:

(2) *Ionization isomerism.* This type of isomerism is due to the exchange of groups between the complex ion and the ions outside it. $[Co(NH_3)_5Br]SO_4$ is red-violet, and in solution gives a precipitate with $BaCl_2$ confirming the presence of $SO_4{}^{2-}$. On the other hand, $[Co(NH_3)_5SO_4]Br$ is red, and does not give a sulphate test in solution, but instead gives a precipitate of AgBr with $AgNO_3$. Note that the sulphate ion only occupies one co-ordination position even though it has two negative charges. Other examples of ionization isomerism are $[Pt(NH_3)_4Cl_2]Br_2$ and $[Pt(NH_3)_4Br_2]Cl_2$, $[Co(en)_2NO_2.Cl]SCN$, $[Co(en)_2NO_2.SCN]Cl$ and $[Co(en)_2Cl.SCN]NO_2$.

(3) *Hydrate isomerism.* Three isomers of $CrCl_3.6H_2O$ are known. From conductivity measurements and quantitative precipitation of the ionized chlorine, they have been given the following formulae:

$[Cr(H_2O)_6]Cl_3$	violet	(three ionic chlorines)
$[Cr(H_2O)_5Cl]Cl_2.H_2O$	green	(two ionic chlorines)
$[Cr(H_2O)_4Cl_2]Cl.2H_2O$	dark green	(one ionic chlorine)

(4) *Linkage isomerism.* Certain ligands contain more than one atom which could donate an electron pair. In the case of the $NO_2{}^-$ ion, either a nitrogen or an oxygen atom may act as donor, hence the possibility of isomerism. Two different nitropentammine cobalt(III) chlorides have been prepared, each containing the $NO_2{}^-$ group in the complex ion. One is red and is easily decomposed by acids to give nitrous acid, while the other is yellow and is stable to acids. This behaviour is analogous to the behaviour of organic nitrites R—ONO and nitro compounds R—NO_2. The two materials are represented below.

red
nitritopentamminecobalt(III)
ion

yellow
nitropentamminecobalt(III)
ion

This type of isomerism might be expected with other ligands, such as CO, CN^- and SCN^-, but no examples are known at present.

(5) *Co-ordination isomerism.* When both positive and negative ions are complex, isomerism may be caused by the interchange of ligands between the two complex ions, for example: $[Co(NH_3)_6][Cr(CN)_6]$ and $[Cr(NH_3)_6]$ $[Co(CN)_6]$. Intermediate types between these extremes are also possible.

(6) *Co-ordination position isomerism.* In polynuclear complexes an interchange of ligands between the different metal nuclei gives rise to positional isomerism, for example:

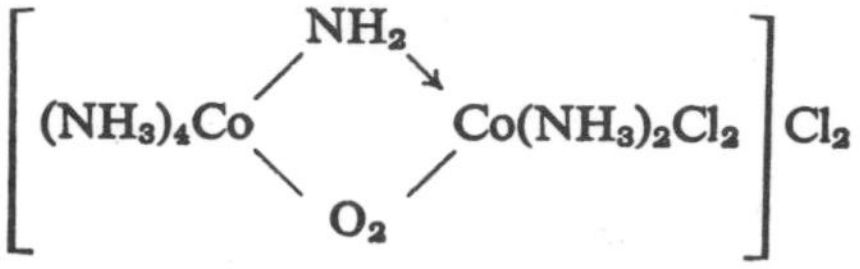

$$\left[(NH_3)_4Co \overset{\displaystyle NH_2}{\underset{\displaystyle O_2}{\diagup\diagdown}} Co(NH_3)_2Cl_2 \right] Cl_2$$

and

$$\left[Cl(NH_3)_3Co \overset{\displaystyle NH_2}{\underset{\displaystyle O_2}{\diagup\diagdown}} Co(NH_3)_3Cl \right] Cl_2$$

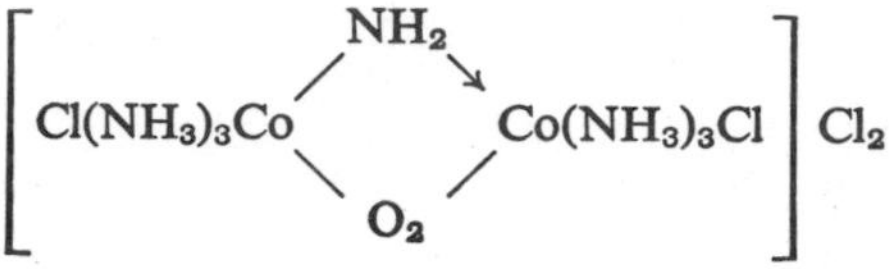

(7) *Geometric or stereoisomerism.* In disubstituted complexes, the substituted groups may be adjacent or opposite to each other. This gives rise to geometric isomerism. Thus square planar complexes such as $[Pt(NH_3)_2Cl_2]$ can be prepared in two forms. If NH_4OH is added to the $[PtCl_4]^{2-}$ ion, the complex formed has a finite dipole moment. However, the complex prepared by the action of HCl on $[Pt(NH_3)_4]^{2+}$ has no dipole. The two complexes are formulated in Fig. 8.11. This sort of isomerism can also occur in

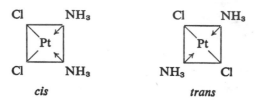

Fig. 8.11

square planar chelate complexes if the chelating group is not symmetrical, for example the complexes between glycine and platinum (Fig. 8.12).

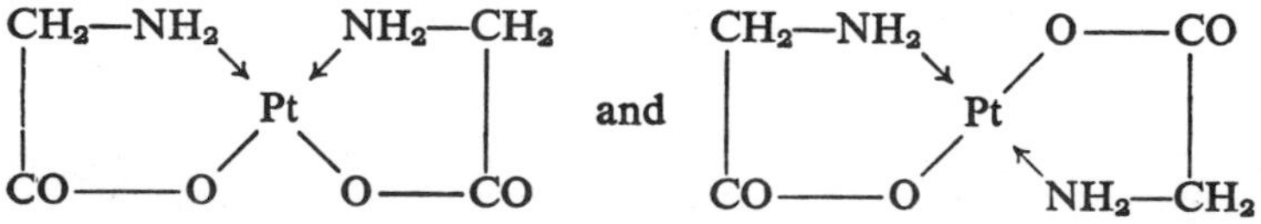

Fig. 8.12

Similarly disubstituted octahedral complexes, such as $[Co(NH_3)_4Cl_2]^+$ exist in *cis* and *trans* forms (Fig. 8.13). (This method of drawing an octahedral complex might suggest that the positions in the square are different

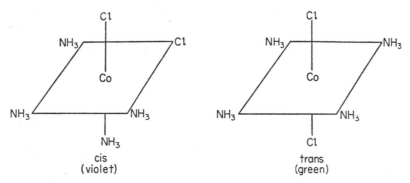

cis
(violet)

trans
(green)

Fig. 8.13

from the up and down positions. This is not the case since all six positions are equivalent.)

(8) *Optical isomerism.* At one time it was thought that this sort of isomerism was associated only with carbon compounds, but it exists in inorganic molecules as well.

If a molecule is asymmetric, it cannot be superimposed on its mirror image. The two forms have the type of symmetry shown by the left and right hands and are called an enantiomorphic pair. The two forms are optical isomers

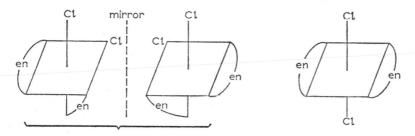

enantiomorphic pair
d and *l cis* dichloro bis
(ethylenediamine)cobalt(III) ion

trans dichloro bis(ethylenediamine)
cobalt(III) ion

Fig. 8.14

and are called either *dextro* or *laevo* (*d* or *l*) depending on the direction they rotate the plane of polarized light.

Optical isomerism is common in octahedral complexes involving bidentate groups. For example, $[Co(en)_2Cl_2]^+$ shows *cis* and *trans* forms (geometric isomerism), and the *cis* form is optically active and exists in *d* and *l* forms (optical isomerism) making a total of three isomers (Fig. 8.14). Optical activity occurs also in polynuclear complexes, such as:

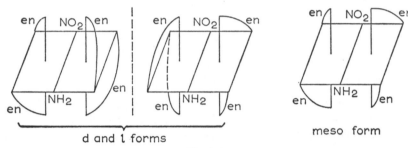

This has been resolved into two optically active forms (*d* and *l*) and an optically inactive form which is internally compensated and is called the *meso* form (Fig. 8.15).

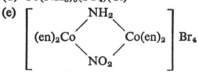

d and l forms   meso form

Fig. 8.15

PROBLEMS

1. List the factors which affect the stability of co-ordination complexes.
2. Describe the methods by which the presence of complex ions may be detected in solution.
3. What methods could be used to distinguish between *cis* and *trans* isomers of a complex?
4. Name the individual isomers of each of the following:
    (a) $[Pt(NH_3)_2Cl_2]$
    (b) $CrCl_3 6H_2O$
    (c) $[Co(NH_3)_5NO_2](NO_3)_2$
    (d) $Co(NH_3)_5(SO_4)(Cl)$
    (e)

$$\left[(en)_2Co \underset{NO_2}{\overset{NH_2}{\diagup \diagdown}} Co(en)_2 \right] Br_4$$

    (f) $Co(en)_2NH_3BrSO_4$
    (g) $[Pt(NH_3)(H_2O)(C_5H_5N)(NO_2)]Cl$.
5. Account for the following:
    (a) $Ni(CO)_4$ is tetrahedral;
    (b) $[Ni(CN)_4]^{2-}$ is square planar;
    (c) $[Ni(NH_3)_6]^{2+}$ is octahedral.

CHAPTER 9

THE ATOMIC NUCLEUS

Structure of the Nucleus

Atomic nuclei are made up of neutrons and protons bound together. The nuclear radius is very small, approximately 10^{-12} cm. Nuclear distances are measured in fermi units $1f = 10^{-13}$ cm. Most of the mass of an atom is concentrated in the nucleus; therefore its density is very high, approximately 10^{13} gm cm^3.

The nucleus is sometimes considered to resemble a 'liquid drop'. The repulsive forces between the like charges on the protons tend to split the drop, and a surface tension effect opposes this. The density of different nuclei is almost constant, and they are regarded as different sizes of drop. The range of nuclear attractive forces is very small, 2f–3f, and so the nucleons (neutrons and protons) can move inside the nucleus rather like the particles in a liquid. Nuclear fission can easily be explained by use of the liquid drop model. As the mass of the nucleus increases, the repulsion between protons increases more rapidly than the attractive forces. To minimize the repulsive force, the shape of the nucleus is deformed. Uranium of mass number 235, ^{235}U, is so deformed that the addition of a little extra energy, e.g. absorption of a neutron, will cause the nucleus to break into two; that is, fission will occur. Nuclei of mass numbers larger than that of uranium are so deformed that they undergo spontaneous fission.

Alternatively the nucleus may be regarded as a 'shell structure' with the nucleons arranged in shells rather like the orbital electrons. This is supported by a periodicity in nuclear properties. Thus elements of even atomic number are more stable and more abundant than elements of odd atomic number. Elements of even atomic number are richer in isotopes and never have less than three stable isotopes (average 5·7). Elements with odd atomic numbers frequently have only one stable isotope and never more than two. There is a tendency for the number of neutrons and the number of protons in the nucleus to be even (Table 9.1.). This suggests that a pairing of nucleons may occur in the nucleus similar to the pairing of electrons which occurs in atomic and molecular orbitals. If two protons spin in opposite

241

directions, the magnetic fields they produce will mutually cancel each other. The small amount of binding energy generated is sufficient to stabilize the nucleus, but is not the most important source of energy in the nucleus.

Certain nuclei are extra stable, and this is interpreted as being due to a filled shell. Nuclei with 2, 8, 20, 28, 50, 82 or 126 neutrons or protons are

TABLE 9.1

Number of protons	Number of neutrons	Number of stable isotopes
even	even	164
even	odd	55
odd	even	50
odd	odd	4

particularly stable and have a large number of isotopes. These numbers are termed 'magic numbers'. The emission of γ-rays by the nucleus is readily explained from the shell model, because if nucleons in an excited state fall to a lower nuclear energy level, they will emit energy as γ-rays.

Thus some nuclear properties imply that the nucleons are free to move within the nucleus, and others suggest that nucleons exist in energy levels.

Forces in the Nucleus

The repulsive forces between protons in the nucleus are electrostatic. In a stable nucleus, the attractive forces must be greater than the repulsive forces, otherwise spontaneous fission would occur. The attractive forces in the nucleus are not electrostatic because there are no oppositely-charged particles, and because the forces only act over a very short distance of 2f–3f. If the nuclear particles are separated by a distance much greater than this, attraction ceases although electrostatic forces only diminish slowly with distance. Further, the same attractive force binds neutrons to neutrons, neutrons to protons and protons to protons; therefore the force does not depend on the charge.

Two atoms may be held together by a sharing of electrons, because the exchange forces result in a covalent bond. By analogy, two nuclear particles may be held together by sharing a particle. The particle exchanged is called a π meson and may have a positive charge $\pi+$, a negative charge $\pi-$ or no charge πo. Exchange of $\pi-$ and $\pi+$ mesons accounts for the binding energy between neutrons and protons, and the transfer of a charge converting a neutron to a proton or vice versa. The resultant attractive forces are indicated by dotted lines in the examples below.

$$\left.\begin{array}{c} n \\ p \end{array}\right\rangle \ \pi- \rightarrow \ \left.\begin{array}{c} p \\ n \end{array}\right. \qquad \left.\begin{array}{c} p \\ n \end{array}\right\rangle \ \pi+ \rightarrow \ \left.\begin{array}{c} n \\ p \end{array}\right.$$

πo mesons are exchanged between protons and neutrons.

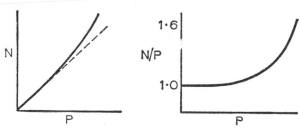

The attractive forces between p–n, n–n and p–p are probably all of much the same strength. A πo meson having a mass 264 times that of an electron and π+ and π− mesons having mass 273 times that of an electron have been detected. All mesons are very unstable outside the nucleus. Less common elementary particles are discussed in articles in *Penguin Science News* 31 and 52. The number of charged particles in a nucleus remains statistically constant, but the particles representing neutrons and protons are constantly changing. The transformation of neutrons into protons and vice versa are first order reactions, and their rates depend on the relative numbers of each type of particle present. In a stable nucleus, these two changes are in equilibrium. The ratio between the number of neutrons and protons is related to the stability of the nucleus.

Stability and the Ratio of Neutrons and Protons

The stability of a nucleus depends in a qualitative way on the number of protons and neutrons present. For elements of low atomic number (up to $Z = 20$) the most stable nuclei exist when the number of protons P in the nucleus equals the number of neutrons N, that is the ratio $N/P = 1$. For elements of higher atomic number the repulsion between protons increases. Entry of a neutron is preferred to the addition of a proton since the neutron increases the attractive force without increasing the repulsive force. Thus the ratio N/P increases progressively up to about 1·6. Above this value the nuclei have become so large they undergo spontaneous fission. These trends are shown in the following graphs of neutron number N against proton

Fig. 9.1

number P, and N/P ratio against proton number for the stable nuclei (Fig. 9.1).

Modes of Decay

Stable nuclei lie near to these curves, and nuclei with N/P ratios higher or lower than the stable ratio will tend to be radioactive. If the N/P ratio is high, i.e. the isotope lies above the curve, the nucleus will decay so that a stable arrangement is reached. The ratio can be reduced by several means which are discussed below.

(a) *Beta emission.* Electrons or β radiation may be emitted from the nucleus when a neutron is converted to a proton, an electron and a neutrino. The neutrino has zero mass and charge, and is postulated to balance the spins. This may be written:

$$_0^1n \rightarrow {}_1^1p + {}_{-1}^0e + \nu$$

The mass numbers at the top and the nuclear charges at the bottom are both balanced in this equation. In this way the N/P ratio is decreased, and if an isotope is not far from the stable N/P line one β decay may be sufficient;

$$_6^{14}C \rightarrow {}_7^{14}N + {}_{-1}^0e + \nu$$

Isotopes further from the stable line may undergo a series of β decays, whereby the resultant nuclei become progressively more stable and have a longer half-life period, until eventually a stable isotope is formed.

$$_{56}^{141}Ba \xrightarrow[T_{1/2}=18 \text{ min.}]{\beta} {}_{57}^{141}La \xrightarrow[T_{1/2}=3\cdot7 \text{ hrs.}]{\beta} {}_{58}^{141}Ce \xrightarrow[T_{1/2}=28 \text{ days}]{\beta} {}_{59}^{141}Pr$$

In β decay the mass number remains unchanged, but the nuclear charge increases by one unit and the element moves one place to the right in the periodic table.

(b) *Neutron emission.* An obvious way to decrease the N/P ratio is for the nucleus to emit a neutron. Since the binding energy in the nucleus is high (about 8 MeV), this form of decay is rare and only takes place with highly energetic nuclei. One of the few examples is given below.

$$_{36}^{87}Kr \longrightarrow {}_{36}^{86}Kr + {}_0^1n$$
$$\xrightarrow{\beta} {}_{37}^{87}Rb \xrightarrow{\beta} {}_{38}^{87}Sr$$

If the N/P ratio is too low, i.e. the isotope lies below the curve, there are three possible modes of decay.

(c) *Positron emission.* Positrons or $\beta+$ radiation (positive electrons) result from the transformation of proton to neutron, positron and anti-neutrino.

$$_1^1p \rightarrow {}_0^1n + {}_1^0e + \bar{\nu}$$

The anti-neutrino is postulated to balance the spins. The positron is ejected from the nucleus and eventually neutralizes an electron. The energy from the positron is released as two γ-rays each with an energy of 0·51 MeV.

This energy came originally from the parent nucleus, and so it follows that the mass of the parent nucleus is greater than the mass of the daughter nucleus.

$$_{10}^{18}\text{Ne} \rightarrow {}_{9}^{18}\text{F} + {}_{1}^{0}e + \bar{\nu}$$
$$_{6}^{11}\text{C} \rightarrow {}_{5}^{11}\text{B} + {}_{1}^{0}e + \bar{\nu}$$

(d) *Orbital or K-electron capture.* The nucleus may capture an orbital electron from the inner or K shell and thus convert a proton into a neutron and a neutrino:

$$_{1}^{1}\text{p} + {}_{-1}^{0}e \rightarrow {}_{0}^{1}\text{n} + \nu$$

Usually an electron from a higher energy level drops back to fill the vacancy in the K shell and characteristic X-radiation is emitted. Electron capture is not common, but occurs in nuclei where the N/P ratio is low and the nucleus has insufficient energy for positron emission, that is $2 \times 0.51 = 1.02$ MeV.

$$_{4}^{7}\text{Be} + {}_{-1}^{0}e \rightarrow {}_{3}^{7}\text{Li} + \nu$$
$$_{19}^{40}\text{K} + {}_{-1}^{0}e \rightarrow {}_{18}^{40}\text{Ar} + \nu$$

Where the difference in mass of parent and daughter nuclei is equivalent to more than the required 1·02 MeV for positron emission, both positron emission and K capture occur.

$$_{23}^{48}\text{V} \underline{\qquad} \beta^+ + (58\%) \quad \rightarrow \quad {}_{22}^{48}\text{Ti}$$
$$\underline{\qquad} K \text{ capture } (42\%) \underline{\qquad}$$

(e) *Proton emission.* Except for nuclei in a very high energy state, proton emission is unlikely, since the energy to remove a proton is about 8 MeV.

γ-Radiation

Following any nuclear change, the neutrons and protons rearrange themselves to take up their most stable positions. Electromagnetic radiation of very short wavelength, called γ-rays, is emitted, corresponding to the change from one nuclear energy level to another.

Half-Life Period

Radioactive decay is a first order reaction, and depends only on the relative number of radioactive atoms present. Thus the size of the sample does not affect the time taken to undergo radioactive decay. The time taken for half of a sample to decay is called the half-life period, and this is a characteristic of a particular isotope.

Nuclear energies are of the order of 10^9 kcal/mole of nucleons whilst the energies involved in chemical reactions are about 10–10^2 kcal/mole. Clearly transmutation of one element to another by chemical means is impossible,

17+c.i.c.

because of the exceedingly high nuclear energy. For the same reason a change in temperature has no observable effect on the rate of decay.

Binding Energy and Nuclear Stability

A stable nucleus must have less energy than its constituent particles or it would not form. Energy and mass are related by the Einstein equation $E = mc^2$ where E is the energy, m the mass and c the velocity of light. Thus the mass of a stable nucleus must be less than that of the constituent nucleons; the difference is called the mass defect.

The mass defect can be calculated, and converted to the binding energy in the nucleus. Clearly the larger the mass defect, the larger the binding energy, and therefore the more stable the nucleus.

Mass of $^4_2$He nucleus = 4·0028 a.m.u.

Mass of 2n + 2p　　= 4·0331

Mass defect　　　　= 0·0303

Binding energy = 0·0303 × 931 = 28·2 MeV

Mass of $^6_3$Li nucleus = 6·0170

Mass of 3n + 3p　　= 6·0497

Mass defect　　　　= 0·0327

Binding energy = 0·0327 × 931 = 30·4 MeV

(931 is the conversion factor from a.m.u. to MeV).

It is quite easy to calculate whether or not a nucleus is stable against decay. Some possible decay processes are given below.

$^4_2$He → $^1_0$n + $^3_2$He

$^4_2$He → $^1_0$n + $^1_0$n + $^2_2$He

$^4_2$He → $^1_1$p + $^3_1$H

$^6_3$Li → $^1_0$n + $^5_3$Li

$^6_3$Li → $^1_1$p + $^5_2$He

$^6_3$Li → $^4_2$He + $^2_1$H

Since the mass of the parent is less than the combined mass of the suggested products, none of the above decay processes occur.

The binding energy of the nucleus varies with the number of nucleons present in it, and to compare the nuclear stability of different elements the average binding energy per nucleon is calculated.

$$\text{Binding energy per nucleon} = \frac{\text{total binding energy}}{\text{number of nucleons}}$$

The graph of binding energy per nucleon against atomic number, for the different elements shows that nucleons are held together with increasing force up to a mass number of about 65. The binding energy for each additional nucleon decreases as the nuclei get larger (Fig. 9.2). The average binding energy per nucleon is about 8 MeV for most nuclei, consequently this amount of energy is needed to remove either a proton or a neutron from the nucleus.

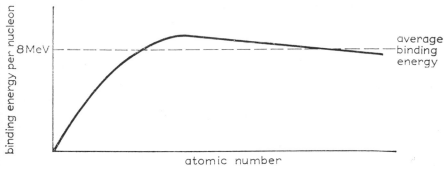

Fig. 9.2

α-Decay

As nuclei get larger, the repulsive force between protons increases and the energy of the nucleus increases. A point is reached where the attractive forces are unable to hold the nucleons together and part of the nucleus breaks off. The α-particle, a helium nucleus $^4_2$He is a particularly stable nuclear fragment, and breaks away fairly readily.

$$^{238}_{92}U \rightarrow ^{234}_{90}Th + ^4_2He + energy$$

The mass of the parent nucleus must provide the mass of the daughter nucleus, and the α-particle plus some mass which is converted into energy. It can be calculated from the mass of the nucleus whether α-decay in any element is energetically possible. Natural α-activity is only possible among elements of mass number greater than 209, since only these elements have the required energy. Conversely 209 is the largest number of nucleons which will fit into a stable nucleus.

If ejection of one α-particle does not completely stabilize the nucleus, further α-particles may be emitted, but since α-decay raises the N/P ratio it may lead to β-emission.

Nuclei of mass number above 230 may undergo spontaneous fission into two elements of lower atomic number. Since elements of low atomic number have a smaller N/P ratio, some neutrons are ejected during fission. These neutrons may be absorbed by another nucleus which then becomes unstable and itself undergoes fission liberating more neutrons, and a chain reaction has thus been started.

Radioactive Displacement Laws

(1) Emission of an α-particle gives an element which is four mass units lighter and the atomic number decreases by two. The daughter element is therefore two places to the left of the parent in the periodic table.

(2) When a β-particle is emitted the mass number remains the same, but the atomic number increases by one and the new element is one place to the

right of the parent in the periodic system. These changes are shown in the following series:

$$^{223}_{88}Ra \xrightarrow{\alpha} {}^{219}_{86}Rn \xrightarrow{\alpha} {}^{215}_{84}Po \xrightarrow{\alpha} {}^{211}_{82}Pb \xrightarrow{\beta} {}^{211}_{83}Bi \xrightarrow{\alpha} {}^{207}_{81}Tl \xrightarrow{\beta} {}^{207}_{82}Pb$$

Radioactive Decay Series

The heavy radioactive elements may be grouped into four decay series. The common radioactive elements thorium, uranium and actinium occur naturally and belong to three different series named after them. They are the parent members of their respective series and have the longest half-life periods. They decay by a series of α and β emissions, and produce radioactive elements which are successively more stable until finally a stable isotope is reached. All three series terminate with element number 82, lead. Following the discovery of the artificial post-uranium elements, the neptunium series has been added, which ends with bismuth, element number 83.

> Thorium ($4n$) series
> Neptunium ($4n + 1$) series
> Uranium ($4n + 2$) series
> Actinium ($4n + 3$) series

The numbers indicate that the parent and all the members of a particular series have mass numbers exactly divisible by four, or divisible by four with a remainder of one, two or three. There is no natural cross-linking between the four series, although this can be performed artificially.

Thorium ($4n$) Series

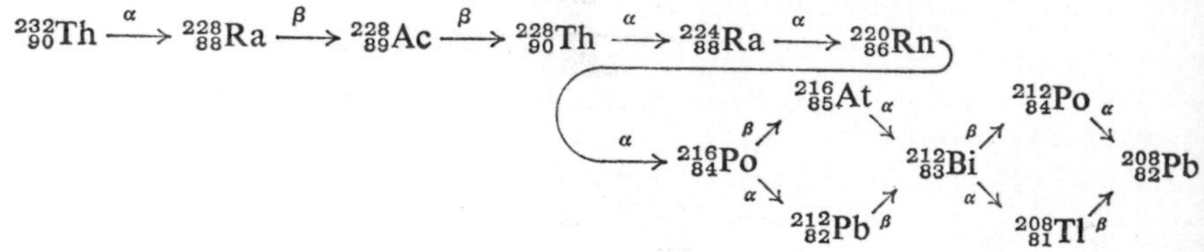

Neptunium ($4n + 1$) Series

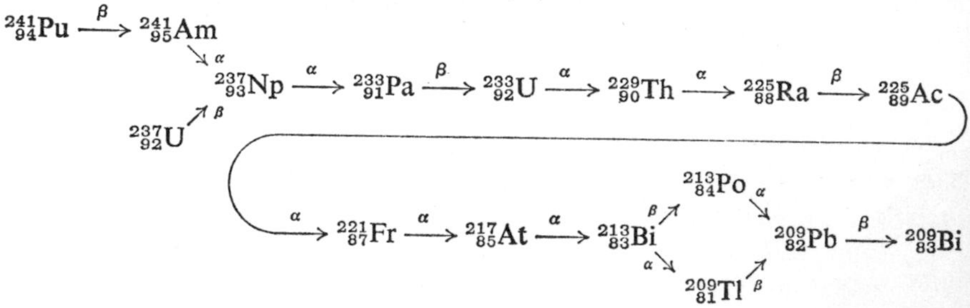

Uranium (4n + 2) Series

$$^{238}_{92}U \xrightarrow{\alpha} {}^{234}_{90}Th \xrightarrow{\beta} {}^{234}_{91}Pa_{\beta}$$

$$^{234}_{92}U \xrightarrow{\alpha} {}^{230}_{90}Th \xrightarrow{\alpha} {}^{226}_{88}Ra \xrightarrow{\alpha} {}^{222}_{86}Rn$$

$$^{238}_{93}Np \xrightarrow{\beta} {}^{238}_{94}Pu_{\alpha}$$

$$\xrightarrow{\alpha} {}^{218}_{84}Ra \quad {}^{218}_{85}At_{\alpha} \quad {}^{214}_{84}Po_{\alpha}$$

$$^{214}_{83}Bi \quad {}^{210}_{82}Ra \xrightarrow{\beta} {}^{210}_{83}Bi \xrightarrow{\beta} {}^{210}_{84}Po \xrightarrow{\alpha} {}^{206}_{82}Pb$$

$$^{214}_{82}Pb_{\beta} \quad {}^{210}_{81}Tl_{\beta}$$

Actinium (4n + 3) Series

$$^{239}_{92}U \xrightarrow{\beta} {}^{239}_{93}Np \xrightarrow{\beta} {}^{239}_{94}Pu \xrightarrow{\alpha} {}^{235}_{92}U \xrightarrow{\alpha} {}^{231}_{90}Th \xrightarrow{\beta} {}^{231}_{91}Pa \xrightarrow{\alpha}$$

$$^{227}_{90}Th$$

$$^{227}_{89}Ac \quad {}^{223}_{88}Ra \xrightarrow{\alpha} {}^{219}_{86}Rn \xrightarrow{\alpha} {}^{215}_{84}Po \xrightarrow{\alpha} {}^{211}_{82}Pb \xrightarrow{\beta} {}^{211}_{83}Bi \quad {}^{211}_{84}Po_{\alpha}$$

$$^{223}_{87}Fr_{\beta} \quad {}^{207}_{82}Pb \quad {}^{207}_{81}Tl_{\beta}$$

Natural radioactivity also occurs in nine of the lighter elements, and it is possible that as the sensitivity of detecting instruments increases, other radioactive elements will be found. Of these, the two most important are $^{14}_{6}C$ and $^{40}_{19}K$. The $^{40}_{19}K$ isotope was probably formed when the earth was created; its present existence is due to its long half-life of $1\cdot25 \times 10^9$ years, though it only constitutes 0·01% of natural potassium, its presence makes living tissue appreciably radioactive. It may decay either by β-emission or K capture.

$$^{40}_{19}K \rightarrow {}^{40}_{20}Ca + {}_{-1}^{0}e$$

$$^{40}_{18}Ar$$

$$K \text{ capture} \uparrow$$

$^{14}_{6}C$ has a half-life of 5720 years and any originally present in the earth will have decayed by now. It is produced continuously from the action of the neutrons in cosmic rays on atmospheric nitrogen, by a nuclear reaction such as:

$$^{14}_{7}N + {}^{1}_{0}n \rightarrow {}^{14}_{6}C + {}^{1}_{1}p$$

Induced Nuclear Reactions

Many nuclear reactions can be brought about by bombarding the nucleus with γ-rays, electrons, neutrons, protons, α-particles or the nuclei of other atoms such as carbon. The nuclei of C atoms which have had the orbital electrons removed are called 'stripped carbon'. The particle may be captured by the nucleus, the nucleus may undergo fission, or fusion of two small nuclei may occur, depending on the conditions of the bombardment.

Natural radiation may be used to induce nuclear reactions, but this limits the energy of the bombarding particle. More usually the charged particles are accelerated by alternate attraction and repulsion using a linear accelerator, a cyclotron or a betatron. In this way particles of a very high kinetic energy can be used to promote the nuclear reaction. This high energy is necessary to overcome the repulsion between a positively charged nucleus and a positively charged bombarding particle. Neutrons have no charge and cannot be accelerated in this manner, but they are not repelled by the nucleus. Some nuclear transformations are given below.

$$^{14}_{7}N + ^{4}_{2}He \rightarrow ^{17}_{8}O + ^{1}_{1}H$$

$$^{23}_{11}Na + ^{1}_{1}H \rightarrow ^{23}_{12}Mg + ^{1}_{0}n$$

$$^{113}_{48}Cd + ^{1}_{0}n \rightarrow ^{114}_{48}Cd + energy$$

In the first example the nitrogen is bombarded with α-particles and a proton is formed, and so this is described as an α,p-reaction. In a similar way the second example is a p,n-reaction. Since the energy emitted in the third example takes the form of γ-rays, this is an n,γ-reaction. The nuclei formed in this way may be stable, or may subsequently decay. The transuranic elements are all obtained by bombarding a heavy nucleus with α-particles or stripped carbon, to produce an even heavier nucleus.

Very heavy nuclei have a lower binding energy per nucleon than nuclei with an intermediate mass. The heavy nuclei are thus less stable. If a heavy nucleus is bombarded with high-energy neutrons, the extra energy may be sufficient to split the already distorted nucleus into two fragments. This is called fission. In the case of ^{235}U, many different products are formed depending on exactly how the nucleus splits up. Three of the more common reactions are:

$$^{139}_{54}Xe + ^{95}_{38}Sr + 2(^{1}_{0}n)$$

$$^{235}_{92}U + ^{1}_{0}n \longrightarrow ^{143}_{56}Ba + ^{90}_{36}Kr + 3(^{1}_{0}n)$$

$$^{135}_{53}I + ^{97}_{39}Y + 4(^{1}_{0}n)$$

The total mass of the fission products is some 0·22 mass units less than the mass of the uranium atom and neutron. This corresponds to an energy release of over 200 MeV, which is more than twelve times the energy liberated in a normal nuclear reaction.

Several neutrons are formed by the initial fission. If these attack other uranium atoms, they release even more neutrons, which attack more uranium atoms and so on, so that a very large number of fissions will occur very rapidly. This is what happens in the atomic bomb, where the branched chain-reaction results in an explosive release of energy. In a nuclear reactor, a moderator is used, so that on average only one neutron produced by fission causes another fission. A chain reaction of this kind continues, but the energy is released at a slow enough rate to be used.

The binding energy per nucleon for light elements is also less than that for elements of intermediate mass. The light nuclei are therefore less stable. Fusion of two light nuclei results in a more stable nucleus, and the extra energy is liberated. If, for example, deuterium is raised to a temperature of several million degrees, fusion reactions occur and liberate an enormous amount of energy.

$$\text{}^2_1\text{H} + \text{}^2_1\text{H} \rightarrow \text{}^3_1\text{H} + \text{}^1_1\text{H}$$

$$\text{}^3_1\text{H} + \text{}^2_1\text{H} \rightarrow \text{}^4_2\text{He} + \text{}^1_0\text{n}$$

$$\text{}^2_1\text{H} + \text{}^2_1\text{H} \rightarrow \text{}^4_2\text{He} + \gamma$$

$$\text{}^2_1\text{H} + \text{}^2_1\text{H} \rightarrow \text{}^3_2\text{He} + \text{}^1_0\text{n}$$

The very high temperature required for fusion can be obtained by a small atomic (fission) bomb, which is used to start the fusion reactions in the hydrogen and nitrogen bombs. Research instruments such as Zeta may also attain this sort of temperature. The energy of the sun is almost certainly produced by fusion, and when a controlled fusion reactor can be built it will supply almost unlimited power.

Some Units and Definitions

a.m.u. = atomic mass unit = $\frac{1}{16}$ the mass of the ^{16}O oxygen atom.

Mass Number = number of neutrons + number of protons.

Mass of hydrogen atom = 1·00814 a.m.u.

Mass of proton ^1_1p or ^1_1H = 1·00759 a.m.u.

Mass of neutron ^1_0n = 1·00898 a.m.u.

Mass of electron $_{-1}^{\;0}e$ = 0·00055 a.m.u.

Mass of helium atom = 4·0039 a.m.u.

Mass of helium nucleus (α-particle ^4_2He) = 4·0028 a.m.u.

MeV = million electron volts

eV = electron volts (1 eV = 23·06 kcal/mole).

1 a.m.u. ≡ 931 MeV.

PROBLEMS

1. What is the nature of the binding forces in atomic nuclei? How does the average binding energy per nucleon vary with the atomic number of the element?
2. In what way is the mode of decay of a particular nucleus related to (a) the ratio of neutrons and protons, and (b) the size?
3. Illustrate the radioactive displacement law by reference to the four radioactive decay series.
4. Compare the processes of nuclear fission and fusion as sources of energy.

Period \ Group	1	2											3	4	5	6	7	0
1	H																	He • .003
2	Li • 65	Be • 6											B • 3	C • 320	N • 46.	O ● 466,000	F • ~900 trace	Ne • trace
3	Na ● 28,300	Mg ● 20,900											Al ● 81,300	Si ● 277,200	P ● 1180	S ● 520	Cl • 314	Ar • .04
4	K ● 25,900	Ca ● 36,300	Sc • 5	Ti ● 4400	V • 150	Cr • 200	Mn ● 1000	Fe ● 50,000	Co • 23	Ni • 80	Cu • 70	Zn • 132	Ga • 15	Ge • 7	As • 5	Se • .09	Br • 1·6	Kr —
5	Rb • 310	Sr • 300	Y • 28	Zr ● 220	Nb • 24	Mo • ~15	Tc —	Ru • .001	Rh • .001	Pd • .01	Ag • .1	Cd • .15	In • .1	Sn • 40	Sb • 1	Te • .002	I • ·3	Xe —
6	Cs • 7	Ba ● 250	La • 18	Hf • 5	Ta • 2	W • ~70	Re • .001	Os • .001	Ir • .001	Pt • .005	Au • .005	Hg • ~·5	Tl • ~2	Pb • 16	Bi • ·2	Po • trace	At • trace	Rn • trace
7	Fr • trace	Ra • trace	Ac • trace	Th ● 12	Pa • trace	U • 4												

ABUNDANCE OF THE ELEMENTS

(Numerical values are given in parts per million in the igneous (volcanic) rocks of the earth's crust.)
(Large circles indicate large values and small circles small values.)

APPENDIX II

Period \ Group	1	2												3	4	5	6	7	0
1	H −259																		He —
2	Li 181	Be 1277												B ~2030	C 3727	N −210	O −219	F −220	Ne −249
3	Na 98	Mg 650												Al 660	Si 1410	P 44	S 119	Cl −101	Ar −189
4	K 64	Ca 838	Sc 1539	Ti 1668	V 1900	Cr 1875	Mn 1245	Fe 1537	Co 1495	Ni 1453	Cu 1083	Zn 420		Ga 30	Ge 937	As 817·	Se 217	Br −7	Kr −157
5	Rb 39	Sr 768	Y 1509	Zr 1852	Nb 2468	Mo 2610	Tc 2130e	Ru ~2500	Rh 1966	Pd 1552	Ag 961	Cd 321		In 156	Sn 232	Sb 630	Te 450	I 114	Xe −112
6	Cs 29	Ba 714	La 920	Hf 2222	Ta 3000	W 3410	Re 3180	Os 2700e	Ir 2454	Pt 1769	Au 1063	Hg −38		Tl 303	Pb 327	Bi 271	Po 254	At 302e	Rn −71e
7	Fr 27e	Ra ~700	Ac ~1050	Th 1750	Pa 1230e	U 1132													

MELTING POINTS OF THE ELEMENTS

(Numerical values are given in degrees Celsius.)

(Large circles indicate high values and small circles low values; e indicates estimated value.)

Data from *Metals Handbook*, 8th edn., Vol. 1 (1961), by courtesy of the American Society for Metals.

Period \ Group	1	2											3	4	5	6	7	0
1	H																	He
2	Li 0·5	Be 1·8											B 2·3	C 2·2	N	O	F	Ne
3	Na 1·0	Mg 1·7											Al 2·7	Si 2·3	P 1·8	S 2·1	Cl	Ar
4	K 0·9	Ca 1·6	Sc 3·0	Ti 4·5	V 6·1	Cr 7·2	Mn 7·4	Fe 7·9	Co 8·9	Ni 8·9	Cu 9·0	Zn 7·1	Ga 5·9	Ge 5·3	As 5·7	Se 4·8	Br 3·1	Kr
5	Rb 1·5	Sr 2·6	Y 4·5	Zr 6·5	Nb 8·6	Mo 10·2	Tc 11·5	Ru 12·2	Rh 12·4	Pd 12·0	Ag 10·5	Cd 8·7	In 7·3	Sn 7·3	Sb 6·6	Te 6·2	I 4·9	Xe
6	Cs 1·9	Ba 3·5	La 6·2	Hf 13·1	Ta 16·6	W 19·3	Re 21·0	Os 22·6	Ir 22·5	Pt 21·5	Au 19·3	Hg 13·5	Tl 11·9	Pb 11·4	Bi 9·8	Po —	At —	Rn
7	Fr —	Ra 5·0	Ac —	Th 11·7	Pa 15·4	U 19·1												

DENSITIES OF THE SOLID AND LIQUID ELEMENTS

(Values are given in g/cm³. Note the value given for carbon is graphite.)

(Large circles indicate large values and small circles small values.)

Data from *Metals Handbook*, 8th edn., Vol. 1 (1961), by courtesy of the American Society for Metals.

INDEX

257